D1272899

The Story of the U.S. Army Signal Corps

THE WATTS LANDPOWER LIBRARY

The Story of the

U.S. ARMY SIGNAL CORPS

Edited by

Lt. Col. Max L. Marshall, USA (Ret.)

SEO Library Center
State Library of Ohio
40780 Marietta Road, Caldwell, OH 43724

FRANKLIN WATTS, INC.
575 Lexington Avenue, New York 10022

FIRST PRINTING
Library of Congress Catalog Card Number 65–11938
Copyright © 1965 by Franklin Watts, Inc.
Printed in the United States of America

237893

This book is dedicated to my son, Terry Allen Marshall (WA5KSY; AD4LNA), and to youngsters like him throughout the United States, who take a serious interest in radio and electronics. It is to them that the Signal Corps' proud heritage of achievement and service rightfully belong. To them also belongs the responsibility for the future accomplishments in communications and electronics required to help keep our nation strong, healthy, and free.

ACKNOWLEDGMENTS
AND EDITOR'S CREDITS

The selections in this book are used by permission and special arrangements with the proprietors of their respective copyrights who are listed below. The editor's and publisher's thanks to all who made this collection possible.

The editor and publisher have made every effort to trace the ownership of all material contained herein. It is their belief that the necessary permissions from publishers, authors, and authorized agents have been obtained in all cases. In the event of any questions arising as to the use of any material, the editor and publisher express regret for any error unconsciously made and will be pleased to make the necessary correction in future editions of this book.

Army Information Digest and R. K. Tierney for "Offspring of the Signal Corps—the Balloon, Dirigible, and Airplane."

Army Information Digest for the following selections: "Getting the Message Through," by Col. G. D. Gray; "Signal Support of 'Special' Warfare," by Col. Harvey J. Pence; "Pictorial Support for the Army," by Col. Arthur A. McCrary; "Teaching Through TV," by Dr. Joseph H. Kanner; "Frequency Management," by Col. W. M. Van Harlingen; "A Step Ahead of the Future," by Brig. Gen. John C. Monahan; "MARS—Military Affiliate Radio System," by Maj. H. C. Beaker, Jr.; "Computers Aid Command and Control," by Maj. Gen. David Parker Gibbs; "Signals in Space," by Maj. Gen. R. T. Nelson.

Army Magazine for "Stratcom—The Army's Global Communications," by Col. Wallace M. Lauterbach, and for "Quiet Please! Electronics Being Tested," by John B. Spore.

Signal Magazine and Col. Kenneth E. Shiflet for "The Inconspicuous Relay," and for " 'Communications Hill' in Korea."

Signal Magazine and Maj. Gen. Earle F. Cook for "U.S. Army Objectives in Field Communications."

EDITOR'S CREDITS

I am indebted to many people for their invaluable assistance in the preparation of this book, but particularly to three individuals.

First—and foremost—to my wife, Constance Beyer Marshall. To her, I would like to express my abiding gratitude for her encouragement, and for the many long hours she spent actively helping me—typing, checking, proofreading, and assisting with the many other painstaking and time-consuming chores that necessarily go into the preparation of any book.

Secondly, I would like to thank Dr. George Raynor Thompson, former

Chief Historian in the Office of the Chief Signal Officer, and currently head of Operations Research and Technical Liaison of the U.S. Army Strategic Communications Command. Dr. Thompson gave unstintingly of his time and effort in assisting me with the necessary research, and contributed greatly to writing much that is contained in this anthology. The vast store of knowledge he possesses concerning the Signal Corps is unique. He has authored many historical and technical articles in *Military Affairs, Signal* Magazine, *Army Information Digest,* and the *Encyclopaedia Britannica.* He contributed to *The Emergency,* the first volume in the Signal Corps official history series, the *U.S. Army in World War II.* He then served as chief author of the second volume, *The Signal Corps: The Test;* and acted in the same capacity in preparing the final volume, *The Signal Corps: The Outcome,* which is in the process of being published. These scholarly, authentic, and documented treasure houses of Signal Corps history are commended to the serious student of military history.

The third individual who contributed immensely to this anthology is Mr. David J. Marshall. Mr. Marshall is the Information Officer of the U.S. Army Signal Center and School, Fort Monmouth, New Jersey, and is also the editor of *Tec-Tac*—subtitled "The Technical and Tactical Training Aid"—which is the professional magazine of the Signal Corps. Mr. Marshall is a professional writer, one of whose books, *Grand Central,* was a best seller in 1946. He had also been a university professor (journalism) and a newspaperman with five years' experience in Europe and twenty-three years' service on the editorial staff of the New York *Sun.* He entered the civil service as Chief of the Tactical Literature Branch of the former Signal Corps Publications Agency in 1952. Mr. Marshall is listed in *Who's Who in America* and a large number of similar publications, including the *Directory of American Scholars* and the British annual *Authors' and Writers' Who's Who.*

I am also indebted to many others—particularly Maj. Gen. Earle F. Cook, former Chief Signal Officer, and Maj. Gen. David Parker Gibbs, Army Chief of Communications-Electronics. It was extremely good fortune that placed me in the position of public relations officer to these two dedicated and outstanding Army officers. My association with them was a privilege, an honor—and an education.

Col. Thomas Matthew Rienzi, Executive, Office of the Chief of Communications-Electronics, likewise provided invaluable assistance. In rendering aid to me, he demonstrated the same perception, enthusiasm, friendliness—and effectiveness—that I came to know during the period that we served together.

I express my warmest gratitude to Col. W. J. "Sparky" Baird, U.S.A. (Ret.), General Manager of the Armed Forces Communications and Electronics Association, and editor of *Signal* Magazine. In his position as bridge between the military electronics community and the nation's communications-oriented industrial firms and educational institutions, he has contributed greatly to the successful military-civilian teamwork needed to keep our country strong. It was my distinct privilege to work closely with him over a period of many months. I express my gratitude to him for his invaluable assistance, and to his able and efficient staff, particularly Brig. Gen. Ralph Glasgow, U.S.A. (Ret.) and Miss Judith Shreve, managing editor of *Signal*.

Lt. Col. Jack Chesebro, editor of the official *U.S. Army Information Digest* lent active assistance—as did Mr. Samuel Ziskind and Mr. Owen Remington, his able aides. Mr. John B. Spore, editor of *Army* magazine, official organ of the Association of the U.S. Army, also provided full cooperation.

I am also indebted to Frank Luther Mott, Dean Emeritus of the Journalism School of the University of Missouri. It is he who sparked my interest in the field of journalism.

Finally, I express my appreciation to my father-in-law, Mr. Ben B. Beyer, for generously making his spacious apartment available as a "working-vacation" summer headquarters—and for his thoughtfulness throughout.

Foreword

The United States owes much to its military services. In addition to preserving the nation in wartime, the armed forces throughout American history have made important contributions in peacetime pursuits.

In the field of education, for example, the U.S. Military Academy at West Point did much pioneering in the teaching of engineering. The Academy's early graduates were in fact among the leading engineers during America's development. Their accomplishments were perhaps most widely recognized and universally applauded after the successful completion of the Panama Canal by the Corps of Engineers.

The Signal Corps, too, has its proud achievements.

The Weather Service was begun by the Signal Corps and turned over to civil authority as an organized entity late in the nineteenth century. The airplane—which has revolutionized civilization in modern times—was likewise nurtured from infancy to manhood by the Signal Corps.

The opening of the West during frontier days owed much to the communications installed and operated by the Signal Corps. Similarly, the Alaska Communications System comprised an undertaking of the greatest magnitude, and was a major factor in developing what was later to become our 49th state.

During World War I, the tremendous strides in radio technology taken by Signal Corps research contributed greatly to commercial communications—and also to the radio entertainment industry which flourished shortly thereafter.

The emergence of motion pictures for use by educators as a training aid was given strong impetus by the Signal Corps, particularly during World War II. Similarly, the use of television for teaching purposes owes much of its start to early sponsorship by the Signal Corps.

Only a handful of people fully appreciate the extent to which our survival during World War II was assisted by radar—another field in which Signalmen have made substantial contributions.

And the pioneering continues to this very day. Now, as we enter the Space Age, we find communications satellites becoming increasingly important. We also find that much of the successful early work in this area has been accomplished by the Signal Corps, or under its auspices. Today, many others are also deeply involved in the field of space communications; however, the Signal Corps continues to play an extremely important role in that field.

Perhaps it is best that we close this Foreword on a note of mutual cooperation. The Signal Corps has never claimed exclusive credit for the many accomplishments outlined herein. In many instances, it has served primarily as quarterback of a team—the Military-Industry-Education team.

These accomplishments, then, are really part of the success story of a great, free people. We are justly proud of the contributions that the Signal Corps, working with its teammates, has made.

Contents

PART ONE

The History of the

U.S. Army Signal Corps

The art of military communication reaches far back into antiquity. In the beginning, the vocal powers of the commander comprised the primary means of relaying messages and commands. As time went on, and as armies became larger and warfare more complex, increasingly sophisticated methods became necessary. All that had gone before was of great interest to a U.S. Army medical officer by the name of Albert James Myer, who was destined to become the "father of the Signal Corps." Dr. Myer's efforts in signaling stemmed originally from his interest in communicating with the deaf. As an Army surgeon stationed in the Southwest, he observed the Indians' signaling methods and studied all available historical literature he could on the subject. From this, he formulated a system which subsequently was to point the way for worldwide military signaling.

The Origins of Military Communications

✠ DAVID J. MARSHALL, *U.S. Army Signal Center*

Albert James Myer was the Army doctor who, just prior to the Civil War, put forward for the first time the modern concept of a separate, trained, professional military signal service. Myer was the human dynamo who, in 1860, became the Army's first signal officer. And Myer was also the fine combative character who, in 1863, became the first Chief Signal Officer. In short, Myer was the father of the present-day U.S. Army Signal Corps.

The concept of an independent signal service, with officers and troops of its own, we owe to Myer; and for this idea, in fact, all the armies of the world are indebted to him. He was the first, in modern military history, to organize and reduce to a system the age-old art of military signaling—to call the signalmen out of the combat arms, to give them a responsible status, and to set before them enforceable standards of reliability and professional skill.

The art of military signaling is very old. It was old when Alexander set forth to conquer the world. It was raised to a science by Hannibal. It was the secret weapon of Genghis Khan. Nor was it greatly enriched when Assistant Surgeon Albert James Myer, U.S. Army, patented, in 1856, a particular system of flag telegraphy, which came in Civil War days to be known as "wigwag." But wigwag is not the thing that Myer is remembered for today. His great work, rather, was in setting up the Signal Corps itself, and thereby

3

lifting the art of military signaling to a new, secure, and lofty basis.

The results of that work are incalculable. To say, for example, that the big-scale operations of modern armies require an elaborate signal system is almost to conceal the truth. For the truth is that the signal service is what makes the big-scale operations of modern armies possible. From the beginning of history, every commander in the world has fought on the biggest scale possible. But the scale has always been limited by the commander's ability to oversee the combat situation and to make his decisions known. Armies have grown as fast as the signal service has permitted them to grow.

So the earliest records emphasize the vocal powers of the commander himself; we are told, for example, that the mighty Finn MacCool had "all the noise of the world in his voice." Armies became larger when the commanders enlisted the aid of heralds— literally, "troop controllers." Splitting the air with their brassy voices, the heralds delivered the commands of a distant captain directly to the troops in combat; and so, apart from minor differences and distinctions, the heralds in fact were messengers and signalmen. They picked up and amplified the voice of command, and carried it all up and down the line of contact. Of all the heralds of the ancient world, the most famous was Stentor, and Stentor, the story goes, had a voice that carried "five miles against the wind."

Armies became bigger when the heralds were first mounted on horseback, and then became bigger still when signaling devices were first used to supplement the human voice. Dr. Myer himself, in the years to come, would write of the Greek military historian Polybius, who described the "moving-light" signals of Hannibal's army and the system of flag-and-torch telegraphy in service among the Greeks as early as 300 B.C. The Greeks' was a long-line system of relay stations, but Hannibal's signalmen were frontline soldiers, who produced the effect of moving lights by waving their torches —which is precisely what Myer's torchmen would do all through the Civil War.

In medieval times the horn had become the principal instrument of military signaling; and so, ambushed in the pass, high up in the Pyrenees, the long-remembered Roland ". . . in pain and woe and great weakness blew his horn. The bright blood was running from his mouth, and the temples of his brains were broken. But the noise of the horn was very great. And Charles (King Charlemagne) heard the signal. And Guenes heard it. And Naimes heard it. And Naimes said: 'Roland is in trouble. Shout the battle-cry! Arm yourselves! Speed the attack! For you hear plainly that Roland is in trouble.'"

4

As the centuries passed, the horn gave way to the trumpet, and the trumpet gave way to the bugle. By the middle of the nineteenth century, the buglers—particular targets of enemy sharpshooters—had become the heirs of Roland. The commander's word went up and down the line by mounted messenger, and the buglers, the combat signalmen of that day, delivered it to the troops. So it was in 1854, when the Light Brigade collided with the Russian guns at Balaklava; and so it was in that same year 1854 on the Great Plains of a still wild-and-woolly West, where the United States Cavalry was constantly on the move and where Dr. Myer was attending the sick, observing the weather, and watching the Comanche Indians in the practice of their uncanny art of signaling.

Up to this time, the armies of the world had not got very far, basically, in their treatment of the age-old problem of troop control. Yet they had got far enough to make one point clear: By giving greater speed and greater range—and greater loudness—to his voice-of-command, the field commander was able to control a larger army. History has never belied that lesson. The whole force of history has been to show, rather, that every step in the growth of combat operations has been preceded by some particular invention to speed the voice-of-command and, at the same time, to extend its range.

True, a host of other factors have contributed to the big-scale operation of modern armies—for example, the rise of modern transportation. The American Civil War was history's first major conflict in which the railroad played a part, and that war witnessed the massing of troops on a previously unheard-of scale. But the Civil War was also the first in which the electric telegraph played a part; and if it is true that the scale of Civil War operations was in a measure made possible by the use of railroads, it is also true that the railroads could not have been used so effectively without the telegraph to direct and coordinate their many movements. Wherefore, the basic rule would seem to stand, that the maximum scale of combat operations is always proportionate to, and cannot exceed, the commander's ability to make his voice heard.

In the end, perhaps, it was not because he invented wigwag that Myer became famous, but because he gave to the Army, together with wigwag, the concept of signaling as an instrument of troop control on an ever-expanding scale.

In 1856, when he invented wigwag, Dr. Myer was twenty-eight years old. He had been commissioned for about two years, and he was serving in the Far West—an untracked wilderness where oc-

5

casional wagon trains were protected by cavalry as they plodded stubbornly toward California, but where, as a rule, there was only time and space and scenery, and what was spoken of, a little nervously, as "trouble with the Indians."

Between the Indian campaigns, when he was not cauterizing snakebites or extracting teeth, Dr. Myer took daily weather observations, as Army doctors had been doing since the early 1800's. But even so he had time on his hands—and by nature he was a man driven, by inner compulsion, to be forever doing something and forever thinking deeply.

In particular, he was impressed by the daily spectacle of the Indians signaling to one another across great distances. Everybody on the post saw what he saw. Everybody took it for granted. And almost everybody shrugged and walked away when Dr. Myer wished to talk about it. Everybody knew, it would seem, that the Great Plains Indians were among the greatest signalmen who had ever lived—but the secret of their art was a mystery that white men simply accepted and seldom tried to penetrate. As a matter of practice, the Army seldom ventured upon a campaign without the signal support of a sizable contingent of Indians.

Like all Indians, those of the Great Plains used smoke signals; but Myer, apparently, was not too interested in that. He was steeped in classical history, and smoke signaling was always turning up in the ancient world. Two thousand years ago the Pictish tribes of present-day Scotland assembled, deployed, attacked, and dispersed in response to a highly developed smoke system; and even in Myers' day smoke signaling was being used by the rebellious Moro tribesmen in the Spanish Philippines. Smoke signaling could hardly have stirred the mind of young Dr. Myer. It was too ordinary, too obvious, and much too lacking in subtlety.

Actually the Plains Indians used smoke only as a last resort, and only when line-of-sight contact was impossible and the distance was very great. As a rule, their signaling was so unobtrusive as to be missed entirely by the white man, who could only say that—somehow—they used lances, blankets, horses, and everything else to telegraph, with remarkable accuracy, great quantities of detailed information. In describing their work as Army scouts, for example, an eyewitness tells us: "The leader, or interpreter, is kept with the commander of the expedition, while the scouts disappear far in advance or on the flanks. Occasionally one shows himself, sometimes a mere speck on a distant ridge, and the interpreter will say at once what the scout wishes to communicate." What he wished to communicate, we are told, could easily have been the exact number and precise whereabouts of the enemy, and the tactic recommended to take him by surprise.

It needs no telling, of course, that this was the kind of signaling that impressed and fascinated Dr. Myer; and his curiosity was sharpened by mystery. For no Indian signalman would reveal the secret of his trade, and no white man had ever fathomed it.

The Army had its generous supply of bugle calls, covering everything from "Squads Right" to "Draw Sabers, Charge," and "Retire," and the Army could hire all the Indians it needed for their kind of signaling. But the Army had no "long-line" system of its own. Dr. Myer's weather reports and all of his commanding officer's dispatches had to be forwarded by mounted messenger, direct to their destinations or else to the nearest post office, some eight hundred miles away. For its signal service outside the combat zone, the United States Army in 1856 was wholly dependent upon messengers, the post office, and the ten- or twelve-year-old electric telegraph —which in that year, however, had not yet crossed the Mississippi.

Dr. Myer reasoned that the Army should be able to signal as the Indians did; and, so thinking, he did his best to penetrate their secret. He never discovered the whole secret, but the day came when he saw two Comanches moving their lances to the left and right as they sat astride their ponies. And that slight observation was what led to wigwag.

Since the Comanches were not a literate people, their signals were essentially "air pictures." What Myer did was to take the lance and marry it to the alphabet. Letter by letter, then, he was able to telegraph words and sentences. And to make the lance distantly visible to white men—whose eyesight, or so it was supposed, was vastly inferior to that of Indians—Myer fastened a flag to it. He developed his ideas slowly, carefully.

Myer was well equipped for such a task. Not merely a doctor, he was also a former telegraph operator, and he had a scholar's grip of the finer points of history—including military history. He had spent his early boyhood in the hills above the Hudson, at Newburgh, New York, within sound of the West Point sunset gun. He had nurtured an ambition to go to West Point, but when his mother died, an aunt took him to live in Buffalo, and as things happened, he attended Geneva College—the present-day Hobart College. From there he passed on to the Buffalo Medical College. During the summer vacation of 1850, he worked as an operator for the New York, Albany, and Buffalo Telegraph Company; and when he was gradu-

7

ated as a doctor of medicine in 1851, his thesis was on the subject of "A New Sign Language for Deaf Mutes."

In this paper he proposed that the Alexander Bain telegraphic alphabet be used as an instrument of speech by the deaf and dumb; such persons could be trained, he argued, to spell out words and sentences by left and right deflections of the hand. And here, too, was a curious foreshadowing of wigwag.

After medical school, Myer spent three years as a practicing physician, and by a brilliant marriage laid the foundations of a no less brilliant career. His wife brought him a substantial fortune, and from that hour forward, happily, Myer was able to lead the life he wished to lead and to do the things he wished to do. In preference to any other, he chose the life of a soldier—and that free choice tells much about the kind of man he was. Soon after his marriage he passed the entrance examination for admission to the Army Medical Staff and was commissioned an Assistant Surgeon.

The early influence of West Point, a boyhood love of the Army, and all else that West Point stood for, a chance job as a telegrapher, a studied concept of a manual sign language, and the fabulous signaling of the Plains Indians—all these things had combined, by 1856, to influence and guide the young doctor in finding the way to his invention.

What Myer invented was a signal system which he called *flag telegraphy*. Then, finding it possible to signal at night by using a flare instead of a flag, Myer spoke also of *torch telegraphy*. And for a generic term to cover both flag and torch telegraphy—and to distinguish these from electric telegraphy—he hit upon *aerial telegraphy*, leaving *wireless* to be applied to somebody else's invention some forty or fifty years later. In the long run, though, wigwag—with its more dramatic connotations—was the name that stuck.

Wigwag was based upon the right and left deflections of a normally centered flag. As he was about to transmit, the flagman held his flag high in front of him; "flag high" was the normal position. Then he "waved" his message across the miles by putting the flag through its motions. What was called the number 1 movement was carried out by swinging the flag to the left, almost to the ground, and then returning it swiftly to its normal position. The number 2 movement was effected by a similar motion to the right. And the alphabet was composed of these two movements delivered separately or in combinations. Thus *A* was set forth in the code as 11; *B* as 1221; *C* as 212; and so on. This was the code, based upon the Bain code, which Myer had worked out for his thesis on a sign language for the deaf and dumb.

Besides the left and right deflections, there was also a number 3 movement—a halfway dip of the flag forward—but that was used only to signal the end of a word (3), the end of a sentence (33), and the end of a message (333).

It was one of the curious things of history that Captain Bolton of the British army and Captain Colomb of the navy, working together, invented roughly the same system of flag telegraphy at roughly the same time as Myer. There is a probability, however, that the American invention came slightly earlier. In any case, the Myer system, as the history of the next few years unfolded, would be used in combat six years before the British system.

When he had fully perfected his invention, the orderly-minded Dr. Myer applied for a patent on it; and when the patent had been safely issued, he sat down one day in the late September of 1856 and addressed a letter to the Secretary of War, Jefferson Davis, itemizing the virtues of flag telegraphy and suggesting the Army's critical need of it. But for two and a half years Myer's letter was not even acknowledged.

Meanwhile there was little to do but wait. Myer continued devoting himself to the duties of an Army doctor on the plains. He waited quietly, patiently, for two long years. Then, abruptly, he was stirred to action by the news of something happening two thousand miles away. . .

It was 0230 hours on August 5, 1858. A stranger banged at the door of the telegraph office at Trinity Bay, Newfoundland; and when the operator had let him in, he demanded: "Is your New York wire working?"

"Yes."

"I've got the end of a cable outside," the stranger said then. "The other end is in Ireland."

The stranger was Cyrus Field, and he had just completed the laying of the first transatlantic cable.

That was one of the great exploits of the nineteenth century, and Myer was thrilled when he heard of it. He gave up hope of ever hearing from the War Department. He penned a second letter, offering his invention to the Navy. The Navy at least was prompt in saying no.

The world, at this particular time, was crowded with remarkable inventions. The Age of Steam was approaching the high noon of its ascendency, and the Age of Electricity was already aborning. The electric telegraph had held the nation spellbound for a dozen years; and many new and fascinating forms of electric telegraphy were still being patented.

Electric telegraphy, in fact, was older than Myer himself. In the early 1820's half a dozen "needle" telegraphs had been invented, one after another, by a galaxy of famous men, including Ampere in France, Steinheil in Germany, and Schilling in Russia. Most efficient of all the needle telegraphs was that of Charles F. Cooke and his partner, Sir Charles Wheatstone—who is today most commonly remembered as the inventor of the Wheatstone bridge—whereas the crowning achievement of his life was the invention (in 1868) of the automatic telegraph with its five-hole perforated-tape transmitter and its ink-wheel receiver, capable of a normal operating speed of one hundred and twenty-five words a minute.

Cooke and Wheatstone patented their needle telegraph, which required two wires in addition to a ground return, in 1837; and one year later an "ardent, hatchet-faced young man," the American portrait painter Samuel F. B. Morse, applied for a patent on a telegraph that required only one wire in addition to a ground return. Ten years elapsed before the Morse patent was issued, though; and that, perhaps, was a fair measure of the complicated claims and counterclaims of men who had brought forth workable telegraphs in the pre-Morse era. Morse had a line working between Washington and Baltimore in 1844. He got his patent four years later.

Meanwhile, in 1846, the Scottish scientist Alexander Bain—who is best remembered today as the father of facsimile transmission—had patented the electrochemical telegraph; and in 1848, with curious consequences for the future United States Army Signal Corps, Bain paid a visit to New York and sold his patent to a Morse competitor, the New York, Albany, and Buffalo Telegraph Company. Two years later the young Buffalo medical student, Albert James Myer, became an operator for this company—which accounts for his knowledgeable interest in telegraphy, and accounts also for his use of the Bain code in wigwag.

In the 1850's, the magic of electricity had taken by storm a world that prided itself on being ultraprogressive and ultramodern. In such a world it was probably true that flag telegraphy had "the odd look of something that was already far behind the times"; and if the War Department looked a little doubtfully upon Dr. Myer's invention, and for the moment laid it to one side, there were reasons for its doing so.

It would seem false, on the other hand, to say that the War Department was "just not interested" in military signaling. The British had made use of the electric telegraph in the Crimean combat zone a whole year prior to Myer's invention of wigwag, and the War Department already had before it—when Myer's letter was received—the report of Major George B. McClellan, U.S.A., describing the work of the British Army telegraphers. And besides the electric telegraph, there were being studied at least two other alternatives to Myer's invention.

In the field of naval signaling, for example, there was a vast experience to fall back upon. Ever since the Battle of Salamis at the dawn of European history, in 480 B.C., combat orders had been transmitted from ship to ship by flag or banner, torch or lantern; and more than two thousand years later Admiral Sir William Penn had devised a method of ship-to-ship signaling with a single flag, thus anticipating Dr. Myer's invention, it could be argued, by two hundred years. Penn's invention gave the British navy a notable advantage, for it was more than a system for signaling thirty or forty commands; it was a system as unconfined as the alphabet, and by its use whole sentences and paragraphs could be signaled up and down the fleet. The king paid a rich reward for the Penn system. The payment was included in the grant of 45,000 square miles of American land—what is today the state of Pennsylvania—to the Admiral's Quaker son in 1681.

The Penn system continued in service for one hundred and fifty years and then, in the last quarter of the eighteenth century, it gave way to a system invented by the English Admiral Richard Kempenfelt—a system of signaling with many flags, one for each letter of the alphabet. With periodic revisions in detail, the Kempenfelt system had been standard among the navies of Europe for a quarter of a century before Dr. Myer was born.

But for many years longer than that—on days when the breeze was light and the flags would not extend; or when the wind was in the wrong quarter and the "spoken" ship could not see the flags, except edgewise—the British navy had also been using semaphore telegraphy.

The semaphore was invented in France in 1792, just as the French Revolution was moving to its climax in the Reign of Terror. It placed peculiar power in the hands of the revolutionaries; many writers believe that semaphore telegraphy, more than any other single factor, is what accounts for the unprecedented success of the French Revolution. The system was introduced into England in 1795, and was brought from England to the United States in 1800.

The English semaphore consisted, essentially, of a high mast with four pivoted arms that rose and fell in response to the pull and release of lanyards. They rose to the horizontal, two pointing to

11

the left and two pointing to the right; or, let fall, they pointed downward. And the high or low positions of any or all of the blades represented, in their various combinations, the different letters of the alphabet.

Lofty, glassed-in semaphore towers were reared above successive hilltops from city to city. Each, in fact, was a relay station; and each was "worked" by two operators. One, with his eye to a telescope, called out each letter as fast as it appeared on the rear semaphore, and the second operator reproduced the letters on the home semaphore as fast as they were called out. The world's most famous line, in the early 1800's, connected the British naval base at Portsmouth with the Admiralty in London; and—except when the English fog settled down and threw the system out of service—the operator at Portsmouth began to write twenty-one seconds after the operator at London, seventy-four miles away, had begun to send.

The British army rigged up collapsible semaphores, and for a time in the Crimean War, in 1855, made use of them in the combat zone.

It becomes obvious, then, that against a background of so many alternatives, it was not easy for the War Department to appraise the value of Dr. Myer's invention. As the event would presently show, the Department had not ignored Myer; nor can Myer, for that matter, be justly represented as having suffered the pangs of martyrdom meanwhile. But he had to wait a long time—to see just where he stood.

At last, the War Department acted in March of 1859 on the letter that Dr. Myer had posted in September, 1856. The Department's answer was to appoint a board of Army officers to inquire into Myer's invention; and the chairman of that board was Lt. Col. Robert E. Lee of the Cavalry.

Lee was much impressed by what he read about the invention. He had known service in the West, and perhaps he saw from the start what others would be slow in grasping—how perfectly the Myer system met the needs of an expedition against the Indians. Where there was hardly ever more than a momentary line of contact, and where the rear was almost always indistinguishable from the front, there was no place for the electric telegraph or even the mechanical semaphore. And where the Cavalry sweep was constantly in progress, and often was at the gallop, there was no place for all the paraphernalia that naval signaling entailed—its large inventory of flags, ropes, and pulleys, to say nothing of tall masts equipped with yardarms.

What distinguished Myer's system—and what in the end was to

make it famous—was the great simplicity of the equipment it required. Any man on horseback could carry a flag or two, a pole that separated into four-foot sections, and a torch; and if he lost his equipment, he still could signal with his neckerchief by day or a burning stick by night.

But if Lee was properly impressed by the peculiar value of flag telegraphy in the field, he was also impressed by the enormity of the training problem its adoption might bring with it; for it was Lee's idea at first, apparently, that the whole Army would have to learn the new language of the flag and torch.

The decision of the board, Lee concurring, was in favor of a trial, and out of that decision came the famous "New York Harbor Tests" which Myer himself planned and carried out with the help of Lt. Edward P. Alexander of the Corps of Engineers—who, for this purpose, was temporarily detached from the faculty at West Point. Myer's first task, then, was to train Alexander; and Alexander, fascinated by the work, swiftly became a master of code and flag. He was a second lieutenant when the tests began in early October of 1859. He was a first lieutenant when they ended twelve weeks later, on the eve of New Year's Day 1860. Within the next year and a half—such is the stuff that history is made of—Alexander would become the first signalman of modern times to influence strongly if not to reverse, the outcome of a major battle.

As the harbor tests began, Myer's system of flag telegraphy was tried out between Sandy Hook, New Jersey, and the two forts that face each other across the entrance to New York harbor—Fort Wadsworth on the Staten Island side of the Narrows and Fort Hamilton on the Brooklyn side. From time to time Myer exchanged places with Alexander, and before the tests were over each man had signaled the other from each of the test positions.

Then, as the late November fogs came rolling in from the Atlantic, Myer several times transferred himself from Sandy Hook to the top of a famous hill in the Navesink Highlands, a few miles inland from the Hook. This was Beacon Hill, which had been a lookout post and signal station in King George's War, more than a hundred years earlier (1746–1748). And from Beacon Hill on November 19, 1859, Myer "waved" a message that Alexander picked up at Fort Hamilton, fifteen miles across the water, and immediately forwarded by electric telegraph to Col. Sam Cooper, The Adjutant General, in Washington. It was Myer's way of dramatizing the capabilities of his invention. It riveted upon him the quick attention of the highest-ranking officers in the War Department.

Locally, the tests were unsupervised. After each day's work Alex-

13

ander addressed a written report to "Dr. Albert J. Myer, Assistant Surgeon, U.S.A.," and Myer forwarded regular reports directly to Colonel Cooper. The decision was in Cooper's hands. With ever-rising interest, Cooper read Myer's reports, and with historic consequences, Colonel Cooper became an ardent apostle of flag telegraphy. Indeed, Cooper perceived in Myer's work the starting point of a major revolution in tactics and troop maneuvers generally.

In his annual report for 1859, the new Secretary of War, John B. Floyd, proposed the adoption by the United States Army of the Myer system of military signaling.

In the spring of 1860, a bill to implement Secretary Floyd's proposal lay before the Military Affairs Committee of the Senate; and there, for the first time publicly, Myer revealed a trait for which he would be severely criticized, and immeasurably praised, for the rest of his life. There, with an idea to fight for, Myer began a fight— careless of the high position of his opponents and careless of the consequences for his own career.

The situation may have stemmed from Robert E. Lee's apparent belief that the whole Army would have to knuckle down and learn the art of flag telegraphy. For a certainty, the Senate committee was proceeding in the spring of 1860 as if the matter before it was simply to purchase the rights to an invention. The concept of organized signaling was missing entirely—and that concept, in Myer's eyes, was the very thing that mattered.

The committee chairman was Jefferson Davis, Democrat, of Mississippi. Davis was the former Secretary of War, to whom Myer had addressed his letter nearly four years earlier; and Davis, more recently, had made a careful study of the Harbor Test reports. At a committee hearing, he put a question to Myer pointblank: "What are your terms?"

Myer's answer was equally concise and brusque: "Create a Bureau of Army Signals and place me at the head of it with the rank of colonel . . ."

"We will create the Bureau of Signals," said Davis drily, "but . . ."

The quiet, drawling voice trailed off. The speaker, curiously erect and soldierly, turned his eyes full upon Myer. There was a subtle change of manner, and it seemed now as if the man was no longer United States Senator Davis, but Colonel Davis, the graduate of West Point and the hero of Buena Vista in the Mexican War.

"But," the quiet voice resumed ". . . I can never consent to lift you over the heads of men who have grown gray as captains."

Davis went on to propose a flat payment of $10,000 or $50,000—

14

the authorities differ on the exact sum—plus a contract under which Myer would become a civilian Instructor of Signals at a handsome salary. Myer refused both offers; and, to his friends at least, it was obvious that, rejecting money, he was fighting for the military rank and authority which alone would enable him to establish within the Army an organized corps of signalmen.

Apparently defeated, he turned about in search of help. He enlisted the aid of another member of the committee, Senator Joseph Lane of Oregon. There was a lifting of eyebrows—for this looked very like politicking, and Myer was still an Army officer. But Myer cared nothing for what it looked like.

There was a showdown. And when the Senate votes were counted, Dr. Myer—though he had to accept a lower grade—had won his main point. He received no reward for his invention. Congress appropriated $2,000 for the purchase of signal equipment and created on the Army Staff the position of Signal Officer.

The story has long been told that Myer was at once commissioned a major of Cavalry and detailed to the Army staff for duty as signal officer. But the fact is that Myer was simply commissioned "signal officer with the rank of major"; and because he was the signal officer, he was *ipso facto* a member of the staff.

The Army staff of 1860, however, differed greatly from the General Staff of today. It was merely the aggregate of officers, each of whom was the head of a "staff department" and each of whom was separately and individually responsible to the Secretary of War.

As signal officer, Myer was head of a signal department that consisted, for a time, only of himself. Under the regulations, though, he had a right to administrative helpers, and when two or three such men were assigned to his office, they gave the department, in the first phase of its existence, its only pretense to bulk and size.

The mission of the signal officer was not at all what Myer had hoped it would be. It was merely to receive details of officers and men from the combat arms, to train them in the art of flag telegraphy, and to return them to their units promptly at the close of each training period. There had been no intention to place him at the head of a separate branch of the Army, nor was it the purpose of the War Department, or of Congress, to place the signal mission in the hands of a new organization. The Infantry would look after its own signaling, and so would the Cavalry and Artillery. It would be Major Myer's job simply to train signalmen.

But things were not going to remain that way for long; there were too many problems to be solved and too few precedents to go

15

by. In the inevitable shakedown period, changes of one kind or another would be inevitable, and with tremendous self-assurance, Myer had decided—prior to accepting his new commission, it would seem—that he would take care of the changes. He would see that all of them, or nearly all, would be in what he himself considered to be the right direction.

At the age of thirty-two years, he was probably the youngest major in the Army; and he knew, apparently, that that was going to tell against him. In any case, he took a decision which can only be explained as that of a very young man defending his right to speak, and speak forcibly, in the presence of older and more experienced men. He decided to continue wearing the uniform of an Army doctor; and consistently, when years later he purchased a five thousand-dollar sword at Tiffany's, he saw to it that the blade inscription read: "Albert James Myer, U.S. Medical Staff." It is the astonishing fact that in his long career Myer never once wore the uniform of the Signal Corps.

Like most determined men, he was not easy to argue with; but he was not, on the other hand, the arrantly difficult person he was often said to be. To be sure, he was schooled and committed to independence of judgment. As a doctor, he had been trained to impress his own opinion upon others. As a doctor, too, he was accustomed to the deference of men, and decidedly not accustomed to the easy give-and-take of line officers. The simple fact would seem to be that Myer had formed early in life, and had carried into the world of affairs, a habit of following his own line, with or without the advice of others. So it was in the matter of a uniform. So it had been in the matter of the Senate committee hearing. And so it would be to the end of his career.

And yet, in spite of everything, Myer was first and foremost a practical-minded man; and once he had paid his respects to the Secretary of War, he decided for himself what his immediate duty was to be. He chose the roughest trouble spot, cleared his plans with the General-in-Chief, and had himself assigned to the staff of Col. Edward R. S. Canby, who at that moment was organizing a first-class expedition against the Navajos in New Mexico Territory.

Canby had the normal field commander's staff of two officers. In accordance with established practice, he would plan and direct his combat operations in person. But he had an adjutant to look after this administrative work; and he had a quartermaster to take care of intelligence and supplies. In accordance with Army regulations, the deputy commanding officer was quartermaster.

Myer became a third member of the staff. Wearing the epaulettes of a major of the Medical Staff, he presented himself at Canby's headquarters at Santa Fe in early October, 1860. He was responsible directly to Canby, and that gave him a strong position. But he chose to work through the quartermaster, and that made his position stronger. A day or two after his arrival in camp, Myer took command of a volunteer detail of two officers and sixteen enlisted men; and in that moment, according to one view of its history, the Signal Department was born.

This was not a permanent organization; strictly speaking, it was not an organization at all, but a temporary training group. Its members, enlisted men and officers alike, had been authorized by their unit commanders to volunteer for the training offered. They would stay with Myer long enough to complete their training—perhaps—and then they would scatter, each man returning to his own unit.

One complication was that every man in training, commissioned or not, continued subject to recall at any moment, at the sole discretion of his unit commander. On the day the group was first brought together, nobody knew how long the combat commanders would allow the experiment to continue.

Canby took the field in the closing days of October. Tentatively, and because Canby himself had somehow taken a fancy to the idea, Myer's training group was kept together. And it was during this campaign against the Navajos that flag telegraphy was used for the first time in the service of the United States Army.

The expedition struck forward among steep and rugged hills, and Myer's men, equipped with only three sets of flags and torches, scaled the steepest rocks to perch their signal stations at the peaks. Their achievement was surprising. The widely deployed columns of Canby's command were kept in close touch with one another; and that was the kind of thing that any combat commander would have been interested in. To perform that service, uncounted scores of messages were transmitted on fifty-two different days over distances of five to twenty miles in all kinds of weather; and that was a clue to the still unsuspected capabilities of flag telegraphy.

But the great surprise of the Canby campaign was the value of the signalmen as scouts and battlefield observers. All this had been unplanned and unforeseen. The signalmen, once they were deployed and on their own, fell into the way of it almost without thinking; and from their high perches they carried out an intelligence mission so effectively and well that Colonel Canby was led to dismiss the bulk of his hired Indian scouts, guides, and spies.

17

It was not a foible of Major Myer's, it was characteristic of the times, that the signal code was known only to the major himself and the two commissioned officers he had trained. The enlisted signalmen knew only the flag movements on which the code was founded, the movements called 1, 2, and 3; and care was taken to prevent their learning what the movements might mean. So a flag-man could receive a message only by jotting down on paper a series of 1's, 2's, and 3's, which only a signal officer could decipher; and he could transmit only if a signal officer stood beside him and called out the numbers, or if the numbers were placed before him on paper.

That this should be their way of doing things is accounted for, at least in part, by the circumstances of their day. Of the general run of enlisted men, for example, few could read or write; and the long-established tradition of the Army had been to entrust secret information only to an officer who could be held accountable for it. On the other hand, there is a possibility—perhaps even a probability—that Myer, even at this early date, was laying the groundwork for a system that would later on enable him to change the code without having to retrain the flagmen.

In any case, Canby's flagmen had been trained exclusively in the physical handling of the flag—in the art of delivering its motions with clarity, precision, and style. But their training, so severely limited, had been good; and their smart, self-confident appearance had the surprising effect of commending the signal service to enlisted men everywhere.

For that matter, to see a flagman at work was intriguing. There was in the work an undeniable touch of the spectacular. There was dash and flourish and the final thrill of knowing that by the magic of a flag contact had been made with far-off men.

Nor was it any job for a softy. The work of a flagman called for a degree of skill that men admired; and it called for strength. It was easy enough, perhaps, to handle a two-foot flag on a four-foot pole—the "action" flag. But a six-foot flag on a sixteen-foot pole was required for transmitting at a range of twenty-five miles, and the management of such a flag was work enough to exhaust a strong man in a few minutes' time unless he had learned his task well. A skillful flagman could avoid fatigue, could work faster, could keep the flag extended through all its motions, and could make the motions plainer to a distant signalman by curving and curling and whipping the flag through every change of direction.

The flagmen who served with Canby had barely mastered the

18

fundamentals of their trade when they found they could use the action flag while lying flat on their backs—in a hollow of the ground or in the shelter of a rock or a log.

The day would come, in the opening phases of the Civil War, when high-ranking officers would expostulate scornfully against the work of the signalman, dismissing it as "contemptible flag-waving" and no job for a soldier. Oddly enough, though, the enlisted men of the Army looked upon the signalman with respect—and their good opinion was one of the factors that eased the way to the final setting up of an independent Signal Corps. Actually, there was no ground for the reproach. Before the close of the Navajo campaign, the usefulness and value of flag telegraphy was so firmly established that there would never again be any valid reason for doubting it.

The day would come too, but later on in the Civil War, when Myer would serve again as Canby's signal officer—and from this new beginning, in the hapless days of his career, would launch the fight that would carry him back a second time to the post of Chief Signal Officer of the Army.

Myer, as we have seen, arrived at Santa Fe in October, 1860. On November 6, the Presidential election was won by a relatively unknown lawyer from Illinois, a man called Abraham Lincoln. On February 18, 1861, Jefferson Davis became the Provisional President of the Confederate States of America, and on April 12, a shot was fired in Charleston Harbor. Caught in the play and interplay of forces rooted deep in her history, the nation had been swept, as fast as that, to the brink of the greatest and bloodiest war ever fought prior to the twentieth century.

Presently the Union armies were marching to a tune that pledged them explicitly to "hang Jeff Davis on the sour-apple tree"; and recalling his appearance before the Senate committee, Myer told a friend—a bit wryly, perhaps—that he at least had stood up to Jeff Davis and bested him.

As he enjoyed his little joke, it may also have occurred to Myer that in two years' time he had met a surprising number of Southerners. For one example, there was Robert E. Lee, who had recommended that the Army try out Myer's invention. On April 15, the day after Fort Sumter fell, General Winfield Scott selected Lee to be his own successor as General-in-Chief of the armies of the United States, predicting that the services of Lee as overall commander would be worth the services of fifty thousand troops. On April 18 the command was offered him in Lincoln's name, and Lee—on the "saddest day" of his life—declined it because, "though opposed to

secession I could take no part in an invasion of the Southern States."
On April 23 Lee became the Major General and Commander-in-Chief of the Armed Forces of Virginia, and on August 15 he became one of the five full generals of the Confederate States Army.

For another example, there was Col. Sam Cooper, who for ten years had been The Adjutant General at Washington. It was he who certified the results of the New York Harbor Tests and became such a fiery apostle of flag telegraphy. In May, 1861 Cooper was made the Adjutant General of the Armed Forces of Virginia; and at once it became strikingly evident which way the wind was blowing, for in this new position, Cooper, with dreams of revolutionizing tactics, had command control over all military signaling. It boded no good for the future, in Myer's opinion, that Cooper became in August the second of the five full generals of the Confederate States Army.

For a third example, there was the young engineer officer Lieutenant Alexander, who had been Myer's assistant in the New York Harbor Tests, and whose mastery of code and flag had equalled Myer's own. In early June, 1861, Alexander became the highly prized signal officer of General Beauregard's army, also on the Confederate side.

And there were many more, among them an ardent young lieutenant of the Cavalry who had vainly applied for signal training at Santa Fe. He too had gone over to the Confederate side, and he, as would soon appear, was a Cavalry genius with a special flair for signaling—J. E. B. Stuart.

The simple fact is that, when the appeal to arms was made and the United States Army in effect became two armies, the Confederate side had drawn to itself nearly all the officers who, in one way or another, had revealed an appreciation of the role that lay ahead for signalmen.

As the summer of 1861 began, the Signal Officer of the United States Army had been left with only one assistant whom he could look to with hope. This was a young West Pointer, Lt. Samuel T. Cushing of the Second Infantry. He had been one of the two officers trained at Santa Fe, and in his person, therefore, the Signal Department, forerunner of the Signal Corps, was linked from its first hour with the United States Military Academy.

After the beginning of the Civil War, Myer's system of signaling was copied immediately by the Confederates with brilliant success. The North was to delay for a long time, and there were to be many dark days ahead.

Early Civil War Signaling

✠ DAVID J. MARSHALL, *U.S. Army Signal Center*

Amid the vast confusion that followed the onset of the Civil War, Maj. James Myer—who for less than one year had been the Army's first Signal Officer—hastened from his first field assignment at Santa Fe to the New York headquarters of Winfield Scott, General in Chief of the Army. Scott assigned him, temporarily, to the War Department in Washington.

But a week's leave was possible; and—as a citizen of New York State—the impulsive Dr. Myer raced up to Albany to interview the governor. Not every young man of thirty-two would have had the temerity to do such a thing; but the story goes that Governor Morgan, as commander-in-chief of the armed forces of New York State, assured him that the officers and men of New York regiments would be encouraged to volunteer for signal training and, except for the most urgent reasons, would not be subject to recall to their units till their training was completed. As early as this, it would seem, Myer had grown impatient of having officers and men withdrawn from training arbitrarily.

Upon reporting to the War Department, Myer was directed to establish a signal school at Fort Monroe—a Union stronghold at the eastern tip of the Yorktown Peninsula; an almost beleaguered stronghold, accessible by water but closed in completely on the landward side by Confederate soil. At the fort, after interviewing many more, Myer selected forty volunteers for training—ten officers and thirty enlisted men—and except for a handful of Regular Army people, they were all taken from New York regiments. To insure and reinsure against failure, Myer had also interviewed beforehand the commanding officers of all forty volunteers, had exacted promises that, after the completion of their training, these officers and men would remain with Myer for just a few weeks longer, to serve as instructors in a greatly expanded signal school.

21

Myer opened his first class at Fort Monroe on June 10, 1861; but for six of the ten officers, the training was abruptly cut short two days later. On June 12 an order was received from Maj. Gen. Benjamin F. Butler sending the first signal party into combat; and—such was the spirit of the moment—the mission was carried out brilliantly.

The battery at Fort Wool in Hampton Roads was to fire that day on the Confederate works at Sewall's Point. As a part of the plan, three signalmen were stationed at the fort, and Myer himself accompanied three others aboard a tugboat that steamed in close to the Confederate position. At a signal from the tugboat, the guns at Fort Wool "spoke"; and as the firing continued, Myer and his fellow signalmen flagged their observations back to the fort and, in effect, laid the guns plumb on target. This was the first Civil War engagement in which signalmen took part under fire.

When it was ended, Myer went back, for the moment, to his schoolmaster's job at Fort Monroe, but he was in the field again just two weeks later, when he established—on June 26—the first permanent flag-telegraph system. By this means Fort Monroe was placed in touch with the port of Newport News, where another Union garrison was holding out on the southern tip of the Yorktown Peninsula. Having trained the flagmen, Myer had also devised the operating plan, which enabled either station to raise the other at any hour of the day or night.

Then, abruptly, Myer was withdrawn from Fort Monroe altogether. Brig. Gen. Irvin McDowell had taken command of an army of five divisions based on Washington. His orders were to attack and disperse the Confederate forces under General Beauregard a few miles south of the Potomac; and for this impending campaign Myer was assigned, on July 17, to McDowell's staff. He requested that one lieutenant and two enlisted flagmen from the school at Fort Monroe be assigned to help him; and when that request had been approved, he turned aside—a bit too anxiously, perhaps—to still another project.

In the first few weeks after the fall of Fort Sumter, three professional "aeronauts" had volunteered their services to the Army; and the enthusiastic Myer had caught sight of a heaven-sent opportunity to dramatize the value of flag telegraphy. He had requested that a balloon be placed at his disposal, and on July 17—the day of his appointment to McDowell's staff—the balloon assigned to his charge was in the final stages of completion.

It was to be a "tethered," or captive, balloon, and Myer's purpose was to place aboard it a signal officer who would continuously flag his observations to the ground. There had been snags, however, and the balloon was not delivered on the day promised. Apparently, then, it was in that anxious day or two of waiting that Myer learned for the first time that, five weeks earlier, Thaddeus Lowe had solved the air-ground signal problem, and solved it brilliantly, by taking aloft in his balloon a Morse "telegraphist" with key and sounder and six hundred feet of "double-conductor flexible cable" that swung loosely from the basket to the ground.

In due course, Myer's balloon was delivered to him at the Columbian Armory in Washington; and Myer had it inflated then and there. There was a protest, an outcry, from the civilian aeronaut. But where, outside the city, would illuminating gas have been available? When he set forth for McDowell's headquarters at Fairfax Court House, Virginia, Myer was disappointed, tired, and cranky. He was at the narrow edge of tuberculosis, weak and overwrought. And he was thirty hours behind schedule.

He left the armory in the early morning hours of Sunday, July 21, and so it came about—as the newspapers duly reported—that late revelers beheld, in the silvery moonlight, a spectacle so disturbingly odd as to send most of them staggering home to sign the pledge. A mounted officer was impatiently, fretfully, attempting to quicken the pace of a slow-moving procession of eighteen or twenty soldiers who cursed and sweated and tugged at a network of ropes while, above their heads, a gigantic ball kept bouncing and bobbing about and causing endless delays by getting itself caught in the trees and telegraph wires along the way.

The sun was rising as they crossed the Georgetown Aqueduct Bridge. As they continued their hike along the towpath of the Chesapeake and Ohio Canal, the soldiers had every so often to enter the water, wading or swimming, to keep the mooring ropes out of the branches of overhanging trees. Finally they made for Fairfax Court House along a road that wound through patch after patch of woodland.

It was a difficult and muddy road, and by 10 o'clock or so it was clogged with carriages and all kinds of merrymakers afoot or on horseback. The impending assault at Manassas (Bull Run) had been seized upon as a happy holiday occasion by thousands of people—notably by Northern congressmen and their wives and families—and they had come pouring out of Washington to see the show. In festive mood, with parasols and picnic hampers, they pushed by Myer and blocked his passage so many times as to leave him frustrated and nearly beaten.

Toward noon, however, Myer was stung to violent efforts by a sudden roar that told him the battle had begun. He ordered the balloon hitched to a wagon and whips laid to the horses. They took off "at a spanking trot," the balloon dragging and bogging behind them, past trees and telegraph wires, till at one point the balloon was caught fast in the branches of a tree. And then, letting his fiery temper get the better of him, Myer ordered the teamster to proceed. The balloon was torn beyond hope of mending in the field.

Thereupon Myer abandoned it, spurred his charger, and was off to his post at McDowell's headquarters, expecting to take command of the signal party from Fort Monroe. But, though four days had elapsed, the lieutenant and the two flagmen had not yet arrived. So the Army's first Signal Officer found himself in his first major action without a command—a signalman with no one to receive his signals. In the circumstances, there was nothing to do but become a mounted messenger—to take part, and a very humble part at that, in a kind of signal service he had done his best to supersede. Myer knuckled down, however, and in the performance of a messenger's duties under fire, he displayed a fearlessness that caught McDowell's attention. Myer was cited for gallantry in McDowell's dispatches.

Northern tradition calls it the Battle of Bull Run. Southern custom calls it the Battle of Manassas. By either name, the battle ended in a severe defeat for the Union forces; late that Sunday afternoon they were in full flight, leaving behind them guns, equipment, and rolling kitchens.

And yet, for the Confederate forces, the victory had not been easy. Early in the day an almost certain disaster had been averted; and the staving off of that disaster had been very largely due to the operations of a signal team commanded by Lt. Edward P. Alexander —the same young officer who had learned the trade of signalman while serving as Myers' assistant during the New York Harbor Tests a year and a half earlier.

At Bull Run, Alexander commanded a party of well-trained enlisted men, all present on the battlefield and all equipped for signal action before the first blow was struck. In fact, the opening shot of the battle, fired by the Union forces, passed through Alexander's tent. But that was unimportant. Alexander and his party carried on, under a very heavy fire, till the battle was done. Subsequently Alexander told his story:

I was watching the flag of our station at Stone Bridge, when . . . a gleam caught my eye. It was the reflection . . . from a polished brass field piece, one of Ayre's Battery. Observing attentively, I discovered McDowell's column in the open field

24

north of Sudley's Ford, crossing Bull Run and turning our left flank, fully eight miles away . . . I signaled (Brig. Gen. Nathan G.) Evans at once: 'Look out for your left. Your position is turned.' . . . (Brig. Gen. Bernard E.) Bee, (Legion Cdr. Wade) Hampton, and (Brig. Gen. Thomas J.) Jackson were all hurried in that direction. The history of the battle tells how they successfully delayed McDowell's progress till, finally, the tide was turned by the arrival of troops in the afternoon.

Alexander's discovery of McDowell's intention, and that swift report that concentrated three brigades at the danger spot after the Confederate flank had already been turned—these, when all is said, were chief among the factors that smashed a victory already in McDowell's grasp. There were other factors. Hampton's legion had fought like demons. Against the main thrust of McDowell's army, Jackson had stood "like a stone wall"—thus earning his immortal soubriquet of "Stonewall"—and Gen. Joseph E. Johnston's forces, arriving from the Shenandoah in the nick of time, had struck with the power of a pile driver. But the one stubborn fact remains that, in a supreme crisis, Alexander had played a decisive part; and the battle, to say the least of it, was kept going till Johnston's troops could strike the mortal blow.

It would seem to follow that Bull Run was the first battle of modern times that was lifted to victory by causes clearly traceable to the use of combat signaling. When the story of Alexander's exploit reached Washington, experienced officers are said to have groaned that a first lieutenant with a flag could have done all that.

Presumably, Myer groaned too. He was human enough to be thrilled that all his preaching, when put to the test of actual battle, had been so brilliantly vindicated; but just the same he was beside himself with rage, he was bursting with indignant wrath, that the vindication had had to come from what he looked upon as the very wrong side of the war.

The excellence of the Confederate signal operations at Bull Run was in sharpest contrast to a series of signal failures on the Union side. The unmitigated fact was that Myer had failed McDowell twice; he had not sent up the balloon with a signalman aboard, and he had not established flag telegraphs in the field, as Alexander had done. Far worse than these, however, was a failure on somebody else's part to get into McDowells' hands a telegram that might have changed the outcome of the battle as effectively as Alexander's signaling had done.

Maj. Gen. Robert Patterson had been sent to engage General

Johnston's forces in the Shenandoah Valley. On July 20, the day before Bull Run, Patterson had sent off a telegram to Washington, reporting that Johnston was on his way to reinforce Beauregard's army with thirty-five thousand men; and, as history records, it was Johnston's army, catching McDowell by surprise at a critical moment of the battle, that finally turned the tide against him and precipitated the rout.

Patterson's warning had never reached McDowell; and there was a disposition all round to blame the commercial telegraph company. Myer concentrated on the possibility that Patterson's telegram, forwarded from Washington, might have been lost between the telegraph office and McDowell's headquarters, ten miles away. Couriers had been used to run messages back and forth over those ten miles. They had been exposed to rifle and gun fire, and Myer reasoned that for every courier killed or otherwise put out of action, there could easily have been a message lost.

Myer's answer to the problem he had thus defined was a proposal to establish electric telegraph lines—Army wire lines—between every major headquarters and the closest commercial telegraph offices . . .

After Bull Run, Myer was back at his training job at Fort Monroe; for now there was a sharp demand for signalmen. And now, too, a great series of exploits for signalmen was about to begin.

Blockade of the Southern seaports had been declared in April; and in June, 1861 the Army and Navy staffs had agreed that, to make the blockade effective, it would first be necessary to establish naval bases and coaling stations at points along the Southern seacoast below Cape Hatteras. A few weeks after Bull Run, the first of several joint Army-Navy expeditions was made ready to sail, under command of General Butler.

But it was Butler who had sent the first signalmen into combat in early June. He had been greatly impressed by the practical results of their work off Sewell's Point; and signalmen, accordingly, went south with Butler—and with all the expeditions that would follow. Scores of signalmen, as fast as they could be trained, would take part in a long-continued effort to capture and hold the required positions from Hatteras to Florida.

At Hatteras Inlet on August 28 a signal officer and flagman were among the first ashore, and then, for the first time in history, troop landings were directed and controlled by flag signals. Next day, when the naval gunners reopened fire on Fort Hatteras, the Army signalmen ashore became the Navy's first fire-direction party.

26

In the violent storms of early November, seven signal officers and fourteen flagmen maintained contact between the sixteen naval vessels and a badly scattered convoy of nearly forty troopships on their way to Port Royal Bay. To prevent their being washed overboard as mountainous seas crashed across the decks, Army flagmen were lashed to the wheelhouse of ships; and the naval commander was so impressed by their work under those conditions that he recommended, as soon as he was able, that the Myer system of flag telegraphy be adopted by the Navy. On November 7, when the warships passed three times between the two forts at the harbor entrance —receiving a heavy fire from both left and right, and replying in smooth succession with heavy broadsides in both directions—the commodore employed those same Army signalmen to pass his orders from ship to ship.

Operation followed operation as the long campaign went forward; and signalmen trained at Fort Monroe—later on, at Red Hill—continued training other signalmen. Ever more signal officers and flagmen were assigned to ever more of the Army-Navy joint expeditions; and the astonishing fact was that they went straight on discovering ever more ways of contributing, through sheer push and self-assertiveness no less than skill, to the effectiveness of combat operations.

At Port Royal Ferry, on New Year's Day, 1862, the Confederate commander assigned a whole battery of his artillery to concentrate on Union signalmen. Apparently, though, their aim was poor, for the signalmen, unscathed, proceeded to lay the fire of gunboats on shore targets invisible to the gunners.

At the reduction of Fort Pulaski, on April 10 and 11, a team of nine signalmen laid the fire of thirty-six heavy siege guns upon a single section of wall that rose twenty-five feet above the high-water line and was eight feet thick at the top; and though the guns were firing at a range of seventeen hundred yards—and though all the military authorities of Europe were agreed that no guns could be effective against a permanent work if the range exceeded thirteen hundred yards—they brought down the wall in twenty-four hours' time. This decidedly, was something new. Commentators explained it by the unprecedented precision which the signalmen had given to artillery work.

When Gen. Ambrose Burnside took command of the expedition to Roanoke Island, he requisitioned a "signal corps" of twenty-five officers and fifty flagmen, but the best Major Myer could do was to lend Burnside the services of nine instructors. In brief order, then, the required number of signalmen, selected from Burnside's own

27

command, were placed under three weeks' intensive training—and after that, seventy-five new signalmen were crowded into a racing schooner. They were five days late in starting, arriving at the scene of action just before dawn on February 7, 1862, just as Burnside was preparing to put eight thousand troops ashore under cover of a naval curtain fire. It was not by accident, then, that the first man ashore was a signal officer. By this time it was standard practice to get the signal flags waving at the earliest possible moment.

The Roanoke Island victory was followed by the capture of New Bern and Moorehead City on the mainland. In these operations, notably, the work of the signalmen had been reduced to a routine—expert, remarkably effective, and almost commonplace—and for a moment it seemed as if the flagmen, as they became more and more efficient, were moving steadily out of the limelight.

But after New Bern and Moorehead City came the capture of Beaufort, and the fall of Beaufort was followed on April 25 by the attack on Fort Macon. Brig. Gen. John C. Parke surrounded the fort, cutting off its communications and placing eleven siege guns in position around the landward sides, while in the harbor, four Union gunboats completed the ring . . .

The fort would not be taken easily. It was heavily constructed of brick and stone, and it mounted nearly fifty heavy guns. The attack began at 0540 hours, and almost at once a signal officer, acting on his own responsibility, took a position whence he and his flagmen commanded the attention of all the ships and all the batteries ashore. He took upon himself the task of directing their fire. He corrected the range of guns by as much as one hundred yards and by 1200 hours he had every shell, without exception, falling in or on the fort. The bombardment continued for four hours after that; the fort surrendered at 1600 hours. And the damage inflicted in those four hours was equal to the damage wrought normally by a continuous bombardment lasting twenty-four hours. The histories of war were ransacked in vain for a parallel; it was concluded that never before had guns been laid so accurately upon a target.

A formula was suggested: Signaling can multiply by six the effective force of the artillery.

When the full meaning of Bull Run struck home in late July of 1861—and the enormity of that disaster was finally understood and the cocksurety of the North gave way to panic and despair—Major Myer was one of the few who kept calm. It might have been otherwise, perhaps, if the situation had merely annoyed him; for he was easily disconcerted and could flare up over trivial things. But in a

28

desperate emergency, he was—not exactly cool, but cold and passionately angry at the same time. And he concentrated the whole force of his suppressed emotion upon the preparation of plans for the future.

Allowing the signal school at Fort Monroe to look after itself for the moment, he was working long and hard these days in the office he had set up for himself in G Street, Washington; and, as a doctor of medicine, he must have known what the cost of such work was going to be. The facts are that he was thirty pounds underweight; that for a long time, bodily weakness and ill health had been creeping up on him; that he was suffering from dizziness, fevers, and chills; that he was plagued by fatigue and frightened by his inability to sleep. Also, there was coughing, accompanied now and then by severe chest pains. And there was blood in his sputum. In short, there were reasons to suppose that Myer's fear of tuberculosis—which had made his life wretched for years—was at long last about to be realized.

But despite that, and with something very like the courage of a lion, Myer addressed himself persistently, relentlessly, to his work in G Street. In that cramped and poorly equipped office he conducted the headquarters work of the Signal Department. There, in a cubbyhole of his own, he kept in touch with all that the signalmen were doing in the seacoast campaigns; and there he wrote his first annual report.

There, too, he kept up a voluminous correspondence with men of importance everywhere. A man of genuine achievement had only to be mentioned in the pages of *The New York Herald* or the Philadelphia *North American;* and right away Myer was writing him a letter—establishing a basis for what could become, and often did become, a firm and lasting friendship. Before long, it may be added, Myer's friends and correspondents included many influential men in Congress and the War Department.

But much more notably, perhaps, Myer carried on from his G Street office two insistent campaigns—one for an independent signal branch, with a status comparable to that of the Infantry, the Cavalry, or the Artillery; and the other for control of electric telegraphy in the field.

On the one hand, Myer was urging upon Secretary of War Simon Cameron a very precise plan for converting the Signal Department into a signal corps with officers and troops of its own. In long letters he described what its place in the Army would be and what its mission would have to be. He drew up a table of organization, and in

29

support of it he brought forward—and for two years to come he would continue to bring forward—an immense amount of pertinent information. Myer, it was said, had a genius for amassing information.

On the other hand, Myer worked equally hard, in the days immediately after Bull Run, to obtain approval of his plan for the use of wire in the field. He was bitter over what had happened at Bull Run. He was stung, no doubt, by the galling memory of his own failures on that occasion. But in the end, as he saw it, the thing that really mattered was the undeniable fact that General Patterson's warning had gone astray . . .

Myer concentrated on that problem of the missing telegram. His answer, as we have seen, took the form of a proposal that the Army set up and operate electric telegraph lines between every major tactical headquarters and the nearest commercial telegraph office. He developed his ideas carefully, and to illustrate their working, he sketched on paper what he called a field telegraph train.

Such a train, as he described it, would consist of two horse-drawn vans, each equipped as a telegraph terminal office. In addition to instruments and batteries, each would carry a great reel of wire and a handsome supply of lancepoles and insulators. No matter where a headquarters might be established, then, the train would proceed to a point midway between it and the nearest telegraph office. There the free ends of wire would be spliced, and the two vans would pay out line as they moved off in opposite directions— one to a point as near as possible to the telegraph office, the other to a point as near as possible to headquarters. Myer thought he could fit five miles of wire on each reel, and thus locate the terminals as far as ten miles apart.

Before he had got too far along with this idea, however, Myer's position was abruptly altered by a change of command. On July 26, 1861, just five days after Bull Run, McDowell was relieved by Maj. Gen. George B. McClellan; and Major Myer, presenting himself at once to his new commander, found McClellan to be as much interested in signaling as he was. It was hardly to be wondered at, perhaps—for this was the same McClellan who had witnessed the British army's use of electric telegraphs in the Crimean War.

Ever since that time, back in 1856, McClellan had pondered over those wire lines, wondering how they could be carried forward to the combat units . . . wondering, too, how the idea could be adapted to the swift advance, the quick and wide deployment, and all the other loose and free-running tactics that were, in effect, the particular repertory of an American Army experienced chiefly in fighting Indians. McClellan, to say the least of it, was well prepared for the ideas Myer had been grappling with.

But that day in late July when Myer first called upon him—still wearing the uniform of a medical officer—McClellan had little time for talk. Before his return to active duty, after an early retirement, he had been the chief engineer of the Illinois Central Railroad; and he had come to Washington fresh from his great victory in that part of Virginia that is today the State of West Virginia. He had found Washington wide open to attack, and he had found the spirit of defeatism so rampant in his new command that he at once pronounced that force unfit for service in the field.

In swift order, though, he caught up the loyalty and trust of the men, and out of what remained of McDowell's army, he built up a new force and called it the Army of the Potomac. Then, on November 1, 1861, while retaining command of that army, he succeeded Scott as General-in-Chief of the Armies of the United States.

For the moment, though, all that lay in a still distant future. In the first week of August, 1861, Myer addressed a letter to Secretary Cameron, describing the telegraph train he had put together on paper, and requesting authority to procure one such train for experimental purposes. As Cameron's lawful adviser on military signaling, Myer had every right to present his case personally. However, he chose to forward the letter through General McClellan; and it was McClellan's endorsement, apparently, that wrought the miracle—for at that particular moment there was hardly a limit to McClellan's influence at the War Department.

In less than ten days' time, the request was approved. No money was made available to cover the cost of a telegraph train, but within the hour Myer had signed the necessary contracts. Who was going to pay the bills? That, it may be stated, was just the kind of question that Myer never let stand in the way of action.

There was no doubt that Myer's telegraph train, with its reels of wire, its batteries, and its electric telegraph instruments, was approved and authorized by the War Department. True, the manner of approval was decidedly offhandish; but that, in all probability, was only one more evidence of the Department's preoccupation with a scheme that was thousands of times more vast.

Simon Cameron would leave office in the end under a heavy cloud of suspicion; but he was, when all is said, a man who was unafraid of large ideas. Long before Bull Run, he had laid before the President a proposal, unprecedented in American history, to bring the nation's railroads and telegraph lines under the supervisory control of the Army.

The principal author of that scheme was Winfield Scott, the General-in-Chief. Scott placed his ideas before the Secretary in April. Ten days later Thomas A. Scott, vice-president of the Pennsylvania Railroad, detached five telegraphers from the railroad service and sent them to Washington. Almost at once, then, the American Telegraph Company, the largest concern of its kind in the East, carried the first telegraph wire into the sacred precincts of the War Department. And on May 3, Thomas Scott entered the War Department as General Manager of Military Railroads and Telegraphs with the rank of colonel.

He was not to remain long in that post, however, for Congress quickly created a higher office for him, and before the summer's end, Thomas Scott—outranking Winfield Scott—became the Assistant Secretary of War for Military Railroads and Telegraphs. The authority bestowed upon him was enormous. By that authority, in August, 1861, he approved Major Myer's telegraph train— perhaps as a courtesy to his fellow railroader, General McClellan— and by that same authority, in the following October, he divided the work of his own office, placing the railroads in the hands of one department and assigning the telegraph lines to what would become famous, in the next few years, as the United States Military Telegraph Department. This brought together under a single head all the commercial wire lines outside of Confederate territory.

Appointed Chief of Military Telegraphs was Anson Stager, who had previously been the general superintendent of the Western Union Telegraph company. In mid-November he was commissioned a captain, three months later he was made a colonel, and by war's end, he had become a brevet brigadier general. His mission was several times defined and redefined, but the broad fact is that, from first to last, he was the commanding officer of the United States Military Telegraphs. For the greater part of the war he made his headquarters in Cleveland, Ohio, which then was a major focal point of the nation's telegraphic network.

Stager had two notable assistants, Thomas T. Eckert and Robert C. Clowry, both of whom were commissioned and both of whom were honored at the war's end for meritorious service. Eckert had been for a time the civilian manager of the American Telegraph Company's office inside the War Department. Stager placed him in charge of all telegraphic operations in the Department of the Potomac; and Eckert, too, came out of the war a brevet brigadier general.

32

Clowry had charge of operations in the West and Southwest, with headquarters first at Little Rock and afterward at St. Louis. He was a very young man; at war's end he held the rank of brevet lieutenant colonel though, even then, he was not yet thirty years old.

Stager, Eckert, and Clowry displayed a quality of teamwork that seldom has been excelled in the history of the United States Army; and it is part of their story that, after the war, all three of these men became gigantic figures in American industry. Stager resigned as vice-president of the Western Union Telegraph Company in 1881 to become the principal founder, and first president, of Western Electric. Eckert was the president of Western Union from 1892 to 1900, when he became chairman of the company's board. And Clowry was the president of Western Union from 1902 to 1910.

It becomes obvious, perhaps, that the United States Military Telegraphs operated, in Civil War days, under a magnificent leadership. Though it began with supervisory control, it took over complete operation of the nation's telegraph lines quite early in 1862. On January 15 of that year Edwin H. Stanton became the new Secretary of War, and exactly two weeks later Congress authorized the President to take over the railroads and telegraphs lock, stock, and barrel, and to operate them. Significantly, the Military Telegraph Department was thereupon placed under the control, not of an Assistant Secretary, but of the Secretary of War himself—and Mr. Stanton, whatever else may be said of him, was the kind of a man who could make his purposes and policies brilliantly clear.

Legally, the Telegraph Department was a civilian bureau within the War Department, and except for that handful of officers at the top—Stager, Eckert, Clowry, and a few others—all of its personnel were civilians. Telegraph Department operators and linemen followed the armies in the field . . . but they took orders only from the War Department.

It was a point of major interest that Clowry, Eckert, and Stager —extremely clever men—were trusted, personal friends of the even more clever Secretary Stanton; and it boded no good for Major Myer that their control over electric telegraphy, anywhere in the United States, in or out of the Army, was exclusive.

For all of that, however, one bright and shiny fact remained: In August, 1861, Major Myer was authorized to procure one field telegraph train—with a view, inevitably, to introducing electric telegraph lines to the combat zone.

Also, in August, 1861, just about the time he was endorsing Myer's letter to the Secretary of War, General McClellan directed—

33

at Myer's request—that all volunteers for signal training within the Army of the Potomac were to be separated from their parent units completely and, finally, that their services were to be offered to interested combat commanders after their training had been completed. In that way, a serious problem was solved—not perfectly, but as well as it could be within the limitations imposed by the act of 1860.

At the same time, McClellan directed Myer to organize and train a "signal corps" for the Army of the Potomac—in those days, any group of signalmen assigned to the same headquarters would be a signal corps—and directed him also to establish along the left bank of the Potomac, from a point above Harper's Ferry to a point below Washington, a chain of watch towers that would serve also as signal stations.

Both directives had been looked for hopefully. And yet they might have disconcerted anyone but Myer; for on the day they were issued every last signalman trained at Fort Monroe had joined Butler's expedition to Hatteras Inlet, and Myer was left with one instructed officer, four torches, and four flags. The officer was that Lt. Samuel Cushing who had served with Myer in the campaign against the Navajos.

Now, with the help of Cushing alone, Myer undertook a formidable task. He looked for volunteers and found them at three different infantry and cavalry camps in Maryland. He called upon the War Department for large quantities of equipment and supplies, and took what he could get. Then, with Cushing's aid, he began teaching; and the long and short of the story was that two teachers had to circulate among three camps which lay ten or fifteen miles apart. Travel was by horseback.

Left alone for the greater part of each day, the officer students made use of their time in memorizing the code and practicing with wands, while the enlisted students struggled valiantly with long-range flags. In one way, things went badly. The mysterious waving of wands and flags was too much for the unimaginative ones. It was openly derided by officers who had never seen a signalman at work —who, for that matter, had never heard of signaling—but who sneered and snorted just the same, and tried their best to dissuade the students from going on with their "contemptible flag-waving."

Myer had foreseen this, and all the while he was knuckling down to a teaching job with Cushing, he was also immersed in the work of setting up a separate, consolidated school—what became known as the Signal Camp of Instruction—at Red Hill, Georgetown, inside

34

the District of Columbia. The new school was established, and the three Maryland schools were closed out, on August 31, 1861.

Red Hill was the first big signal training center; its opening sessions were attended by a hundred or more enlisted men and by sixty or seventy second lieutenants from one or another of the combat arms. In addition to its work for the Army of the Potomac, then, this camp took on the job of meeting the demand for ever-increasing numbers of signalmen to take part in the attacks along the Southern seacoast—at Port Royal Bay, Roanoke Island, and all the other places except Hatteras Inlet, which had fallen two days before the opening of Red Hill.

Myer placed Cushing in charge at Red Hill—made him, as Cushing afterward asserted, the "post commander, quartermaster, ordnance officer, adjutant, commissary, signal officer, and superintendent of schools." As supply officer, Cushing found the prevailing prejudice against signaling to be such that "it was only by the most obstinate persistency that I could get my requisitions approved and, afterward, filled."

To prevent a further spread of prejudice, Myer had acquired two gigantic hospital tents to house the officer department of the school, and thus conceal from unfriendly eyes the spectacle of commissioned officers waving wands. The enlisted flagmen continued their schooling out of doors, however. The code was still kept secret from them, and they still were trained exclusively in the movements of the flag; but it soon became evident that some of those fellows were figuring out the code for themselves. That was a cause of increasing worry to Myer, who presently set about devising a systematic means of changing the code at regular intervals.

The oddities of Red Hill were many; but the most telltale of all was football, for this was distinctively a college game, and its appearance at Red Hill was the outward and visible sign of the presence of college men at the camp. In accepting officer volunteers for signal training, Myer had taken a clear line in favor of college graduates, and he had found, to his delight, that he could have as many of them as he wished.

There was a general dislike of them, however, for the college men of those days were intended, almost exclusively, for the ministry or medicine, and there was something to be said for the argument that they were not quite the kind the Army needed. But Myer, significantly, was just the kind of man to prefer them. He was passionately interested in the idea of a highly educated officer corps; and at Red Hill he was already consciously at work on a scheme that would have its effect, in the years to come, upon the whole Army. Thus a writer in the *Army Information Digest* for July, 1956, in describing the Army's first serious efforts to test the educational fitness of officer candidates, declared: "It was the Signal Corps . . . which instigated this major reform." Actually, the testing traces back to the Signal Department, and to Major Myer's experiment with college graduates at Red Hill.

In August, as we have seen, there had been only two signalmen in the whole Army of the Potomac: Cushing and Myer himself. But eight weeks later Myer was able to report to The Adjutant General that he had the officers and flagmen needed to man the Potomac Line—the chain of signal towers along the left bank of the river— and that he also had twenty-one signal teams ready for assignment to units in the field.

Each team comprised two officers and four flagmen. Each team was mounted, each was equipped to move, camp, and care for itself independently, and each was supported by a supply wagon that carried, along with other necessities, twelve hundred colored lights and five hundred signal rockets. It was somewhat of a triumph for Major Myer that each of the enlisted men carried a carbine.

In his report to The Adjutant General, Myer pointed out that for normal operating purposes, each team would divide itself into two half-teams, both of which would move to their respective positions at the gallop and be instantly ready, on arrival, to start signaling. Every officer had been trained to select the right perch, or flagging position; and every team, said Myer, could transmit and receive at the rate of three words a minute over distances, on a clear day, of as many as ten miles.

The teams were "advertized." Whereupon all twenty-one were promptly gathered in by various unit commanders; and it was looked upon as remarkable that each team began moving off on one hour's notice. Before they left, Myer issued to each a set of final instructions, which became, in effect, the first statement of Signal Department policy:

> *The officers in charge will report to the commanding general the readiness of the party to move with the column.*
> *It is particularly enjoined upon signal officers to proffer to the commanding general their services whenever they can be of use, as in crossing rivers, keeping up communication between different bodies of the same command.*
> *In the case of battle, signal officers should always aim to*

keep the communication between the line engaged and the reserves. . . .

No opportunity for communication should be lost at any time, each signal officer remembering that, by his readiness for duty and his expertness, he must expect to gain his distinction and the favorable notice of his commanding general.

Myer, it would seem, had been preaching that doctrine for a long time—for these twenty-one teams of signalmen, the first to serve with the Army of the Potomac, acquired at once a reputation for their special eagerness to demonstrate the value of signaling to their commanding officers.

They took the field on October 30, 1861. Then, one or two weeks later, the Potomac Line was completed, and the first messages were flagged back and forth over its entire length of eighty-five or ninety miles. This line extended from a western terminal at Maryland Heights, on the Maryland side of the Potomac just above Harper's Ferry, to an eastern terminal at Fort Washington, on the estuary several miles below the capital. It was this line that proved the effectiveness of flag telegraphy in a system of fixed relay stations, and proved its superiority to the electric telegraph in a situation hopelessly exposed to the attention of men with wire clippers. (The Baltimore & Ohio Railroad telegraphs were always being cut.) On the other hand, it was the Potomac Line that caught the imagination of the American people; and it was this line, then, that gave currency to the phrase, "All quiet along the Potomac."

Tradition ascribes that phrase to the signal officer in charge of a station that was reared above the lopped-off branches of a tree atop the precipice where the Great Seneca flows into the Potomac. Myer's regulation called for a daily report from every station above and below Washington. As a rule, these reports went forward just before sundown, and to avoid the tiresome chore of relaying so many separate messages from further up the valley the signalman one day epitomized them all in the phrase, "All quiet on the Potomac." Thereafter, receiving no report, he and his deputy made a practice of using the formula whenever it fitted the facts.

Then a correspondent of the *New York Herald,* who had been a frequent visitor at the treetop station, used the phrase in one of his dispatches; and the copy editor found it concise and telling enough to be used as a headline, but to achieve the required balance he changed one word. Then—with its lower bank—the resulting headline was:

37

ALL QUIET ALONG
THE POTOMAC

Picket is Killed by
Rebel Sniper

Ever since Bull Run Confederate snipers had been busy picking off sentries on the left side of the river, and with its explicit reference to the killing of still another, the "All Quiet" headline struck in the reader's mind a note of irony and pathos. Ethel Lynn Beers of the *New York Ledger* found it so, in any case, and was inspired by it to write the verses beginning:

> *All quiet along the Potomac tonight,*
> *No sound save the rush of the river,*
> *While soft falls the dew on the face of the dead—*
> *The picket's off duty forever.*

Her verses became immensely popular; yet Mrs. Beers was only one of a score of writers who, directly or indirectly, fed a growing popular interest in the Potomac Line. Besides the *New York Herald* man, many another newspaper correspondent also found the signal stations a heaven-sent source of information; they visited the perches daily, they copied messages straight out of the station files, and they repaid the courtesy by their published tributes to the work of the signalmen. In effect, they called the miracle of flag telegraphy —and the organizing ability of Major Myer—sharply to the attention of Congress.

In early March, 1862, the Army of the Potomac stood ready to take the offensive against Richmond. The Red Hill training camp had been closed out, and the camp commander, now Captain Cushing, had become the Chief Signal Officer on General McClellan's staff. The overall plan was to feint in the direction of Bull Run and, under cover of that maneuver, to move the bulk of the army by steamboat to Fort Monroe, on the Yorktown Peninsula, for an attack on Richmond from the rear.

On March 8, however, the situation was abruptly complicated by the appearance in Hampton Roads of the Confederate iron-clad *Virginia*, the former USS *Merrimac*, which played the devil with a considerable concentration of Union warships, sinking the *Cumberland*, forcing the *Congress* to surrender, and driving the others into the safety of shallow water. For a moment, then, it looked as if the Confederate Navy had completely frustrated McClellan's purpose.

Next day the *Virginia* sallied forth again, but this time she met the Union ironclad *Monitor,* which had arrived overnight from New York. Their hours-long battle ended in the *Monitor's* retreat. Unable to follow, the deep-draft *Virginia* then quietly retired to Norfolk. And there, surprisingly, she went into drydock. Even more surprisingly, the Confederates at once withdrew from a series of strong positions they had held along the lower Potomac; and so, at the last moment, the way was made clear for the water-borne phase of McClellan's campaign.

There had been a scare, however. There had been a time of waiting for the outcome of the *Virginia's* sorties. And while he waited, McClellan thought of something else. Accordingly, on March 9, the day the two ironclads were fighting "the most momentous naval conflict ever witnessed," McClellan wired Major Myer in Washington from his headquarters in Virginia, directing Myer to dispatch a field telegraph train to Fairfax Court House.

This order, an accidental result of an unexpected hitch in Mc-Clellan's plans, lifted Myer to the first peak of his Army career. Simon Cameron had only recently been forced out of office in connection with frauds in the letting of government contracts, and the War Department, seething under the lash of the new Secretary Stanton was too busy to concern itself with Myer's problems. But McClellan's order was all the impetuous Myer needed to set him to work, doing furiously the job he had so long wished to do. As the history of the next year and a half would prove, McClellan's order unkeyed the arch and released the avalanche; and before the War Department could catch up with events, Myer had forty or more electric telegraph trains already operating in the field. For the part he played in this affair, tradition long remembered McClellan as the godfather of the Signal Corps.

For the moment, though, all these developments lay in the lap of time. Bright and early on the morning of March 10, 1862 no teams of galloping horses went careening down to Fairfax Court House with the wonderful train McClellan had demanded; and the simple reason for that was that Myer had no such train to send forward. The one he had contracted for in the previous October had been found unfit for service. Delivered, tested, accepted, and finally paid for—after endless paper work—it nevertheless had proved a failure at Red Hill.

As the Peninusla campaign was about to begin, Myer was confronted by two difficult problems in the quest for a satisfactory train. First was the problem of transporting the batteries—the open tanks

39

of weak sulphuric acid that served in those days "to set in motion this wonderful agency or influence, the electric fluid." And second was a personnel problem, for the Military Telegraph Department had hired all the telegraphers it could lay hands on, was appealing for more, and—perhaps with a warning nod in Myer's direction—was loudly asserting its exclusive and prescriptive right to their services. So far as Myer could learn, there was not a single telegraph operator left in Washington to help man a field telegraph train.

In the face of these difficulties, Myer cast about for new ideas. On March 10, the day after he had sent his fateful message to Myer, McClellan launched his offensive in the direction of Bull Run and, seven days later, he began the movement of his main force to Fort Monroe.

Although Cushing was the Chief Signal Officer, Army of the Potomac, he took no part in this campaign, but instead, at his own request, remained in Washington, where he took charge of Myer's office in G Street, thus relieving Myer of a difficult chore and enabling him to follow the army in the field. In effect, the Chief Signal Officer, A.P., and the Signal Officer, U.S. Army, changed places; and not the least of Myer's services in the Peninsula was to reorganize the A.P. Signal Corps along lines that today would doubtless be called functional.

Cushing's offer to remain in Washington is explained in part by the large amount of work being done at that crowded G Street office; for by March of 1862, Myer had multiplied his own activities many times over. In particular, he had set up a center for the testing and distribution of signal equipment and signal stores; and he had brought in two officers to develop in a hurry some form of cryptographic machine. Myer's office had become, in effect, the Army's first signal laboratory.

There was reason enough for Myer's interest in cryptography. He was annoyed that the enlisted flagmen at Red Hill had by this time broken the flag-telegraph code; but what whipped and stung him to furious action, and what gave urgency to the project, was a report from Hilton Head, off the coast of North Carolina, that Confederate signal officers, armed with telescopes, were concealing themselves in the tall swamp grasses of the mainland, and with admirable skill were reading the combat orders of the Union commanders.

Out of the new project came a variety of mechanical devices for changing the code. The best was essentially a disk to which a revolving smaller disk was attached by a center pin. The letters of the alphabet were inscribed on the smaller disk, and on the larger

40

one was inscribed various combinations of the number 1 and number 2 movements of the flag. In a later form, the letters of the alphabet appeared on the smaller disk in random order, and finally a form was arrived at in which the alphabet was scrambled in a variety of different ways on a variety of smaller disks, any one of which was attachable to the larger disk.

From time to time, and from place to place, it passed through minor changes, but essentially this last was the "cipher disk" that won for the Signal Department unaccustomed praise, and that was used by Union Army signal officers throughout the remaining years of the Civil War.

More than Myer, though, it was Captain Cushing who supervised the cipher project—in addition to caring for a multiplicity of other tasks devolving upon the Office of the Signal Officer. From first to last, Cushing's administration of the office was exceptionally good and in this assignment, so close to the War Department, the captain made a reputation for himself as a charming person, immensely easier to get along with than Myer was. He won the personal friendship and favor of several highly placed officers, and for a time there was talk of his being made a lieutenant colonel—in which case he would have outranked Myer. But nothing came of that. The story goes that, out of loyalty to Myer, Cushing rejected the promotion and thereby offended those who had laid themselves out to help him.

Unquestionably, and as early as this, there were a few unpleasant fellows out gunning for Myer, whose chief offense, apparently, was that he answered carping criticism by a show of stiffnecked imperturbability and pride. It was a well-known technique—effective, but enraging, and somewhat out of place in the Army. Yet Major Myer could win the loyalty of a superior like General McClellan and a subordinate like Captain Cushing.

From Myer's point of view, the Peninsula campaign was twice notable: it was the first major offensive in modern times to have the support of a fully organized system of flag telegraphy; and it was the first in history to witness the use of the electric telegraphy well forward of army headquarters.

Myer had reorganized the signalmen, assigning teams and groups to three separate functions—reconnaissance, fire control, and general communication. Officers and men of the reconnaissance service kept the scouting and security patrols in instant touch with the columns they protected; and at the head of each advancing column, by order of General McClellan, were two signal teams—one with

41

white flags for general-service messages, and the other with red flags for directing the fire of the supporting artillery and gunboats. On the peninsula, there was hardly a fight in which fire control was not in the hands of Major Myer's signalmen.

There was hardly a day when the signalmen were not among the first to enter a new position or among the last to leave an abandoned one. In the sunny days, when the drive was prospering, signalmen on more than one occasion had to be restrained from entering positions the Confederate forces had not yet been driven out of.

The sunny days were coming to a close when the telegraph train arrived. It was late in May, 1862, and the Army of the Potomac was already approaching Richmond. McClellan had pitched his tent near Williamsburg, and his Chief of Cavalry, Brig. Gen. George Stoneman, was at Mechanicsville, within seven miles of the Confederate capital. Though he had taken the better part of three months to do it, Major Myer had finally succeeded in piecing together and delivering the train that McClellan had ordered in early March.

The principal item of the train's equipment was a more or less new type of electric telegraph set called a Beardslee. This had been patented by George Beardslee in 1859, and—justly or otherwise— it was held in scorn by the commercial telegraph companies. However, it had the peculiar advantage of requiring neither a battery nor a trained operator. Also it had the immense advantage of having been rejected by the Military Telegraph Department. In choosing an instrument in which that department had no interest, Myer, to say the least of it, was acting with prudence.

The Beardslee telegraph required no battery because it had a built-in magneto; and it was operable by anybody who could read and write. Outwardly, it consisted of little more than a dial and pointer. The letters of the alphabet and the numerals appeared in sequence round the face of the dial, and—to transmit a message— a soldier had only to seize the pointer by its knob and, as it were, to move it round and round the clock, pausing briefly before each of the letters needed to spell out the words. By moving the pointer he also moved a pile of magnets, and so produced the current required to move the pointer of the distant instrument. And to receive a message the soldier had only to watch the jerkily moving pointer and note the letters in the order in which the pointer called them out.

It goes without saying, perhaps, that the first electric telegraph ever used by the United States Army posed for its operators a difficult problem of synchronism; but it had its good points just the

42

same, and as long as it stayed synchronized, an experienced soldier could transmit and receive at the rate of fifteen words a minute—which was five times the speed required of the flagmen trained at Red Hill.

Myer's train was placed in service between McClellan's headquarters and Stoneman's; and for the first time in history, then, a field commander was in touch with a subordinate headquarters by Army wire. The arrangement lasted from May 24 to June 26, when the Confederate victory at Mechanicsville sealed the doom of the great Peninsula campaign; and the best that could be said for it was that in that period of thirty-three days, an indifferent sort of telegraphic service was maintained. It was a point worth Myer's remembering, on the other hand, that the Military Telegraph Department had all along been building pole lines in the Peninsula, and before the end was operating Morse telegraph systems as far forward as corps headquarters.

Myer was greatly disappointed that his soldier-operated train—which could rush in almost anywhere in almost no time at all—had turned out so poorly. But Myer was also quick to search out a number of ways in which he could improve matters. The reels of wire, for example, contained only four miles of inferior copper line coated with gutta-percha instead of the five miles of properly insulated wire he had counted on getting. And a good part of the trouble had been due to the cutting of the wire by Union soldiers who had heard about the miracle of electric telegraphy, who were anxious to send home to their families as souvenirs a few inches of the wonderful wire, and who had no idea that their snitching such tiny bits would be noticed. In the future, Myer decided, patrols would be needed to defend his wire.

Before the end of another year, the ever-sanguine Myer had his two-score telegraph trains in service in various combat zones. But one fateful consequence of that was to stir dissatisfaction with the Beardslee and to give rise to a widespread demand, among signal officers, that Morse telegraphy be substituted for the Beardslee system. When that cry went up, an overworked Myer, suffering the cumulative effects of chronic fatigue, was thrown abruptly into a violent row with the powerful Military Telegraph Department.

Meanwhile, with notable consequences for the future, signal flags made their first appearance in combat west of the Appalachians. This was in late March of 1862, just as the Peninsula campaign was getting under way; and, as happened at Bull Run, the flags were in the hands of Confederate signalmen.

43

At Pittsburg Landing in April, General Sherman confessed he had never heard of signalmen. A few days later a signal team sent out by Major Myer was arrested outside of Grant's headquarters by an officer who declared that only the Confederate Army had signalmen and that Myer's men, therefore, must be spies. A few days later the "ex-spies" were having trouble keeping back the crowds of spectators they attracted, and when the flagging ring was invaded once too often, an exasperated signalman roared at the intruder an angry, "Get out of here!" The intruder this time was General Grant, receiving his first impression of flag telegraphy.

Back in the East, and just a month or two after the close of the Peninsula campaign, General Lee crossed the Potomac some thirty miles above Washington, and he had reached the outskirts of Frederick, Maryland, before the tail end of his supply train was discovered—by a signal officer—steadily and smoothly fording the river. The signalman was at the Sugar Loaf Mountain perch, an inland backup station supporting the Potomac Line; and his report, flagged to the mainline station at Point of Rocks, was believed to be the first that Washington had had of an invasion that was already two days old.

Beset by scores of other problems, Myer was dumbfounded by that freakish failure that allowed a whole army to slip unseen through the highly publicized Potomac Line. And Myer was confronted by still more problems when it turned out that the invasion had in fact been instantly detected and instantly reported, but that a misuse of cipher disks had prevented one station from understanding what another station was trying to say, and that a misguided sense of responsibility had prevented one signal officer from flagging forward a message he could not understand.

Myer would have been less than human if his misery was not increased by finding out that the Secretary of War, without the help of signalmen, had been aware of what Lee was up to, and had promptly set the Army of the Potomac marching for Frederick.

The South's success in using Myer's signaling system contributed substantially toward the belated adoption of his methods by the Union. With this, came authorization for the establishment of the Army's Signal Corps.

The Birth of the U.S. Army Signal Corps

✠ DAVID J. MARSHALL, *U.S. Army Signal Center*

From his office in G Street, Washington, Major Myer had long been waging a campaign for an independent signal branch that would have a status comparable to that of the infantry, the cavalry, or the artillery. Before the close of 1861, he had urged upon the Secretary of War, Simon Cameron, a very precise plan for converting the Signal Department into a signal corps with officers and troops of its own. On learning that the Confederates had created such a professional corps, Myer intensified the battle.

He had, of course, a great new ground for his argument: the ground that the Union army could not afford to be excelled by the Confederate army in any field at all. But he would now no longer be facing Simon Cameron. He would be dealing, instead, with Edwin H. Stanton. . . . Myer labored hard to gather all the information he could find to support and buttress his argument.

As the law stood, the Signal Department could only train signalmen and send them back to the combat arms; and, on the whole, the department had been doing this job well. But there had been difficulties. There was the need, for example, to hunt out officers and men of the combat arms and persuade them to volunteer for signal training; and there was still that basic difficulty of holding onto the trainees. In spite of all that Myer could do, disappointingly large numbers of these continued to be recalled by their unit commanders before they had learned anything useful.

In the summer of 1862, on the other hand, Myer was aware of all the new tricks that signalmen were learning in the field, and he was strongly of the opinion that there ought to be a way of keeping the earlier-trained signalmen abreast of these developments. But the Signal Department had no way of doing this, nor any way of guarding against a general deterioration of efficiency on the part of signalmen once they had passed beyond the training stage. For that matter, the department had no way even of keeping itself abreast of the experience the men were accumulating in the field.

There was still another difficulty, perhaps the worst of all: Under the Signal Department's operating system, the arguments were, on balance, decidedly against any man's volunteering to accept signal training. The story was already going round, for example, that within a combat unit there could be no hope of promotion for a signalman. And, apparently, there were good grounds for that opinion. No matter how well he learned his job, or how unflinchingly he stood up to his duty under fire, a signal officer in the eyes of a combat commander would always be a signal officer, and a flagman would always be a flagman, and there could be no reason why the one should be a captain or a major instead of a lieutenant, or why the other should be a corporal or a sergeant instead of a private.

That, from Myer's point of view, was not a good situation; and it was being made worse by the average combat commander's refusal to allow a good signal officer to revert to his former assignment and thus resume his place in the line of promotion to a combat command. The moral was glaringly apparent that the more skillful a signalman became, the worse his chance of promotion would be; whereas the signalman who deliberately garbled his messages stood a good chance of being returned to combat service where, in 1862, promotions came swiftly. To Myer, it was clear that things could work out no other way, unless something radical was done about it.

Being sure that this was so, Myer addressed to the Secretary of War his letter proposing the organization of a signal corps "to serve during the present war and to have charge of all telegraphic duties of the Army." His basic argument was that in such a corps, there would be normal promotions, and there would be at least the possibility of maintaining standards of efficiency and thus of furnishing genuine signal support to the Army as a whole.

His suggestion that the proposed corps be authorized only for the duration of the war was intended, apparently, to push into the future the need of another act of Congress. Myer was attempting, as he had attempted before, to get the signal corps established and working if only on the basis of what he conceived to be the Secretary of War's emergency powers.

His reference to "all telegraphic duties of the Army" represented on the other hand, his request for control over electric as well as flag telegraphy. It was Myer's way of insisting that electric and flag telegraphy were, in substance, the same thing; and that every argument against disunity was an argument in favor of consolidating, in his proposed signal corps, centralized control over telegraphy in both of its forms.

For a time at least nothing came of all these representations.

But meanwhile combat signaling was continuing to grow in prestige, and the men in the field, by their exploits, were continuing to astonish the combat commanders—and continuing, no less, to strengthen Myer's hand. . . .

Antietam was fought in a kind of amphitheater, cradled in mountains; and flag stations commanded the whole of the battlefield and all of its approaches. From the high peak known as Washington's Monument, Lee's initial disposition of his forces, and all subsequent troop movements on the Confederate side, were observed and flagged to McClellan's headquarters. From Elk Mountain, all the redeployments of Lee's infantry, the shiftings of his batteries, the regroupings of his cavalry, were likewise observed and flagged to McClellan's headquarters—and that headquarters in turn was interconnected with those of General Burnside, on the left, and General Meade, on the right, by second-generation field telegraph trains.

As the battle approached its climax, the signal officer on Elk Mountain spotted Stonewall Jackson's cavalry racing up from Harper's Ferry, and signaled Burnside: "Look well to your left. The enemy are moving a strong force in that direction." Burnside was about to enter Sharpsburg when the signal reached him. He reacted instantly by falling back upon the bridge across Antietam Creek; and the effort to turn his flank was frustrated.

Neither side "won" the battle of Antietam; but Myer learned a little later, and presumably was comforted to know, that the Confederates thought—as one of them argued in a Richmond newspaper—that they would have won the battle had it not been for McClellan's signalmen, whose "little white flags" in the mountaintops reported every Confederate maneuver to the batteries below.

On the day before Antietam, the story goes, the Army of the Potomac's new Chief of Cavalry, Brig. Gen. John Buford, stood watching a flagman at work, then summed up the spectacle as so much *wigwagging*. It was a telling description and, cut short to wigwag, it became another name for flag telegraphy. Even Myer himself in the end came to speak of his invention as wigwag; and it was not too many years before wigwag became its official name and was used in Army publications.

In early November, 1862 Gen. Ambrose Burnside took the place of McClellan in command of the Army of the Potomac. Burnside was the general who had taken the advice of a signalman and reversed his march when Stonewall Jackson was about to turn his flank at Antietam; and Burnside, too, was the general who had called for twenty-five signal officers and fifty flagmen before the attack on Roanoke Island. He had always liked the idea. Now he was more than ever a believer in signaling.

Captain Cushing, who had relieved Major Myer in Washington throughout the Peninsula campaign, now resumed his post as Chief Signal Officer, Army of the Potomac; and it became obvious in the early planning stages that the flagmen and the telegraph trains would have roles to play in Burnside's drive on Richmond from the north. Then, early in December, General Burnside began the offensive that culminated in the Battle of Fredericksburg.

That town lay on the far side of the Rappahannock, on low ground between the river and sharply rising hills where the Confederate artillery was emplaced and ready, and where the Confederate infantry lay back of a low, but miles-long, masonry wall.

The battle began on December 11 with a frontal attack that was intended to carry across the river, through the town, and up the steep slopes back of the town. Signalmen gave tight control as, by the numbers, the pontoon bridges were thrown in place under a heavy fire from the heights. Signalmen served as fire-control parties as the artillery continued its long bombardment of the Confederate positions; and when the infantry struck across the bridges, signal parties accompanied the first wave of the assault.

Two signal officers and four flagmen of Franklin's grand division were the first men to reach the south side of the river. They galloped to a hilltop, where they set up a station and flagged back across the Rappahannock the results of their first look-around. But they had barely begun to swing flags when they drew upon themselves a concerted fire from farther up the heights. They were driven off the hills, and as they moved across an open space, all six of their horses were shot from under them.

That was in the early hours of the fight. As the situation developed, the signalmen made their way back to their hilltop, where they reestablished their station and held it till that nightfall.

When Couch's corps struck across the Rappahannock, two signal officers were in the first wave of the attack; and two days later, when the main battle was fought, they shared their signal station—in the steeple of the county courthouse—with General Couch, who made it his command post.

Signalmen accompanied the assault troops up the lower part of

48

Marye's Hill. They went as far as that stone wall that stretched for miles across the path of the attack. They plied Couch with signals from the frontline commanders, and they received his combat orders and delivered them. In going as far as the wall, they went the whole way of the attack; for back of the wall, and shielded by it, were the closely packed units of Confederate riflemen.

Meanwhile a signal station had been perched on the roof of a private house at the north end of Fredericksburg, and the Confederate artillery—commanded by Brig. Gen. Edwin P. Alexander: the same young man who had been Beauregard's signal officer at Bull Run—was quick to find out about it. By the fifth day of the battle "the roof under our feet, the trees over our heads, the houses next to ours, everything near us, was either broken, riddled by shells, or tumbled in ruins. The sentinel in front of our station was killed, several men in the house were wounded, and in a neighboring hospital fifteen of the wounded men were killed by one shell." The signalmen stood their ground, however; and at last they had to be ordered to close down their station, because it was drawing fire upon the hospital.

On the night of that fifth day of battle, Burnside's forces withdrew from Fredericksburg, leaving their dead piled three deep in many places along the wide approach to the stone wall. (The military history of the world could show few parallels to "the horror of Fredericksburg.") The troops moved back across the Rappahannock under cover of darkness, and the signalmen, using torches, had much to do with the swift and orderly execution of that maneuver. Signalmen had been the first to cross when the assault began; they were the last to leave Fredericksburg.

The badly shattered Army of the Potomac lay for the next four months on the north bank of the Rappahannock, directly opposite Fredericksburg. The Confederates made no move to counterattack. In Richmond, a few days after the fighting, General Lee was assured—but would not believe—that the last great battle of the war had now been fought; that the panic produced on the New York Stock Exchange by the Fredericksburg disaster had given rise to severe pressure upon the White House; and that peace could be expected within thirty or forty days.

The pickets of both armies patrolled the opposite banks of the river. They struck up friendships, and—off duty—they played cards together, exchanged rations, and traded coffee for tobacco. The flagmen on both sides of the river exchanged the *good morning* and *good evening* signals daily, and presently were exchanging all the gossip of their respective armies. . . . Things went on this way for four long months.

In this long period of inaction that followed Fredericksburg, while the opposing armies lay in winter camp along the Rappahannock and the war to a large extent was frozen under, the United States Army Signal Corps was born.

For a whole year Major Myer had been spending the greater part of each month in the field. He had been with McClellan in the Peninsula, and he had been with him again at Antietam. But all this time, as Signal Officer on the Army Staff, he had also been writing letters to the Secretary of War in support of his campaign for an independent signal corps.

There were signs he might succeed and, just as often perhaps, there were disappointments. Thus on April 20, 1862—when the Peninsula campaign was still in its early stages—the House of Representatives passed a bill to create a separate signal service, but the Senate allowed this bill to die in committee.

A day or two after Antietam, Myer resumed his place in the Office of the Signal Officer in G Street. There he worked a little harder to bring into existence the kind of corps he thought necessary. And just as the fall of 1862 had given way to winter, powerful help came unexpectedly out of the West. In late December, a day or two before the Battle of Murfreesboro, General Rosecrans, commanding the Army of the Cumberland, addressed a high-priority telegram to The Adjutant General in Washington in angry protest against the transfer of three of his signal officers. In the normal course of events, the telegram went before Myer; and by way of endorsement, Myer —who was thirty-five years old now—declared flatly and firmly: "I cannot supply the demand for signal officers."

That statement, simple and brief, was surprisingly effective; and on January 20, 1863, Myer followed it up with a letter in which he recalled to the Secretary of War that the Confederate States Congress at Richmond had long since created an independent signal service within the Confederate army. "The contest," he added, "is not a fair one." The inference would seem to be inescapable: The Signal Department, as organized under the Act of 1860, could not compete against the Confederate Army Signal Corps.

On March 3, 1863, the last full day in the appointed lifetime of the Congress elected in 1860, a huge appropriation bill was enacted, and—quite unimpressively—one of the clauses of this bill authorized the creation of the United States Army Signal Corps.

It was the junior of the Confederate Corps by almost eleven

50

months; and the authority of its existence was not even a separate Act of Congress, but only a clause—a rider which, at the last minute, had been stuck into the Appropriations Bill. Notably, the Signal Corps was established as a temporary organization—it was set up merely for the duration of the war.

But in spite of its temporary nature, Congress laid out in close detail the organization of the new Corps, which comprised in part:

One Chief Signal Officer, with rank of colonel . . $211 a month
One lieutenant-colonel . . . .$180 a month
Two majors . . . .$163 a month

In addition to these top-ranking officers, there would also be for every Army Corps and every Military Department:

One captain . . . .$130 a month
From one to eight lieutenants, as deemed
    necessary . . . .$114 a month

And for every commissioned officer, there were to be enlisted or detailed:

One sergeant . . . .$34 a month
Six privates, 1st and 2d class . . . .$17 and $13 a month

The enlisted men would receive ration and housing allowances in addition to their pay. But the officers would receive their salaries and nothing more; and their pay—except for the first $50—was subject to a 3 per cent income tax, deducted by the Paymaster.

There was a point about the new law that would be long remembered. Prior to this time no enlisted man could hope, as a rule, to become an officer of the United States Army. The officer corps was composed chiefly of West Point graduates, and for the rest, with few exceptions, it was made up of men who had held commissions in foreign armies and of men who, having achieved a certain status in their respective communities, were commissioned directly from civil life. But under the new law and its implementing orders, enlisted men for the first time in the history of the United States Army —not counting a handful of earlier exceptions—"were given an opportunity to become officers."

The implementing orders were composed by Major Myer. Two of their paragraphs are historic, for they represent the first serious effort made to base appointments on ability and to introduced definite and adequate tests for determining the moral as well as the educational fitness of the candidates to hold commissions:

Candidates for commissions shall be examined upon Reading, Writing, Composition and Arithmetic; Elementary Chemistry,

and the elementary branches of Natural Philosophy, and Field
Telegraphs; and . . . upon the mode of conducting Signal
parties in the field, and in the presence of the enemy, and upon
rendering the proper papers and reports . . .

No person shall be recommended for appointment . . . in
the Signal Corps who is not of good moral character . . .

A little more than six months went by—and the Battle of Gettysburg had been fought—before the Act of Congress could be fully implemented; and those six months were a period of intensive preparation . . . a period also of great confusion. It was taken for granted that Myer would be the new Chief Signal Officer, but nobody else knew what the future held. The attached personnel of the Signal Department were notified that they would all have to take and pass the prescribed examinations for admission to the Signal Corps; and, what was a great cause of difficulty, there were now more majors and captains attached to the Signal Department than there were spaces in the new Corps.

This was a curious situation brought about, the story goes, not by granting promotions to signalmen, but by the behavior of certain combat commanders who, more or less panic-struck, had pushed officers into signal training regardless of rank. In any case, the situation was such that many signal officers were forced, in the end, to accept reductions in rank in order to stay with the signal service. Many other excellent officers, unwilling or unable to make this sacrifice, returned to their parent units and thus were lost to the Signal Corps.

On the other hand, the new Corps's emphasis on brains had the effect, as Myer apparently had hoped it would, of attracting from outside the Signal Department an especially good type of candidate for both commissioned and noncommissioned rank. Such men applied for admission to the Signal Corps in large numbers, and in the competitive examinations, to Myer's great surprise, they scored "too high." The result was to pose a problem which Myer, who was ardently religious, met in his own particular way. His answer took a form of a more positive and more rigid test of morals.

The transition from Signal Department to Signal Corps was long, and was attended by undeniable difficulties. In the end, however, all the preliminary work was completed, and on September 18, 1863 Myer was appointed Chief Signal Officer with the rank of colonel, to date from March 3, 1863, the official date of the founding of the Signal Corps. Typically, the first thing Myer did was to change his

52

epaulettes to those of a colonel of the United States Army Medical Staff.

For Myer, the showdown came right after Gettysburg. The Act of Congress creating the Signal Corps had had a basis in the many schemes and proposals he had put forward; but the Signal Corps, as finally established, had no control over electric telegraphs anywhere.

That, from Myer's point of view, was bad; and Congress had barely acted when it became known that the War Department was planning steps to keep out of the hands of the new Signal Corps the forty or so telegraph trains the Signal Department had by this time placed in the field. Myer reacted to this news by addressing a confidential circular to the chief signal officers of the several armies, declaring in part: "If, in your opinion, transfer of the Field Telegraph lines and apparatus to another organization is deemed injurious to the service, it will be your duty to make such representations in writing to the commanding general."

Some time later, confessing that the Beardslee telegraph was too imperfect a thing to enable the train crews to furnish even a half-way efficient service, Myer took the decision that subsequently led to trouble. He decided to equip the trains for Morse telegraphy; and he advertised for Morse operators. In an army journal on September 8, 1863, he published an advertisement headed: "Commissions for Telegraphers."

Conflict with Secretary of War Stanton leads to Myer's removal from the post of Chief Signal Officer, and to some interesting events.

Removal of the Chief Signal Officer

✠ DAVID J. MARSHALL, *U.S. Army Signal Center*

Myer strove ardently to keep control over the electric field telegraphs. As always, he took and followed his own line. In particular, he took the position that the new law amended, but did not repeal, the act of June 21, 1860; he was able to show that Congress laid it down, in that earlier act, that the Signal Officer of the Army "shall have charge . . . of all signal duty"; and he took *all* to be the governing word of that clause. "Colonel Myer was not in favor with the Secretary of War," a close friend of his would later on recall, "and . . . his persistency in claiming that the *law* gave him the charge of all signals, both electric and other, . . . was getting him disliked."

For Myer at this time, two dates and three occurrences are significant. On September 8, 1863 he published the advertisement that offered Signal Corps commissions to Morse telegraphers. On September 18, the Signal Corps was formally activated; Myer became a colonel and the first Chief Signal Officer of the U.S. Army. And also on September 18 Myer issued a circular stating in part: "The attempt seems to be making simultaneously in the different departments to take the signal telegraph lines, and in some instances the wire and instruments, from the control of the proper officers of the Signal Corps, for the purpose of throwing the management into the hands of the American Telegraph Company. *This is injurious to the Corps, and is an interference with a part of their legitimate duties.*"

The circular went on to urge all signal officers to vigorously defend their right to control the electric telegraph trains by writing to their commanding generals and by insisting that no one use their lines except under the direct supervision of signal officers.

Four days later, on September 22, The Adjutant General took action on the newspaper advertisement. He was sharply critical of Myer. He spoke of serious harm to the interests of the Military Telegraph Department.

Myer was instant in retort, denying flatly that he had exceeded his authority. Having entered this denial, however, he proceeded quietly to point out that the advertisement had been forwarded for publication "through The Adjutant General's Office." He argued that, since he had presented it for approval prior to publication, it was—technically—not he who had published the advertisement, it was The Adjutant General himself. Then, as if to suggest that the harm to the interests of the Military Telegraph Department could not have been very serious, Myer declared that the advertisement had produced only two applications anyhow, and that neither of the applicants had been of a sort to interest the Signal Corps. He added the reminder that, even if a qualified telegrapher were to be recommended for a commission, the recommendation would still have to go to the Secretary of War for his approval.

In rejoinder, The Adjutant General notified Myer, formally and frigidly, that he had no right to recruit wire telegraphers; and almost at once a report was heard that the Department had "withdrawn" Myer's right to recruit telegraphers. The report was patently absurd. . . . Myer had taken his stand upon the act of 1860, and The Adjutant General's letter had no bearing on that.

Just the same, Myer had pinned his hope, not inconsistently, upon still another factor of the situation . . . his sufficient authority for the actual purchase of electric-telegraph trains, and for placing them in service in the field, was General McClellan's directive of March 9, 1862. Myer knew that the directive, inspired by McClellan's own confidence in the necessity of Army-controlled wire circuits, ran counter to the wishes of the Secretary of War; but he hoped that, in operation, the trains would justify their own existence and then would receive the inevitable accolade of official approval. It was this approval of the trains for their own sake, and quite apart from any question of authority, that Myer was working for in the late summer of 1863; and seen in this light, the letter of The Adjutant General was, to say the least, disturbing. It left Myer no alternative in defending the usefulness and therefore the existence of the new Signal Corps, except to fall back upon the argument he knew to be enraging—the argument that his authority over the electric telegraphs forward of Army headquarters came from Congress itself.

Then, on October 27, the Military Telegraph Department placed before the Secretary of War a formal request that all the electric telegraph trains in the hands of the Signal Corps be turned over to that Department forthwith. Col. Anson Stager, the Chief of Military

Telegraphs, prepared for the Secretary a long and detailed justification of his request, and in this he made a series of assertions: "The Field Telegraph of the Signal Corps . . . has failed to meet the requirements of the military authorities. On several occasions . . . the Commanding General directed the operators of the Military Telegraph to take possession of the field telegraph wire and operate the same . . . after the Signal Corps had repeatedly failed to transmit with accuracy or promptness the important dispatches entrusted to it. To overcome these failures and to make the Field Telegraph a feature of the Signal Corps, it has become necessary for it to adopt a system"—the reference here is to Morse telegraphy—"which requires the practical experience of military telegraphers, and the Signal Corps is now making efforts to secure the best electricians in the service by offers of rank and increased pay, which it is enabled to do through its military organization, an advantage not possessed by the Military Telegraph Department."

Colonel Stager concluded his letter by recommending "that the management of all field and military electric telegraphs be confined to . . . the United States Military Telegraph Department, or that that Department be abolished . . ."

This demand for a final showdown was under advisement when Secretary Stanton laid hands, apparently, on a copy of the circular Myer had issued to the Signal Corps three weeks earlier, ascribing to the War Department a scheme to take the wire lines away from the Signal Corps "for the purpose of throwing the management into the hands of the American Telegraph Company." This, on the face of it, was only another way of saying that Stanton's purpose was to increase the profits of the American Telegraph Company, and that allegation was all the more serious because Stanton was, in fact, a director of the Atlantic & Ohio Telegraph Company and a very close friend of the president of the American Telegraph Company.

On November 10 Myer was peremptorily ordered to appear before Stanton who was, among other things, the foremost lawyer of his day, and who had a reputation for approaching an adversary as he approached a hostile witness for cross-examination—"like a tiger."

For a certainty, Stanton was not a man to be trifled with. It was true that he was a wealthy man, and that some of the wealth was invested in the telegraph business; but it was also true that he was a tremendous fighter for personal and public honesty. He had twice insulted Lincoln, yet Lincoln held him in great respect—precisely because of his unshakable honesty. He became the Secretary of War six weeks before the start of the Peninsular Campaign, and he worked at high pressure for the almost incredible total of twenty hours a day, seven days a week, for five consecutive months. It was said of him that he worked under a head of steam of two hundred pounds to the square inch—which in those days would have exploded the biggest locomotive boiler in the world.

Harsh and peremptory, but tremendous in action, he uncovered fraud after fraud in the War Department, he threw out a horde of dishonest contractors, he threw out another horde of corrupt officials, and when his curt commands were carried out, at least the armies were well supplied. On the whole, Stanton was not the kind of man who would let pass suggestion that his policy—and every War Department policy was Stanton's own personal policy—had back of it an improper motive.

It is not on record what Stanton said to the thirty-six-year-old Colonel Myer at their interview of November 10. But nobody should have been surprised that Colonel Myer emerged from that interview "crushed and shaken"—and stripped of his assignment.

Pending the outcome of researches now being made in the Department archives, the story of all that happened to Myer has yet to be told. We know, however, that his appointment to be Chief Signal Officer had not yet been confirmed by the Senate; and we know that Stanton at once withdrew the nomination. Apparently, too, Stanton began the prescribed process of stripping Myer of his commission. . . .

Immediately, then, by order of the War Department, the Signal Corps turned over to the Military Telegraph Department all its field telegraph trains, all its electric telegraph equipment, and all personnel who had been trained in the operation of electric telegraphs.

Myer had been called before Stanton on November 10. The interview had barely ended when WD Special Order No. 499 was placed in his hands, directing him to proceed at once to the headquarters of the Army of the Mississippi at Memphis, Tennessee, where he would serve—temporarily—as Signal Officer. In the late afternoon of that same day, Myer addressed a farewell letter to the Signal Corps, bidding the officers and men goodbye, thanking them for "the zeal and gallantry with which they have brought forward this infant arm of the service," and expressing the hope that, "directed by others, their progress may meet with better success and higher regard."

On Myer's removal from command, the Assistant Adjutant General—Brig. Gen. Edward Canby—was directed by Stanton to audit the accounts of the Signal Corps; and five days later, on November 15, 1863, Maj. William J. L. Nicodemus became the Acting Chief Signal Officer. Up to this time Nicodemus had had charge of signal training activities; and three years before this, in the campaign against the Navajo, Canby had been the first commanding officer to witness the use of signals in combat. His audit showed the receipts and expenditures of the Signal Corps, throughout the Myer administration, to balance perfectly.

Nicodemus served as Acting Chief Signal Officer for a little more than one year. In the course of that year, in May of 1864, he moved his office to a larger building in F Street; and there he installed a printing press for use in turning out the required hundreds of copies of orders, circulars, and letters addressed to signal officers in the field. It was the first Signal Corps printing press, and toward the close of 1864 Nicodemus used it to print his annual report, in which he criticized the West Point authorities for their attitude toward military signaling, boldly recommended that the field telegraph trains be returned to the Signal Corps, and revealed in a score of other ways an attitude that was distinctly, and loyally, Myer's own attitude. Then, having printed his own report, Nicodemus distributed copies throughout the Signal Corps, without the prior approval of the Secretary of War—and that was what brought the thunder and lightning down upon his head.

When Stanton heard about the distribution of a report which he himself had not yet seen, his reaction was instant and typical. He sent a detachment of troops to take over the Office of the Chief Signal Officer and to seize the printing press, the original manuscript of the report, and all printed copies still remaining on the premises. It goes without saying, perhaps, that as quickly as Stanton could lay hands to paper, Nicodemus was summarily stripped of his commission and dismissed from the service. . . . But here again, it would seem, the skeins of history are tangled; for it was not long before the ousted Major Nicodemus turned up as Lt. Colonel Nicodemus. . . .

On December 26, 1864, Lt. Col. Benjamin B. F. Fisher succeeded Nicodemus as Acting Chief Signal Officer, and because the Senate had not yet confirmed his formal nomination for the post, Fisher was still the Acting Chief Signal Officer at the close of the Civil War.

At the time of his dismissal as Chief Signal Officer, back in early November, 1863, Myer left Washington at once for Memphis. There he took over as Chief Signal Officer, Army of the Mississippi, and almost at once got himself transferred to Cairo, Illinois. He had barely arrived in Cairo when he persuaded the commanding officer there to give him ten days' leave, and from Cairo he rushed on to Cleveland, Ohio, the headquarters of the United States Military Telegraph Department.

The superintendent of the Military Telegraphs was that Col. Anson Stager, whose letter to the Secretary of War, demanding a showdown on the question of the electric telegraphs, had done so much to bring about Myer's downfall. Now Myer confronted Stager face to face, told his side of the story—and won the tremendous respect, and the cordial friendship, of that astonished man.

The two men sat down together and drew up a tentative procedure for governing the future relations of the Telegraph Department and the Signal Corps; and Stager undertook to lay the procedure before Stanton for approval. Under the arrangement agreed upon, the Signal Corps would receive back its wire facilities, but the recruitment of wire telegraphers for service in the Signal Corps would be in the hands of the Military Telegraph Department. Stager summed up one aspect of the agreement when he declared himself impressed by Myer's "suggestion of combining at Army headquarters the duties of the field lines of the Corps in the hands of the experts from the Military Telegraph, commissioned in the Signal Corps." The important point was that the Signal Corps would be responsible for all telegraphy forward of army.

But the proposal so readily agreed upon was never approved by Stanton. Stanton had something to say about it, though. He called the matter to the attention of The Adjutant General, and General Canby, the Assistant Adjutant General, was directed to find out why, and by whose authority, Myer had been in Cleveland. Canby's letter calling Myer to account was written from Washington on March 21, 1864; and on April 16 Myer replied to Canby in a courteous letter that was notable for its detailed explanation.

This letter was received in Washington at quite a tremendous moment of the war, and the wonder was that Canby would have found the time to read it. There was a particular trouble spot that had to be attended to. The trouble spot was Mobile Bay, and what made Mobile Bay important was its great and furiously busy shipyards. Newly launched upon the bay, though not yet ready for sea, was the latest Confederate ironclad, the C.S.S. *Tennessee*, a monster of unheard-of size with a hide of armor plate five inches thick. For some time now the lamps had been burning late in Washington. . . .

Of course, it would be a joint operation. Admiral Farragut would command the naval forces and—what caused considerable surprise—Canby himself, raised to the rank of major general, was chosen to command the land forces. He arrived at his new headquarters on May 7, 1864, and then, as commanding general of the Military Division of West Mississippi, he drew the floodlights of attention upon himself by his choice of a Chief Signal Officer. He got the man he wanted, though. The man was Myer.

So, after seven months in exile, the former Chief Signal Officer of the Army was called to a responsible position. At Canby's headquarters he swiftly organized a signal training group. He trained and drilled both officers and flagmen for a joint operation of considerable magnitude. Some he drilled for service with the troops ashore. Others he drilled for service aboard the warships, where signal officers of necessity would do their own flagging.

He laid hands on a couple of field telegraph trains which the Military Telegraph Department had discarded, and—within Canby's command—he again made Signal Corps men responsible for wire telegraphy. . . . It can be argued that Canby had been through all that, and that Canby stood responsible. It can also be argued that Myer believed his understanding with Stager, so carefully expounded in his letter to Canby, had had a real effect upon the situation. It can be argued, too, that Myer would not have had the temerity to do this if only he had had the cunning to think of his own career first and the Army next. But it needs no arguing, perhaps, that an IG [Inspector General] report finds its way, almost invariably, to Washington.

Within a week or two of his reporting to General Canby, Colonel Myer proposed a new service which Canby assigned at once to the Signal Corps. Canby's order of May 30, 1864 read: "Deserters, refugees, and other persons coming in at any military post in the Division of West Mississippi, or any of the spots on the east bank of the Mississippi River, will be carefully examined by a discreet officer, and the information obtained from them compared and collated with that derived from scouts and other sources, and reported direct to the Chief Signal Officer at these headquarters, Natchez, Mississippi. . . ."

Subjoined to this order was the statement of Colonel Myer: "I have the honor to . . . request that the duty of procuring, collating, and forwarding the information . . . be assigned to some particular officer . . . of your command, and . . . [that such information be] reported at once to the Chief Signal Officer at these headquarters."

60

This is said to be the first effort ever made in the United States Army to systematize and develop this particular source of military intelligence. . . .

Meanwhile, besides all his other work, and surrounded by feverish preparations for the coming campaign, Myer found time to write a field manual for joint use by Farragut's fleet and Canby's land force. This was the famous *Manual of Signals*. It brought up to date the many developments which had taken place in the art of flag telegraphy since the beginning of things in the Navajo campaign of 1860; and down to the present hour it continues to be spoken of as the first Signal Corps manual. However, it was published privately, out of Myer's own pocket; and it was used, apparently, only within Canby's command and, by Army signalmen, within Farragut's. In the end, Farragut was deeply impressed by the service the Army signalmen afforded him, and said so in a letter of commendation which he addressed to Myer.

The campaign so long in preparation was launched on August 4 with an assault on Dauphin Island, west of the entrance to Mobile Bay. Myer was present with the landing force on this occasion. He and his aides coordinated the land-sea attacks on Fort Gaines, and two days later, as the ranking Army officer present, he accepted the surrender of the fort. He was the first signal officer ever to perform such a function.

The main battle began just before sunup on August 5, with Army signalmen perched upon the topmasts of the fighting ships—like, as one of them said, "the angels at the tops of Christmas trees." Admiral Farragut paid the highest tribute to their work, and the admiral's compliment was one of the triumphs of Myer's life. But the moment of triumph was brief.

For on that same day, August 5, 1864, General Canby received a directive from the War Department, declaring that Myer was not an officer of the United States Army and was not to be allowed to serve as one. . . .

The mystery of what Myer did next would seem to be a mystery still. It is made piquant by the revelation, long after the fact, that Myer had played a hero's part at the Battle of Allatoona Pass. . . . At the end of August the Confederate General Hood withdrew from Atlanta and began a series of raids on Sherman's long supply line, with a view of forcing General Sherman back into the Tennessee Valley. On October 3, Hood went after the supply depot of Allatoona with its rich store of three million rations and seven thousand head of cattle. Essential facts were: (1) that the depot was defended by a garrison so small it could not hold out for long against a heavy assault; and (2) that Hood's army stood between the garrison and Sherman's army. General Corse was at Rome, however, with a force of roughly fifteen hundred men; and, signaling over the heads of the intervening Confederate army, Sherman directed Corse to race to the aid of the garrison, thirty-six miles away. His message went by flag telegraphy to Allatoona Pass and from there by wire to Rome.

Sherman's headquarters was at Vining's Station, and from there contact with Allatoona Pass was through a flag relay station perched at the top of Kennesaw Mountain. Cut off and surrounded by Confederate cavalry in the first day's fighting, the relay station nevertheless continued operating; but early next day a heavy fog settled down, and contact was lost. Then, as the Confederate forces were closing in on Allatoona, helped along by that same fog, the signal station at the Pass had to be abandoned. But the signalman transferred himself and his flag to the rampart of a nearby fort, and when the fog lifted that afternoon, he was in touch again with the relay point . . . It was October 5, 1864.

At Vining's Station that day Sherman stood beside the flagging ring for hours, issuing commands—"Hold the fort"—encouraging the garrison—"Corse is coming"—and eagerly awaiting news of the battle. It was the first time in history that a commanding general had fought a battle by remote control, and when he received word of the final victory, he told the signalmen their services had been worth a million dollars to the Government.

Nor was he satisfied to drop the matter there. Instead, he laid himself out to do what a general in the field has little time to do: he wrote a long letter to the War Department, in the course of which he declared: "Had it not been for the services of this Corps on that occasion, I am satisfied we should have lost the garrison at Allatoona, and a most valuable depository of provisions there, which was worth to us and the country more than the aggregate expense of the whole Signal Corps for one year."

Sherman was not alone in being pleased. The newspapers seized upon the story, and the people were deeply stirred by what seemed to them the miracle of flag telegraphy. Presently the feat was celebrated in a long poem which appeared in *Harper's Magazine* under the title of "The Flag That Talks," and for the next half century revival meetings all over the country rang with the words of a favorite hymn: "Hold the fort, for I am coming . . ."

Back of all this, apparently a secret member of General Sherman's staff, stood the figure of Albert J. Myer.

As we have seen, the Confederacy was quick to grasp the significance of the new system for military signaling, establishing its own Signal Corps early in the Civil War. Because of the favorable attitude maintained toward the fledgling branch of the Confederate army by both the civil and military heads, and because of its outstanding leadership and the professional skill of its members, it rendered invaluable service to the South throughout the Civil War.

The Confederate Army's Signal Corps

✠ DAVID J. MARSHALL, *U.S. Army Signal Center*

The Confederate States Army Signal Corps was the first independent branch of professional signalmen in the military history of the world. It was organized in the spring of 1862, when McClellan was in the Peninsula and the Army of the Potomac was battering its way toward Richmond. True, there was back of it the history and the combat experience of many small signal units. But formally, as an independent branch, it dated from the nineteenth of April, 1862—four score and seven years to a day after the historic ride of Paul Revere, whose "one if by land and two if by sea" had made him the exemplar, if not the first great hero, of all American signalmen.

The Confederate Corps was a remarkable organization, and it was heir to a number of remarkable predecessor organizations. It used the Myer system of flag telegraphy; and one of its branches specialized in reading the combat orders of Union commanders. It also used electric telegraphy—which Myer's men were forbidden to do. It was authorized to take over and use commercial wire circuits anywhere any time. And finally, it had the two "most romantic" missions: military intelligence and blockade running. Espionage was their inevitable corollary.

The whole responsibility for military intelligence was in the hands of the Confederate Signal Corps; and that, if it seems odd today, seemed only reasonable then. Myer himself had argued the affinity of intelligence and communication, and surely the Confederate signal officer who specialized in reading Union army combat signals was an intelligence officer. The idea was at least more reasonable, and in practice it proved immensely more effective, than the arrangement made on the Union side of the war, where the intelligence mission, for a time at least, was committed to the Pinkerton Detective Agency.

The Secret Service was the undercover branch of the Confederate Signal Corps; and that branch had operatives, both military and civilian, both men and women, who worked inside the Union lines, in cities all over the North, and in all the key cities of the British Isles and of continental Europe. They gathered military supplies as well as intelligence. They formed a network, a regular spider's web of communication lines, that had its focus and nerve center in the private office of the Chief Signal Officer. It was the latter's duty to report to Jefferson Davis every morning, and to place before him the clear versions of incoming dispatches, the bulk of which were enciphered.

Military information from the North was received on regular schedule three times a week, but the newspapers came in daily through Washington. The Baltimore papers arrived on the day of publication, and the New York papers one day after publication. Mail to the operatives up North or in Europe was relayed by couriers to a secret signal camp on Mathias Point, and from there was rowed across the Potomac and posted inside Washington. And so too were the reports of a certain New York newspaper correspondent who was supposed by his editor to be in Washington but who actually was in Richmond and in the pay of the Confederate Signal Corps. . . .

For nearly four years, too, the Confederate Signal Corps maintained a secret flagging station within a block or two of the War Department in Washington. This station was in hourly touch with a sister station across the Potomac, deep in Confederate territory. Its presence in the heart of the Federal capital was undiscovered to the end.

During all those years Confederate signalmen were ferried back and forth across the Potomac in considerable numbers. A Confederate sympathizer, Thomas Jones of Maryland, was one of the ferry masters. He was arrested in Washington at least once in 1861, but a few months later he was back at his job, at the personal request of the Confederate Chief Signal Officer; and from that day to the war's end he maintained his secret ferry service without a hitch, dispatching boats two miles across the Potomac as many as four times in a single night.

On the other hand, it was the Chief Signal Officer and his military aids who directed and controlled all blockade-running operations. They chose the hour and the point at which the effort would be made, by sea or by land. They assigned the secret identification signals to every ship and every overland packtrain. They arranged for their physical protection; and they arranged also for attacks and diversions that would open up pathways, by land or sea, into Confederate territory.

It was a tribute to the valor of American signalmen that those on the Confederate side, no less than those on the Union side, achieved their greatest fame in combat; and it was not for nothing that signalmen before long were looked upon as the proudest, cockiest swaggerers in the whole Confederate army.

The art of combat signaling made a curious appeal to Southerners; Lieutenant Alexander's case was typical. The first thing Alexander did upon joining Beauregard's staff was to make signalmen of his own two brothers. And when the fiery Jeb Stuart transferred himself to the Confederate cavalry, he at once looked round for a signal officer and chose for that assignment his own first cousin, Hardeman Stuart—who rose to the occasion by a superb mastery of the signalman's art. Jeb Stuart himself had volunteered for signal training at Santa Fe in the fall of 1860, the third U.S. Army officer to do so; and Myer, reluctantly, had had to turn him away.

On June 12, 1862, as McClellan's campaign in the Peninsula was approaching its climax, Jeb Stuart received orders to reconnoiter the Union commander's right flank, and under the pretext of obeying orders he carried out brilliantly one of the war's most daring raids. With twelve hundred men and two guns, he rode entirely around McClellan's army, destroying supplies, capturing prisoners, and gathering a fund of critical intelligence; and from first to last he was guided on this raid by a teen-age trooper of the Third Virginia Cavalry, Richard E. Frayser. The youngster, born and raised in the neighborhood, had been chosen for his knowledge of the countryside; and he served so well that Jeb Stuart saw to it that he was properly rewarded—with a sword from the Confederate Congress and a captaincy in the Confederate Signal Corps.

A little over two months later, Capt. Hardeman Stuart "was killed at the storming of Groveton Heights, among the foremost"; and the next day, in succession to the general's cousin, Captain Frayser became Jeb Stuart's chief signal officer.

Oddly, Stonewall Jackson also lost his chief signal officer in the assault on Groveton Heights—but only for a time, for Capt. R. E. Wilbourn, though gravely wounded, recovered in the end. And Wil-

65

bourn was at Jackson's side when, a little after 2100 hours on May 2, 1863, Jackson was reconnoitering the field at Chancellorsville . . . There was no clear line of contact, and as they pushed forward in the gathering dusk Jackson and his whole staff almost fell into the hands of Union Army troops. Fired upon, they wheeled their horses and ran for it; and, as they galloped back to safer territory, they were mistaken for a Union cavalry patrol. It was their own men who fired upon them. Sergeant Cunliffe of the Confederate Signal Corps was killed. General Jackson received three bullets. He reeled in his saddle, began to fall; and it was Captain Wilbourn, his chief signal officer, who caught him and lowered him to the ground.

A few minutes earlier, the second in command, Lt. Gen. A. P. Hill, had also been wounded; and it was General Hill's chief signal officer, Capt. R. H. T. Adams, who flagged over to Captain Frayser the signal that Jeb Stuart was now in command of Jackson's corps.

The story goes on and on to the end of the Civil War. The variations are endless, but the more we trace the story through, the more clearly we see the prominence in that war, the undeniable faithfulness and valor, of the Confederate signalman.

In addition to his brothers, Lieutenant Alexander had two other flagmen in his command at Bull Run; and those four—trained, equipped, and ready—shared with Alexander the credit for that job of signaling that went so far toward raising the battle from an almost certain defeat to a stunning Confederate victory. In the weeks and months that followed Bull Run, Alexander's tiny unit attracted scores of volunteers. It became, for a time, a training unit; and it became, in the end, the nucleus about which the Confederate Signal Corps was formed.

Meanwhile, and within a week or so of Bull Run, a call went out at Alexander's request, all up and down the Confederacy, for spyglasses and telescopes. The appeal brought a supply of glasses that lasted for several months; but the other item was in short supply to the war's end. One powerful telescope was borrowed from a citizen of Charleston, and it was this, emplaced on the Virginia side of the Potomac, that was used for reading signals of the Confederate flagmen inside Washington. Smaller telescopes were received on loan from the astronomy departments of Southern colleges; and still others, as time went on, were brought in by the blockade-runners from Europe. . . .

Meanwhile too, in the early part of the war, other signal units, totally unconnected with Alexander's, sprang up spontaneously in the Confederate service; and one of these practiced for a considerable time the art of naval signaling. That was an outfit organized in General Magruder's army in the Yorktown peninsula. It was commanded and trained by Capt. William Norris, who had had some years' experience at sea; and its history, to say the least of it, settled the question of whether naval signaling—with its high masts, lines, and pulleys, and its large inventory of flags—could be used effectively ashore. Norris had guessed what the problems would be, but for a long time he was unwilling to admit they were beyond coping with. He gave up the effort in the end, and his unit was retrained in the Myer system of flag telegraphy. A little later still it was absorbed into the Confederate Signal Corps.

Yet, there was one signal unit that was never absorbed, but continued its own separate existence to the last hour of the war. This was a "Myer flag system" outfit from the start. Its first unit was organized by Capt. James F. Milligan at Norfolk in February, 1862, and less than two years later it comprised a battalion of nine commissioned officers and one hundred and thirty enlisted men. Throughout its long combat career, it was known to the Confederate service as the Independent Signal Corps.

On the day after Bull Run, Lieutenant Alexander was lifted over the heads of older officers and made Chief of Ordnance of Beauregard's army. In his new assignment, however, he was allowed to continue in charge of the signal mission, and presently Alexander was sending out trained signal parties for service in every part of the Confederacy.

So it was, in fact, that flag signaling made its first appearance in combat west of the Appalachians—and brought a full-scale battle to a sudden stop. It was in March of 1862. Union gunboats, at the moment, were driving home their attack on Island No. 10 in the Mississippi. A Confederate flagman placed himself atop the breastworks of a battery on the riverbank and attempted, in face of the naval gunners' fire, to make contact with a distant battery. At once the guns fell silent all around, for the signal flag was mistaken for the white flag of surrender.

A lieutenant from the Union commander's flagship went forward in a small boat to receive the surrender; and the Confederate general raced his horse madly around the river bend to find out "why the hell the battery was giving up." As the lieutenant was about to land under the truce flag, the general met him at the water's edge and confessed that he himself had also been fooled. He explained, however, that it was all the fault of "a newfangled signalman"— and he'd be greatly obliged if the Union commander would kindly resume shooting.

In October, 1861 Alexander wrote to Jefferson Davis suggesting

67

one line of fixed flag-relay stations along the Eastern seacoast—where the Union forces were carrying on their historic joint operations—and similar lines between vital points in the West, where the wire shortage was acute. Davis approved the suggestion promptly and with an unexpected show of enthusiasm; and out of this exchange of letters came, among others, the famous Mississippi Line.

It was this way: New Orleans fell in April and Memphis fell in June, 1862; and after that the Confederate forces had undisputed control of only two hundred miles of the Mississippi extending from Vicksburg in the north to Port Hudson, Louisiana, in the south. To capture this final reach of river, and thus to drive a wedge between two parts of the Confederacy, a joint force under Cdr. David Porter and General Grant struck down from Memphis while another joint force, under Admiral Farragut and General Banks, struck up river from New Orleans.

At the siege of Vicksburg, beginning in late May, 1863, the Interception Service, Confederate Signal Corps, picked up a message, Porter to Grant, in which the naval commander protested against having to divert his gunboats from fighting to other purposes. The commander of the city decided that this was a hopeful sign. Instead of surrendering, as he had planned to do, he held out a little longer.

After a siege of forty-five days, Vicksburg surrendered on July 4, 1863, the day after Gettysburg, and Grant had the fact of the surrender flagged to Porter. This message too was picked up by Confederate signalmen, who swiftly passed it down the Mississippi Line to the military commander at Port Hudson. This officer decided that the news was anything but a hopeful sign. Instead of holding out a little longer, as he had planned to do, he surrendered at once. And for having had this unforeseen effect, Grant's message to Porter was seized upon by the newspapers and played up as "the most momentous signal in American history."

Credit for the great spread of signaling in the Confederate service, for the initial push, belonged in quite considerable measure to Alexander and his original unit of four flagmen—"Alexander's original four." . . .

In November, 1861, Alexander's greatly expanded unit was, by Act of the Confederate Congress, converted into the Signal Bureau, a subdivision of Sam Cooper's Adjutant General's department. The position of Chief Signal Officer, with the rank of colonel, was offered to Alexander, and Alexander turned the offer down, preferring field service to any staff position anywhere. He thereupon, toward the close of 1861, withdrew from the signal service. . . . At Fredericksburg, however, less than one year later, he was Brigadier General Alexander, chief engineer and superintendent of artillery of the Confederate First Corps.

Then as things turned out, Captain Norris—the seafaring man who had tried his luck with naval signaling ashore—became the Confederate Chief Signal Officer with the rank of major; and Lt. William N. Barker became his chief assistant. Barker was one of the original four who served with Alexander at Bull Run.

Early in 1862, just as Norris was settling down in his new assignment, the Confederate service produced the world's first signal manual, an admirably complete "pamphlet of instruction" covering the Myer system of flag telegraphy. It was classified *Confidential,* and the Confederate Secretary of War was careful to point out in his report to Jefferson Davis that there was in it everything about the "principles of the art" but nothing at all that might betray the key to any cipher. It was in print for a whole two years before Major Myer was able to publish a manual of his own. Its author was J. H. Alexander, one of the two brothers of E. P. Alexander and, like Barker, one of the original four.

As created by the act of April 19, 1862, the Confederate States Army Signal Corps was, like the Signal Bureau before it, under the immediate supervision of enthusiastic Sam Cooper. At first, the Corps consisted of a Chief Signal Officer plus ten other officers below the rank of major, ten sergeants, and such additional personnel as General Cooper might consider necessary. But the law was quickly amended; Cooper saw to that. The ten sergeants became twenty sergeants; the ten captains and lieutenants became one major, ten captains, and twenty lieutenants; and the additional personnel, selected and assigned to signal duty by Cooper himself, rose rapidly to fifteen hundred officers and men.

The Corps had barely been established when Cooper, by Special Order No. 40, directed every officer of The Adjutant General's Corps to master the art of flag telegraphy, and called upon every Confederate general to assign to the Signal Corps for training, in suitable sequence, every staff officer and aid. How many of the generals responded to Cooper's invitation no one seems to know, but every adjutant became a signalman; and it was on this account that, before long, all Confederate signal officers came to be spoken of, loosely, as adjutants.

Nor were things allowed to rest with No. 40. On the heels of that famous order Cooper assigned two signalmen—one officer and one sergeant—to the staff of every general, lieutenant general, and

69

major general in the whole Confederate Army. And presently, urged along by the adjutants, enlisted men of the combat arms came trooping into the Signal Corps for training . . . North of the Potomac nothing like that was happening to help along the cause of Major Myer.

From first to last, the Confederate signalmen were woefully short of just about everything but flags; and much of their history is explained by the shortages they endured. The flags they owed to Lieutenant Alexander, who took it upon himself as Chief of Ordnance, right after Bull Run, "to start in Richmond a little factory of signal apparatus." So flags, poles, and torches were in good supply. And so too were horses—for all Confederate signalmen, officers and men alike, were mounted . . .

Most serious was a shortage of insulated wire, required for field telegraphy. Therefore all the wire the Army could lay hands on was carefully spooled and hoarded—and much of this, it may now be stated, had to be captured from the Union forces in combat. Confederate signalmen quite early in the war learned how to raid for wire.

They never got round to adopting a uniform of their own. Signal officers wore the uniforms of the general staffs to which they were assigned; and flagmen wore the uniforms of the combat units in which they served, but with a badge of one kind or another that authorized them to enter restricted areas and, in general, to come and go without question.

And yet the Morse telegraphers had a kind of uniform. Every Confederate signalman who had qualified in that specialty had a Morse key strapped to his thigh and a sounder hung from his belt. He also, but less evidently, had a pair of climbing irons in his saddle roll. . . . He laid wire where it was called for—and if he had any —but nine times out of ten he climbed a pole and cut in on the commercial wire that was there. It was part of his job to know the route of every wire of every pole line standing in a wide zone of military operations; and the fact is that, with the help of the commercial operators in their different offices all up and down the lines, he was almost invariably able to get his message through.

Among the rarest breed of men, a kind of Signal Corps elite, were the telegraphers attached to Confederate cavalry commands. These fellows—all of whom had also qualified as flagmen—rode at the head of every such command, and during many raids into Union territory, they tapped all the wires they came across. With astonishing skill, they switched military traffic to wrong destinations, they transmitted false orders into the headquarters of Union commanders, they cast suspicion upon all orders that came by wire. And when they had finished a job, they cut all the wire in sight and took home with them as much as they could roll up in a hurry.

A Confederate army signalman, Sgt. George E. Tabb, was aboard the CSS *Virginia* when that ironclad, better known as the *Merrimac*, fought her great battle with the USS *Monitor* in Hampton Roads in early March, 1862; and that small item is important for the light it throws upon a vaster phase of Civil War history. The fact was that the Myer system of flag telegraphy had been carried into the Confederate navy, and that the Confederate navy, with possibly a few exceptions, depended upon the Army to keep it supplied with signalmen.

At sea, however, they did their best work aboard the blockade-runners; and the day was swift in coming when no ship's captain would attempt a run to harbor from the open sea without a Confederate army signal officer aboard. In this work, though, the flags and torches were retired in favor of lanterns that cast their rays of light through long tubes. Two lanterns were used. Their tubes were aimed like rifles at a particular point ashore, and generally, therefore, their lights could be seen only at, or along the line to, the target. The lights were red and green, and the code was the same as for flag telegraphy, the red standing for a leftward and the green for rightward swing of the flag.

Service aboard the blockade-runners was of course not unconnected with the Confederate Signal Corp's responsibility for the overseas procurement of military supplies.

For other reasons too it was a duty that signal officers competed for. It gave them opportunities to purchase privately abroad the many things they could not buy for their families at home. It also gave them opportunities to buy and sell general merchandise on their own accounts and to reap small fortunes on the side.

At Yorktown in the spring of 1862, the newly created Confederate Signal Corps sent up its first balloon. It was not to be compared with that of the Union Army Corps of Engineers, in service at the same time and place. The Confederate balloon was only a large cotton bag, coated over with a sticky substance to make it airtight, and attached by a cone of cords to a good-sized basket in which the observer rode. The balloon was anchored by half a mile of rope which was fed out or hauled in by a windlass. It was inflated quickly by building a great bonfire of pine knots and turpentine under a flue, the other end of which opened into the balloon. The balloon would stay aloft until the hot air within it cooled.

In this crude contraption John Randolph Bryan made three ascents. He was a twenty-one-year-old flagman serving as an aid to General Magruder when General Johnston, the army commander, requested the services of someone who was well acquainted with the country. Bryan rashly volunteered, expecting scout duty. Instead he found himself, in spite of his vigorous protests, alone in the homemade balloon, hanging above the treetops, a target of special interest to the Union batteries and sharpshooters, as he sketched their positions.

Coming down was the worst part of that first ascent. When the air in cooling allowed the balloon to settle, Bryan wigwagged to the ground crew to begin hauling in the rope. The process was perilously slow, with the ground crew sweating at the windlass and the entire Union Army, it seemed, concentrating its fire on the defenseless balloon. But somehow the balloon and Bryan escaped unhurt.

General Johnston was greatly pleased with the sketch and complimented the artist. But he received with surprise and disapproval Bryan's application for a transfer back to his former duty. "I fear you forget," he said, "that you are the only *experienced* aeronaut I have."

The descent was made less leisurely, the second time, by hitching six artillery horses to the end of the rope and riding them at full gallop down the road. The trick worked well, and the aeronaut is said to have felt a little better. . . . He was already known as "Balloon Bryan."

The third ascent was scheduled for a moonlit night, and the huge blaze that was needed to inflate the bag drew a horde of curious lookers-on. Then, as the rope was being paid out and the balloon was rising above the treetops, one of the crowd stepped into the coil beside the windlass. The rope tightened around his leg. He screamed. A comrade cut the rope with an axe, and the balloon, untethered, shot high in the air. Caught by an air current, it floated over Union territory. Another current sent it back over the Confederate lines, but far from its home ground, and now it was fired on by Confederate guns. Then a freshening wind carried it over the York at a place where the river was three or four miles wide.

Bryan began to strip for a swim. Unable to remove a pair of new and very tight shoes of which he was excessively proud, he slashed them open with his pocketknife and dropped them into the river. The water was now so near he could hear the splashing caused by the dangling rope. But suddenly the wind changed, he was blown inland near Williamsburg, and there he took a chance and slid down the rope to safety. Then he secured the balloon by tying the rope around a tree.

72

But all the time he was aloft and helpless in that free balloon, Bryan had been doing his duty, and in his own words: "The information which I was able to give General Johnston . . . enabled him to prepare for an attack which was made early the next morning, just before day. I was among those who awaited their approach, and you will pardon me if I say it gave me no little satisfaction to aim my rifle at those who had so recently and so frequently taken a wing shot at me."

What happened in the end to Bryan's balloon is not on record, but we know it was replaced by a better one almost at once; and we know that E. P. Alexander, though he had left the signal service four or five months earlier, went up at least once in the second balloon. This was the work of Dr. Edward Cheves of Savannah. According to an oft-repeated story, it was made of bits and pieces of all the silk dresses remaining in the wardrobes of the ladies of the Confederacy. According to Alexander, it was "made from silk of many patterns, varnished with gutta-percha carsprings dissolved in naptha, and inflated at the Richmond Gas Works with ordinary city gas."

Alexander saw from it the Battle of Gaines' Mill, and from it reported the crossing of the Chickahominy by General Slocum's division to reinforce Fitz-John Porter.

Later, when the Union forces reached Malvern Hill, the balloon was each day inflated at the gas works and was taken down the river on a tugboat. Ascents were then made from the boat's deck— day after day, till one fatal day the tugboat grounded during a fast-falling tide. It was July 4, 1862. The Army of the Potomac had already been eight days in retreat, and McClellan's great campaign in the Peninsula was within four days of its close. But the stranded tugboat could offer no defense. A boarding party from a Union gunboat captured the last Confederate balloon. For the Confederate Signal Corps, that was the end of aerial reconnaissance.

The Confederate cipher disk—the device for encoding and decoding signals—was invented by Capt. John Barker, who had been the fourth of Alexander's original flagmen. The device consisted, essentially, of an alphabet square to which a key word had to be applied. The first letter of the key word was found at the top of the square; the first letter of the outgoing signal was found on the left-hand margin; and at the intersection of the perpendicular and horizontal columns was found the first letter of the encoded signal.

Barker further matured his invention by pasting the alphabet square on a cylinder that revolved under a bar. The letters of the alphabet were then arrayed along the length of the bar, and a

73

pointer was moved along the bar to the letter that was first in the key word. The cylinder was then revolved until the first letter in the outgoing signal appeared under A on the bar. The pointer then rested upon the letter to be used in the encoded signal.

This equipment was in the widest use, since the Confederate Signal Corps was responsible not only for observation, scouting, battlefield surveillance, and military signaling in general, but also for encoding and decoding all official correspondence of the Confederate government.

On the Union side of the war, enlisted men were not supposed to know even the flagging code. The truth is, of course, that the Union flagmen figured it out for themselves.

On the Confederate side, these matters were differently arranged. The cipher system and the key word—which was changed every day—were not kept secret from any Confederate signalman, commissioned or enlisted. But no Confederate soldier, on the other hand, could be trained as a signalman unless he took a formal oath of secrecy. And it was perhaps the highest tribute ever paid to signalmen anywhere that, after the close of the Civil War, it could be stated that no Confederate signalman had ever deserted, and that none, so far as history knows, had ever betrayed his oath.

The impact of signaling upon tactics, foreseen by Sam Cooper, was never lost sight of by the Confederates. So an eminent ex-Confederate officer, some years after the war, wrote that he had never understood why the Union commanders gave up the use of balloons early in 1863, for even if the observers never saw anything worth reporting, the presence of the balloons, he argued, was of itself alone a cause of annoyance and delay to the Confederate forces "in trying to keep our movements out of their sight."

That same writer told of the Union army's signal station on Round Top at Gettysburg, and said that he himself, as superintendent of artillery of the Confederate First Corps, had been "particularly cautioned, in moving the artillery, to keep it out of sight of . . . Round Top." That was one of the details in his description of Pickett's charge. And further along, in his account of the battle as a whole, he wrote: "That wretched little signal station upon Round Top that day caused one of our divisions to lose over two hours, and probably delayed our assault nearly that long. During that time, a Federal corps arrived . . ."

This writer was, of course, Brig. Gen. E. P. Alexander. A few weeks later, in reply to a letter, he assured the historian of the Signal Corps Association, the Union veteran group: "You are more than welcome to the compliment I paid the signal station on Round

Top . . . I have forgiven all my enemies now; and though you fellows there were about the last I did forgive, I took you in several years ago. . . ."

After Appomatox, the U.S. Army Signal Corps moved rapidly to the verge of extinction. By the summer of 1865 only a handful of tiny units were left. One was operating a line of twelve flag stations inside Washington. Two were on the Mexican border, and two or three more were serving against the Cheyennes in what today are the States of Wyoming and Montana.

In August, however, a wire line was completed, and the signal stations in Washington were closed down. A final signal was flagged in from Red Hill to the War Department: "So passeth away the glory of the world." That's what the signal meant, but the signalmen—being gentlemen and scholars—flagged it along through all the intervening relay stations in Latin, and thereby saved four words: *Sic transit gloria mundi*. That same day they were mustered out, and there was not one signalman left on field service in the Military District of Washington.

In October the signal units on the border were mustered out; and then there were no signalmen left in the field save those on service in the Northwest. So far as anybody at that time could tell, the expedition against the Cheyennes was to be the last campaign of the Signal Corps—which, after all, had been explicitly established for the mere duration of the Civil War.

But there was a something in that Northwest situation that nobody had quite foreseen. The expedition against the Cheyennes included a notable assortment of ex-Confederate volunteers who had been taken into the U.S. Army at a moment when almost everybody else wanted only to get out; . . . and then, in the person of a dozen or more signal officers and flagmen, that old Confederate signal service became a living, throbbing part of the U.S. Army Signal Corps.

Those ex-Confederate signalmen became for a time, in fact, a predominant element of the Corps. They brought into the Corps their special way of doing things; and their way became, in some instances, the Signal Corps way. But they also brought into the Corps —what was greater than any bag of tricks—the special spirit and tradition of the Confederate Corps. During the lean years that followed the Civil War the effect of that spirit and that tradition would become ever more evident. There was a fusion; and almost a century later there would seem to be but one conclusion possible: that today's U.S. Army Signal Corps is the daughter service of those that fought on *both* sides of the Civil War.

75

Myer's frustrations and disappointments of many years were vindicated as he finally triumphed over Secretary Stanton and was reinstated as Chief Signal Officer. He went on first to preserve, then to build up the Signal Corps in the post-Civil War era.

Myer's Triumph and the Postwar Signal Corps

✠ DAVID J. MARSHALL, *U.S. Army Signal Center*

It was the day of his collision with Stanton on November 10, 1863. It was the day of the Battle of Mobile Bay. It was the day of the Battle of Allatoona Pass. Whatever the day—and it doesn't matter which—Myer chose to fight for reinstatement as Chief Signal Officer of the U.S. Army. He took the position that his removal was illegal, that the injustice to himself was intolerable, and that, as a gentleman, he had no choice but to throw down the gage and fight. He was a rich man; at least he had all the money needed to fight with. He planned an all-out war and retained as counsel the law firm of Chipman, Hosmer, Gilmore, and Brown. He launched a campaign and pushed it forward for two years on every judicial, legislative, and political front in Washington.

Politics? It was an age of politics, and Myer played politics for all he was worth—cleverly, astutely and, above all, with the dignity that became a doctor of medicine. And the hour came when Washington, in shocked surprise, could say that Dr. Myer had beaten Mr. Stanton at his own game.

As a New Yorker, Myer began his campaign by appealing to the senior Senator from New York, Ira Harris. Harris arranged to have him see President Lincoln personally, and Myer assured Mr. Lincoln that (1) he had been examined and approved by a military board, (2) his appointment was based upon the board's action and, therefore, was legal, and (3) henceforth the Executive Department had no discretion but was obliged to forward his name to the Senate for confirmation. The withholding of his name from the Senate, he added, or its withdrawal, was "contrary to law."

This interview took place, apparently, on January 2, 1865, for on that day Myer wrote Harris that "I have the promise of the President that he will not fill the office of Chief Signal Officer . . . until he shall . . . be himself satisfied" concerning the justice of Myer's claim.

On January 29 Myer placed on the desk of every Senator a "Memorial Address" in which he requested that the Senate investigate the circumstances of his removal and that, pending the outcome of investigation, the Senate refuse to confirm the nomination of any other Army officer to the grade of colonel in the Signal Corps. This address was magnificently printed on the finest paper: it took the form of a large brochure contained within an envelope, and the gossip was that the printer's bill alone ran to a thousand dollars.

Presented in such attractive dress was the whole story of Myer's connection with the Signal Corps and of his efforts to obtain reinstatement. This was Myer's own story, told by himself, but told objectively, in the third person—a plain tale, without missionary fervor, and therefore remarkably effective. As if to add to its impact, the story was backed up and supported by a series of endorsements that bore the signatures of General Grant, General Sherman, General Thomas, General Howard, Admiral Farragut, and Vice-Admiral Porter.

On February 14, 1865 Myer wrote Stanton a long and courteous letter, explicitly requesting reinstatement and denying that there had been on his part any intent of insubordination.

On March 9 the nomination of Colonel Fisher to be Chief Signal Officer was forwarded to the Senate for confirmation; and Myer demanded an investigation by the Attorney General of the United States.

He had still heard nothing from President Lincoln. He appealed once more to the Republican party leaders, and a second interview was arranged at the White House. That meeting was scheduled for the morning of April 15, 1865.

On the night of April 14 Lincoln was shot.

On June 28, 1865 Myer addressed to the new President, Andrew Johnson, a letter beginning: "I respectfully request that I may be restored to my position as Chief Signal Officer of the Army." In four additional sentences, all equally brief, Myer then told the history of signaling throughout the Civil War and of his own connection with it. He added: "I believe I am justly entitled to the position."

Two months later, on August 28, the President endorsed Myer's letter to General Grant for "examination and recommendation," and nearly two months later still, on October 26, Grant replied: "The services rendered by Colonel Myer in organizing the Signal Corps have been of great value to the service. . . . Why he was displaced as Chief Signal Officer I never knew. . . . If reasons do not exist for keeping him out of the place of Chief Signal Officer, I think that his restoration to that place would be but an act of simple justice."

On receiving this letter, on October 30, Johnson endorsed the file to Stanton: "Respectfully referred to the Secretary of War for report. This case was once before referred to the War Department for report, but no report has been received." It becomes apparent, perhaps, that Stanton had never replied to Lincoln's request for information on the Myer case; and there is evidence, too, that Stanton bypassed Lincoln in forwarding Fisher's nomination to the Senate.

Johnson waited more than six months for any sign of a reply from Stanton. Then, on May 9, 1866, the President took his own copy of the Myer file and endorsed it directly to Brig. Gen. Joseph Holt, Chief of the Bureau of Military Justice. To the usual endorsement formula he added: "Gen. Holt will examine such persons and papers as may be necessary, and report in writing to the President. A copy of this report will be furnished Colonel Myer."

On July 28, 1866 Congress passed the Armed Forces Act, one effect of which was to make permanent the position of Chief Signal Officer of the Army; and two days later, acting on his own initiative, Grant addressed a special letter to the Secretary of War in which he recommended, as General in Chief, that Myer be appointed Chief Signal Officer.

Fisher's nomination was placed before the Senate for the first time on March 9, 1865, since which time the Senate had thrice refused to confirm the appointment. By late July, 1866, Myer had many personal friends among the Senators. They engaged in cloakroom campaigns on his behalf, and on the day Grant was writing Stanton on Myer's behalf, a "Memorial Address to the President," requesting that Myer be nominated for Chief Signal Officer, was being passed among the Senators for signature. This document was signed by a majority of the whole Senate and by every member of the Senate Committee on Military Affairs.

On October 24, 1866 Sam Chamberlain of Buffalo, a power in the Republican party politics of New York State, called at the White House and had a long interview with Johnson "in support of Myer's application for the appointment to be Chief Signal Officer of the Army." Chamberlain laid before the President a series of documents, including: (1) the Memorial Address to the Senate with its endorsements by Grant, Sherman, Thomas, Howard, Farragut, and Porter; (2) Grant's letter of October 26, 1865, favoring Myer's reinstatement; (3) a letter from General Sheridan, commending Myer; (4) a letter in commendation of Myer's book on signaling from Rear Adm. Charles H. Davis, Superintendent of the Naval Observatory; (5) a letter from Admiral Porter commending the same book; (6) the Senators' Address to the President requesting the appointment of Myer; and (7) Grant's letter of July 30, 1866, recommending the appointment of Myer.

The day after he received these documents, Johnson gathered them together in an envelope, and on the face of the envelope he endorsed the entire packet over to Stanton with a directive, thrice underscored, peremptorily ordering Stanton to see "that this appointment be made."

Five days later, on October 30, 1866, Myer was appointed Chief Signal Officer with the rank of colonel to date from July 28, 1866, the day on which Congress passed the Armed Forces Act. The appointment was confirmed by the Senate on February 21, 1867. So the Army's first Chief Signal Officer returned to the command from which he had been ousted.

For challenging the authority of the President, Stanton was suspended from office on August 12, 1867. Grant became the *ad-interim* Secretary of War, and by General Order 92, October 1867, Grant directed the Chief Signal Officer to "equip and manage the field electric telegraph for use with active forces." And that was the end of a long quarrel. Henceforth the Signal Corps, and the Signal Corps alone, would be responsible for wire telegraphy in the combat zone.

Then, on November 30, 1867, Grant ruled on a question of military law. His decision was that Myer had not been stripped of his commission on November 10, 1863.

Finally, on December 11, 1867, a regular starburst of honors was showered upon Myer. For gallantry in combat, he was brevetted a lieutenant colonel as of May 27, 1862, a colonel as of July 2, 1862, and a brigadier general as of October 5, 1864. But October 5, 1864 was the day of that battle made famous by its inspired signaling, the Battle of Allatoona Pass. Thus it became known that, after his dismissal from Canby's headquarters, Myer had secretly attached himself to Sherman's.

Now—and this was the whole effect of his brevet commission— the Chief Signal Officer was "General Myer." He was still a colonel in rank and authority, and he still drew the pay of a colonel, but for his bravery under fire he was authorized, by vote of the United States Senate, to wear the uniform of a brigadier general and to be addressed as general.

Actually, the Signal Corps was down to one lieutenant and two clerks when the Armed Forces Act of July 28, 1866 rescued it from extinction by making permanent the position of Chief Signal Officer. Section 22 of the act provided that there should be "one Chief Signal

Officer of the Army," and that he should have the rank, pay, and emoluments of a colonel of cavalry.

That was not to say, of course, that there should be a Signal Corps; the law made no mention of any such organization. And yet by that same law the Signal Corps was reconstituted—for Section 22 went on to authorize the Secretary of War to detail "for the performance of signal duty" six officers and not more than one hundred enlisted men of the Corps of Engineers.

It was not a new idea, nor was it one that Congress hit upon by accident; the British had long since made military signaling a function of the Royal Engineers, and the French, the Prussians, and the Austrians had followed the lead of the British. To many an American congressman, conscientious enough to study foreign precedents, it seemed only proper to commit the signal mission to the Corps of Engineers. Why not? It has been suggested, by way of answer, that the United States had Myer. He had made a powerful impression upon the leaders of Congress; and their choice, or so the story goes, had been to make him a colonel of the Corps of Engineers—hardly the right prescription for a doctor of medicine—or else to continue in existence the position of Chief Signal Officer and to accept, in consequence, the fact of a more or less independent Signal Corps. In any case, Myer became the Chief Signal Officer, and in tribute to the European experience, a kind of compromise was effected by filling the rest of the Corps with engineer personnel.

But the Corps was not filled up overnight. When Myer took over as Chief Signal Officer for the second time, in the autumn of 1866, his command jurisdiction extended to the one lieutenant and the two enlisted clerks. Less than one week later he advanced a proposal that military signaling and telegraphy be reintroduced as subjects of study at West Point. He visited the Point and spoke before the Academic Board; and the result of that talk was the establishment of a Department of Practical Military Engineering, Military Signaling, and Telegraphy, which continued in existence down to World War I.

Myer's next move was to visit the Naval Academy at Annapolis. Signaling had been taught there since early in the Civil War, but minor deviations had crept in, and the Navy had had no opportunities to share in the rapid development of military signaling ashore. Myer placed before the Annapolis board a concrete plan to bring about a uniformity of teaching at both of the service academies; and what came of that scheme he was able to illustrate in his annual report for 1868. In the summer of that year, he wrote, the midshipmen's cruise took them up the Hudson for a visit to

West Point, and the "anchors of the fleet were hardly down before questions and answers were waving back and forth with handkerchiefs, between midshipmen and cadets, on ship and on shore."

The textbook at both academies was Myer's own *Manual of Signals,* edition of 1868. Myer had had the first edition privately printed, as we have seen, while serving as Canby's Chief Signal Officer in 1864. A second edition was brought out in 1866 by Van Nostrand, the New York technical publishers, and this was very widely distributed, the reviews and commendations—in particular, those received from European war ministries—being used in Myer's campaign for reinstatement. And the third edition, that of 1868, likewise was published by Van Nostrand. Understandably, in the light of all the circumstances, the copyright to this book was Myer's personal property.

In 1868 Myer also established his quite remarkable Signal Training School. In the summer of that year, the Corps of Engineers detailed eight of its officers to the Signal Corps for training, one from each of the eight territorial departments of the Army; and the plan was that, upon returning to his parent unit, each of the eight officers would train one other officer and two enlisted flagmen.

To accommodate that original class of eight, Myer opened up a classroom in his own suite of offices. He furnished the room with eight tables and chairs, he equipped every table with instruments, battery, and switchboard, and by using great coils of wire to give the effect of distance, he interconnected all the tables in a complex system of eight Morse telegraph stations. That was the first classroom in which the Signal Corps gave formal training in wire telegraphy.

A few weeks after this course had been started, however, Myer transferred the school to Fort Greble, which lay, dreary and desolate, on the southern edge of Washington. Greble was one of the abandoned wartime defenses of the capital—its parade ground used as a city dump, its temporary housing in a state of disrepair. A detachment of fifty men worked for six weeks to rehabilitate the place. Myer also established there a signal training center for enlisted men. The first officer graduates included two latecomers— lieutenants of the Swedish army.

In 1869 Myer inaugurated regular courses in signaling at the Artillery School of Practice, Fort Monroe, and the Engineer School of Practice, Willett's Point, New York. This was the beginning of an Army-wide spread of interest in signaling; and wherever the training courses were established, Myer's manual was the textbook.

Also in 1869 Myer transferred the school from Greble to Fort

Whipple in Arlington, Virginia, just across the Potomac from Washintgon. Whipple was immensely bigger than Greble; there was room there for big-scale telegraph-train maneuvers; there was also room for an experimental field wire-pole line forty miles long; and from there across the valley, wigwag drill could be carried on at a range of thirty miles. Fort Whipple became the first "Home of the Signal Corps."

The fort was connected with Myer's office in Washington by a field telegraph line upon which the most elaborate experiments were centered. This line was ten miles long, and was strung with four different types of wire, enabling Myer to report conclusively, before the close of the year, that steel wire was the strongest, galvanized iron the most durable, American compound (copper and iron) the best conductor, and plain iron the cheapest.

Finally in 1869—and this was an evidence of the stir that Myer was causing in Washington—Congress created the position of Chief Signal Officer of the Navy, and imposed upon the Army and the Navy chief signal officers a common responsibility for arranging ciphers, correlating signal training, and contributing jointly to the improvement of signal services on land and sea.

In 1870 the Navy Department adopted Myer's *Manual of Signals,* and numbers of naval and Marine Corps officers were at once detailed to the Fort Whipple Signal Training School.

Though General Myer had been Chief Signal Officer since the late fall of 1866, his mission was not clearly established and defined till almost a full year later. Then it was set forth in a series of directives addressed to Myer and contained in War Department General Order No. 92, October, 1867. Again, however, there was no explicit mention of a Signal Corps.

> *The Chief Signal Officer of the Army is to furnish two full sets of signaling equipment and two copies of the* Manual of Signals *to each company and post.*
>
> *Telescopes and binoculars are to be furnished companies on requisition.*
>
> *All signal equipment is to be accounted for to the Chief Signal Officer.*
>
> *The Chief Signal Officer will equip and manage the field electric telegraph for use with active forces.*

There was a word in that final directive, and Myer seized upon it. The word *manage* afforded the one slender grounds—but possibly, hopefully, a sufficient grounds—for inferring the existence of a Signal Corps. Myer was worried.

By late October, 1868, he had worked out a plan of organization and equipment which, to say the least, presumed the existence of a very active Signal Corps; and he had the unit right there in the field, on active duty. It was a field telegraph train company, organic to corps and consisting of a captain, four lieutenants, and one hundred and thirty-four enlisted men. It was equipped and trained—it was drilled "a thousand times" in the first year of its existence—to lay four telegraph lines simultaneously from corps to each of the four divisions.

Then came General Order No. 88, War Department, October 22, 1868, prescribing the uniform to be worn by the "enlisted men of the acting Signal Corps." After all, it was the first War Department order to recognize the existence of even an "acting" Signal Corps. It was said that General Myer shrugged.

There was a long wait after that, but then—on February 28, 1870—Myer was directed by a joint resolution of Congress to set up and operate this country's first weather bureau. Behind that resolution was clearly visible the hand of Myer himself, grasping for something that would keep the Signal Corps alive. He had many ideas. The weather service was one; and he liked it because it could not exist without long-line communications, and because long-line communications could not exist—outside of the country's populated areas—without a Signal Corps.

Thus the nation's first weather service began. At 0735 hours on November 1, 1870, "dead on the minute," the first reports were filed by twenty-four Signal Corps sergeants in twenty-four different cities from Boston to Santa Fe and from Key West to Cheyenne. By the close of 1871, the weather stations had been extended to the Pacific coast and "as far north as Canada." By 1872, they had been extended into the West Indies. One year later a total of ninety-three stations—of which fifteen lay outside the United States—were reporting three times a day to the Office of the Chief Signal Officer in Washington.

From the day the service began, the reports went directly to the Telegraph Room in Myer's office, for the wires of all the principal companies of the United States converged upon that room; and it was a matter of pride to General Myer that this was so. In Cleveland, toward the close of 1863, he had confronted Anson Stager, the superintendent of the U.S. Military Telegraphs. He had won that man's friendship and admiration. Now Stager was the vice president and general manager of Western Union, and it was chiefly through his help that Myer had succeeded in bringing the wires of a score of different companies directly into his office.

An enormous volume of reports came pouring in. They were collated and studied by two experts, Professor Cleveland Abbe and Professor T. B. Maury, and by a group of officer-scientists who included, notably, 2d Lt. Adolphus Washington Greely . . .

Meanwhile, in 1873, Congress directed the War Department to install a telegraph office in every lighthouse and lifesaving station along the Atlantic seacoast of the United States, to man those many offices, and to build the great wire systems that would connect them with one another and interconnect them with commercial lines; and Congress also directed the War Department to construct and operate telegraph lines through thousands of miles of the country's wilder frontier sections. It goes without saying, perhaps, that both jobs were turned over to General Myer.

But also in 1873 Myer was in Europe to represent the United States at the first International Meteorological Congress, where he sponsored and, in effect, established the present-day system of international exchange of weather data. While in Europe, he had the satisfaction also of learning that the methods and techniques embodied in his *Manual of Signals* had been adopted by the armies of all the principal countries of Europe. Thus he was now a figure of worldwide reputation, the father of the American Signal Corps and, as it were, the grandfather of every other signal corps on earth.

Surprisingly, too, he was famous for his concept of tactical operations—for combat commanders could not continue fighting battles as they had done before the dawn of flag signaling and electric telegraphy. Wigwag had introduced something new into their calculations, and tactics could never be the same again. And back home in Washington, all through the 1870's, Myer kept harping on this. General Sam Cooper had seen the point. General Lee had based his tactics upon it. But the generality of combat commanders, governed by precedent, had been definitely slow to see it; and being the kind of man he was, Myer rammed it, often truculently, down their throats . . . He had a sharp mind, and he had systematized his own thinking. As a part of his mission to promote the welfare of the Signal Corps, the old Army doctor was now the advocate—and, in a way, the author—of a new and stimulating concept of faster-moving combat operations.

He was a hard man to work for, apparently; and if he was an outstanding leader, he was also a driver of men. Yet he drove himself no less brutally . . . Till the day he died in harness, his responsibilities were ever growing.

The seacoast telegraph lines, begun in 1873, were completed

section by section, the first in a few months' time, the last some two or three years later. With the aid of electric telegraphy, the life-saving service was able for the first time to organize its rescue operation, and a huge number of new observatories began contributing weather reports to Washington. In addition, Myer threw flagmen into the work, and thereafter for many years, signalmen went out with the lifeboats and flagged back to the shore the ship and sea conditions; in many an instance received from the flagman ashore —who was also the telegrapher and the meteorologist—the advice that enabled a master to maneuver his vessel out of a critical situation. Early reports tell of signalmen who, in the course of a rescue operation, trudged as far as thirty-two miles through deep, gale-swept sand; of Morse operators who, for as many as twenty-six hours, pounded their keys without relief; and of other operators who, in raging gales, laid as many eight miles of wire, singlehanded, prior to setting up their temporary telegraph stations at the scenes of disaster.

Like the seacoast lines, the frontier telegraphs were begun in 1873; and in seven years' time, under General Myer's direction, seven thousand miles of line were placed in operation in a wilderness that no commercial telegraph company would have presumed to enter. They formed three separate systems which, by commercial wire, were connected with one another and with Myer's office in Washington. The first, a network of twenty-four stations, extended from Fort Sill to Brownsville and from Denison, in the eastern part of Texas, to Fort Davis, in the Texas Panhandle. The second system, of twenty-nine stations, ran from Santa Fe, New Mexico, to San Diego, California. And the third, a string of twenty stations, extended—in Myer's time—from Bismarck, in Dakota Territory, to Fort Ellis, in what is today the state of Montana. Those seventy-three telegraph offices, of course, were also seventy-three weather stations.

The weather service was begun in 1870, and both the seacoast lines and the frontier telegraphs were begun in 1873. Two years later still—and perhaps inevitably—came the act of March 3, 1875 by which Congress, for the first time since the Civil War, gave an explicit grounds for the existence of the Signal Corps. Strictly, the act of 1875 did not establish or reestablish the Corps; it simply authorized the Corps to enlist a personnel of its own—including not more than 150 sergeants, 30 corporals, and 270 privates.

There were further stipulations that no man could be assigned to the Signal Corps until he had completed the requisite courses of instruction at the Signal Training School, and that no man could be promoted within the Corps until he had completed higher courses of instruction at that same school. Here again the hand of General Myer was seen, still advancing the cause of professional skill. But the main point was, of course, that Myer at last had gotten from Congress the assurance he had wanted that the Signal Corps would continue to exist.

It was noticed at the time that out of a total of four hundred and fifty enlisted signalmen, exactly one-third were to have the rank of sergeant—an enormously high percentage. The explanation was that a sergeant of the Signal Corps was, almost by definition, a meteorologist . . .

It was also in 1875 that Myer found himself squarely in the middle of the historic clash between the government and Western Union; for it was the weather service, imposing its inexorable demands upon the commercial telegraph companies, that brought that issue to a head.

The dispute was rooted in the act of Congress of June 24, 1866, the purpose of which was "to aid in the construction of telegraph lines and to secure to the Government the use of the same for postal, military, and other purposes." Subject to certain limitations, the law gave to the telegraph companies, without charge, the right to build pole lines over public lands and the right to take from public lands the stone and timber required for construction purposes; it also gave them a grant of thirty acres of land for every telegraph station established; and in return, the United States and all its agents were to have top-priority service over the companies' lines at rates to be fixed by the Postmaster General.

The Signal Corps began its weather service four years after the passage of that law. The service grew, and the requirement imposed upon the telegraph companies in many instances exceeded their capabilities. Without additional compensation, the companies could not extend their lines to remote weather stations, nor could they maintain all-night services where there was no corresponding commercial need. What was more, the companies denied that the act of 1866 required them to do these things.

In the early stages of the quarrel, Myer had the Signal Corps build lines of its own from the more out-of-the-way observatories to the nearest commercial telegraph offices. But the companies would not permit these lines to be interconnected with their own, and Congress replied to this refusal by passing the act of June 10, 1872, assessing heavy fines and penalties against any company convicted of refusing or neglecting to transmit government telegrams. This act was followed by a series of Post Office Department and other regulations, culminating in War Department General Order No. 72, June 30, 1874, which laid down a prison penalty for willful interference with the telegraphic business of the government.

In a rejoinder, Western Union denied the validity of both laws and regulations; and while the lawyers argued the constitutional question, General Myer worked to save—with justice to both sides —what he considered the vital principle of cooperation between the Signal Corps and the commercial telegraphs. He devised a system of telegraphic codes to reduce the length of government messages, and he offered to place enlisted Signal Corps telegraphers in outlying Western Union Offices to clear government traffic. Not all of his ideas were accepted, but many were, and—what really mattered in the end—it was Myer's plan that formed the basis of the historic compromise that brought the litigation to a close in 1875.

Meanwhile, the weather service continued expanding, and as it grew Myer's office remained open later and later very night, until soon the service was operating twenty-four hours a day, seven days a week, the whole year round. Not without pride, Myer said—in 1878—that he was receiving eight reports daily from each of 224 weather stations, including one in the Aleutian Islands; and that he was in direct telegraphic touch with Canada, the West Indies, South America, and Europe, and in reasonably close touch, by lines extending eastward from London, with Egypt, India, and the far eastern seaboard of Asia.

Gradually, too, in these years, Myer's office had become virtually a publishing house, printing an average of thirty-five bulletins and sixty weather maps a day, and distributing them to nine thousand post offices; publishing from time to time voluminous studies of particular tornadoes, hurricanes, and blizzards; and also publishing a weekly *Weather Chronicle* and a twice-weekly weather report called *Synopsis and Probabilities*.

This last was written or edited by General Myer himself who, as an Army doctor, had taken weather observations as far back as 1854. By 1874, thanks largely to Myer's literary efforts, there was a certain popular excitement over the new and mysterious art of predicting tomorrow's weather. By 1876 boys were dreaming of careers in meteorology. And by 1878 Myer had become known, affectionately, to newspaper readers all over the United States as "Old Probability."

Clearly Myer was immersed in a great variety of jobs, and the question was being asked how any one man could keep abreast of all of them. Myer did, however; and Myer still had the alertness and the liveliness of mind to be ever on the lookout for something new. Surprisingly, it was General Myer who introduced the telephone to the service of the U.S. Army.

The first Army telephones were installed on the line that connected Myer's office in Washington with the Signal Training School at Fort Whipple, over in Arlington, Virginia; and they were in service in early October of 1877—just eighteen months after Alexander Graham Bell had taken out his first patent. Several types were tried out and tested, and the rules were never allowed to stand in the way of some new experiment . . . It was the astonishing fact that General Myer telephoned Fort Whipple almost every day in years when even the most progressive American business firms looked upon the telephone as a pretty toy.

In the summer of 1879, Myer was again in Europe, representing the United States at the international congress that planned "the Arctic year" that would begin in the summer of 1881. But even before he left for Europe it was becoming evident that Myer's strength was running out. After all, he had shown symptoms of tuberculosis even as a boy at medical school.

On June 16, 1880, Myer, who for more than a dozen years had been a brigadier general by brevet, attained the permanent rank of brigadier general; and a few weeks later, he was forced by recurring illness to leave Washington on leave. For years his friends had been urging him to do this—to rest and relax; perhaps even to retire. But his reply had always been: "What rest would it be for me if I left my work unfinished?" Now he had, in fact, rounded out his work, tying up the loose ends and leaving the affairs of his office in what he considered "apple-pie order." Thus, with a clear conscience, on August 3, 1880, he took off for the last time his uniform with the epaulettes of a brigadier general, medical staff, and left for his home in Buffalo. There, while still on active duty, he died on August 24, 1880 at the early age of fifty-two.

General Order No. 63 was issued by the War Department that same afternoon:

The Secretary of War is pained to announce to the Army the death of Brig. Gen. Albert J. Myer . . .

General Myer's attention was early turned to the subject of signaling by sight, in which he has since achieved such remarkable success, establishing that branch of the military service during the late war on a basis of usefulness and im-

88

portance that has proved of the greatest benefit, and caused its knowledge to become an important part of education, not only for the Army, but also for the Navy. . . .

Assigned . . . to the duty of taking meteorological observations and giving public notice of the approach and force of storms, he brought to bear remarkable ability for organizing this service and making its usefulness felt, not only in every seaport, but in every hamlet of the land.

In this comparatively unexplored field of science and usefulness General Myer displayed the enterprise of practical investigation and study of meteorology, and with the production of useful results, which has made his name familiar to every one of his countrymen and proved of incalculable benefit to various interests. These services have been highly appreciated, both at home and in foreign countries. His perseverance . . . affords . . . the only full and satisfactory data extant for the study of meteorology.

Struck down at the meridian of his usefulness, the country has lost a most distinguished and promising officer, and the Signal Service an able, efficient, and zealous chief. The officers of the Signal Corps, and on duty therewith, will wear . . . mourning for thirty days.

One year later Fort Whipple, the home of the Signal Corps, was rechristened Fort Myer.

From the beginnings of Army signaling in 1860 until the turn of the century and the Spanish-American War, two giants dominated Signal Corps' history. General Myer of course was one; the other was General Adolphus Washington Greely. Each had extremely long terms of office. Perhaps best known for his dramatic scientific expedition to the North Pole (from which only he and a handful of starved survivors returned), Greely made many other contributions.

Adolphus Washington Greely

✠ DAVID J. MARSHALL, *U.S. Army Signal Center*

In 1873, for a variety of reasons, Congress passed the first of a series of acts directing the War Department to construct and operate its own telegraph lines in the country's wilder frontier sections. This job was turned over to the Signal Corps, and within the next ten years the Corps had built eight thousand miles of pole line and was operating three distinct and separate telegraph systems.

All three of the systems covered vast areas. The first, a network of twenty-four stations, extended from Fort Sill to Brownsville and from Denison, in the eastern part of Texas, to Fort Davis, in the Texas Panhandle. The second system, of twenty-nine stations, ran from Sante Fe, New Mexico, to San Diego, California, and from Fort Bliss, in Texas, to Camp Apache and Camp Verde, in present-day Arizona. And the third, a network of twenty-four stations, stretched from Fort Bennett, on the Missouri River in what today is South Dakota, to Dayton, on the Columbia River in what today is the state of Washington. In all, they comprised seventy-seven frontier telegraph offices—which were also seventy-seven weather observatories —and, by commercial wires, the three systems were connected with one another and with the Office of the Chief Signal Officer in Washington.

The frontier telegraphs were to play a tremendous role in the Indian wars and the final conquest of the continent; and to an extent that would today seem unbelievable, the building of those lines was the exploit of one man—Lieutenant Adolphus Washington Greely, Weather Service Division, U.S. Army Signal Corps.

Greely had been wounded three times in the course of the Civil War, and though he had entered that war as a private, he had come out of it a brevet major. In 1876 he was commissioned a second

90

lieutenant of the infantry. One year later he was detailed to the
Signal Corps, and upon the establishment of the weather service,
toward the close of 1870, he was assigned by the Chief Signal
Officer to the headquarters of that new division—which twenty-
one years later was to become the U.S. Weather Bureau. It was
typical of Greely that he began at once to compile a bibliography of
books on meteorology; and it was typical of him too that, when he
was reassigned, the bibliography was "tremendous."

He was reassigned in 1873—by then he had become a first lieutenant of cavalry and was, next to General Myer himself, the highest ranking officer in the Signal Corps. He was directed, briefly, to
build the telegraph lines.

His first step was to train a detachment of men at the Signal
School, Fort Whipple, where for several weeks he had them practicing pole-line construction. Then he led them to Texas and looked
around, as he had known he would have to do, for poles. Fort Concho
—which was to be the braincenter of the new system—lay in a
treeless prairie, one hundred and sixty miles from the nearest frontier town; and Greely, in the end, was forced to haul timber overland the better part of five hundred miles northward from the Rio
Grande Valley and to send to the Dismal Swamp, along the coastline
of Virginia, for more.

To hasten the work, Greely borrowed platoons and companies of
men from all the nearby garrisons, and so, necessarily, he had to
give a great deal of his time to training problems. Week after week
he worked as many as twenty hours a day, and at the end of one year
he had completed 1,100 miles of line at a total cost of $110,000, or
just about $100 a mile.

As the event showed, however, Greely had driven himself too hard
on that job, and in the hope of recovering his badly affected health,
he was forced to take a six months' leave of absence. It was the first
of many times that this would happen; for Greely was one of those
men who worked when there was work to do and never cared about
the cost.

Returning to duty half a year later, he had to rebuild a hundred-
mile stretch of Signal Corps line between Cape Henry and Cape
Hatteras which a hurricane had destroyed; and when he had barely
completed this job, he was hustled West again to build the two-
thousand-mile-long line from Santa Fe to San Diego. This cut across
desert country where the annual rainfall was less than five inches
and the temperatures rose as high as 119 degrees in the shade; and
it also cut across a mountainous country that was almost inacces-
sible by horse-drawn wagons.

On this job, however, the work was lightened by the fact that several short lines already existed along the route that Greely was to follow. These ran, as a rule, only between two neighboring forts, and even the best of them were poorly constructed, weatherbeaten, ramshackle affairs. They were repaired and strengthened, however and then incorporated into the through line from Santa Fe to San Diego. Thus Greely was able to save a substantial mileage and to install the new line in six months' working time.

Next, Greely returned again to Washington "for less arduous duty." But this was in 1878—and 1878 was the year the Army was left unpaid. Congress had simply failed to appropriate the funds. Now the nation was confronted by a serious deterioration of its armed forces and, concurrently, by an equally serious uprising of the Indians of the Northwest.

Defrauded again and again by dishonest agents of the government, the Indians had reason to be embittered. Driven by hard necessity, the unpaid Army officers were resigning, the unpaid men were deserting. The total strength of the Army fell to fewer than 20,000 effectives, and in the Army's extremity, it seemed, was the Indians' opportunity.

Congress took emergency action. One of many projects authorized was the construction of a military telegraph line from Bismarck, in Dakota Territory, to Fort Ellis, Montana; and after four months' rest in Washington, Greely was sent out to build that line, plus a branch line to Deadwood. He was instructed to have the whole job completed "before the snow flies."

The job was to connect Bismarck and Deadwood alike with Fort Stevenson, Fort Buford, Fort Keogh, and Fort Custer. The beginning point was Fort Buford, on the left bank of the Missouri, two thousand miles upstream from St. Louis; and general supplies had to be transported from that city against a current that for hundreds of miles was too swift for bathing. Poles had to be hauled overland from a region hundreds of miles deep in Canada, or transported down the Yellowstone River.

The Yellowstone was unusually low in the summer of 1878, but time was passing and the need was great. Each time the steamboat came to a shallow spot, the poles had to be unloaded and—when the hurdle had been passed—reloaded again. The crew mutinied. The punishment for this was to be placed ashore and left behind. Jeered one of the mutineers: "They'll never be used. Them poles will be worn out with loading and reloading."

Before the first snow fell, however, Greely had in fact completed his work, and had the lines operating. He so reported to Washington from Deadwood, the new gold-rush town in the Black Hills; and the answer from Washington was a directive ordering Greely to conduct a personal inspection of the lines and, after that, to return to Washington.

With a sergeant and two privates, the only escort he could find, Greely set forth in a four-mule wagon on the verge of winter. Two days out, they were caught in a blizzard in the Bad Lands, and the storm, accompanied by sub-zero temperatures and gales of hurricane force, lasted thirty-six hours. At Powder River the party was discovered by a troop of cavalry on reconnaissance from Fort Keogh. Astounded, the captain demanded: "What damned fool sent you into Indian country with three men?"

"A distinguished colonel of Civil War experience," Greely answered drily.

"You had a nerve to come."

"What else could a lieutenant do?"

Despite the deep snow, the cold, and the Indians, Greely completed his tour of inspection, crossing the ice-clogged Missouri at Fort Buford the day before it froze.

But, for Greely, a far more severe test lay ahead . . .

As Chief Signal Officer and head of the weather service, General Myer had represented this country at the first two meteorological congresses in Europe, and it was he who sponsored the resolution setting up the first international system for exchanging and collating weather information on a worldwide basis. Out of this, in due time, came an international effort to gather weather data in the Arctic for a limited trial period, with a view to tracing the influence of Arctic weather upon that of the North Temperate Zone, and with a further view to establishing, if possible, the value of systematic observations taken within the Arctic Circle.

In January, 1879, while Myer was still the Chief Signal Officer, Congress passed the first of a series of acts approving this country's participation in the Arctic project and directing the War Department to establish a temporary weather station at Point Barrow, Alaska, and another at or near the shore of Lady Franklin Bay, in Grinnell Land, across the strait from the northwest coast of Greenland. Eleven nations were taking part in the project, and the plan was to encircle the North Pole with an aggregate of fifty observatories.

Inevitably, the task of establishing and manning the two American stations fell to the Signal Corps; and wave after wave of high

93

excitement swept over the country as, little by little, the plans were made public. In the popular imagination, Point Barrow was unbelievably far beyond the Arctic Circle; it lay within 1,300 miles of the Pole. But Lady Franklin Bay, just recently discovered by Sir John Franklin and named for his wife, was calculated to be but 500 miles from the Pole. In 1879 that was breathtaking.

It was typical of the country's wild enthusiasm for the project that the Congressional Record for April 15, 1880 was able to forecast, in minute detail, the problems to be encountered, and to suggest an exact solution of each. Newspapers from Sandy Hook to San Diego continued to point out, meanwhile, that this was the first international effort in which America had ever participated in time of peace. America, they said proudly, was taking her place in the family of nations.

It was not till the summer of 1881, however, that the effort was made, and then—a whole year after Myer's death—the project was in the hands of a new Chief Signal Officer, Brig. Gen. William Babcock Hazen. It was he who directed all the immediate preparations, and who gave the order that the two expeditions were to sail—one from the west coast and the other from the east coast. Thereafter he set to work at once on plans to resupply the stations in the summer of 1882.

The expedition to Point Barrow was almost without a history. It was the case of a mission carried out perfectly and without incident; from first to last, not one man of this expedition suffered injury or was sick for even a day.

Commanded by Lt. Patrick H. Ray, they arrived at the Point—a long, low, sandy spit projecting into the Arctic Ocean; bare of all but moss and lichens in the few weeks of summer, bare of all but snow and ice in the long and dreary months of winter. With their own hands they built their shelter. They established their station, and they ran it for the better part of two years. And then, in October of 1883, they came home with a complete record of hourly observations covering a period of nineteen months.

It was an outstanding piece of work—a flawless performance. And it was made the more notable by the fact of the men's returning with an unmatched collection of specimens of the plant and animal life of northern Alaska, including varieties that the world up to that time had neither seen nor heard of.

The expedition to Lady Franklin Bay had a history that men are likely to remember to the end of time—for it was the story of human fortitude and courage against a background of naked tragedy. It was the story of twenty-five men of whom, with one exception, it could be said that "they did what men can, they bore what men must." And it was, above all, the story of one man's superb leadership and example.

Lieutenant Greely was in command at Lady Franklin Bay. With him were two second lieutenants of infantry, one assistant surgeon, five sergeants of the Signal Corps, fourteen noncommissioned officers and men assigned from the combat arms, and two Eskimo guides.

In the summer of 1881 they were landed on the north shore of the bay with a plentiful supply of timber and other building materials, an array of the latest scientific instruments, a steam launch, and a stockpile of fuel and provisions sufficient for the needs of two years' existence in the Arctic. They built a stormproof structure and established themselves within it. It was merely a timber house, but they called it Fort Conger, and as Fort Conger it was entered on the War Department maps at Washington. It was the most northerly human habitation in history.

Throughout the fall of 1881, and the winter that followed, the twenty-five men learned to work and live together. They were well enough housed; they had, in fact, a commodious dwelling, with a good kitchen, a room for the officers, and a room for the enlisted men and the Eskimos. There was also an office where the work of the station could be carried on—where the hourly weather observations could be entered in the record books, where the usual entries could be made in the station log, and where the records could be safely stored.

There was also a tiny cubicle opening off the kitchen. This contained a bathtub and a hopper that fed water through a long spout into the tub. To take a bath, one had only to shovel the hopper full of snow and allow the heat from the kitchen to have its effect.

During the first winter of his Arctic command, Greely revealed himself a leader of considerable ability. Only the doctor and the two Eskimos had had prior experience of the Arctic; and only the five Signal Corps sergeants were accustomed to the tedium of service at a weather station—Israel, the astronomer; Jewell, Ralston, and Gardiner, the observers; and Rice. Rice was unique. Sgt. George W. Rice was the first, and up to this point the only, Signal Corps photographer.

For the rest, the garrison consisted of the two second lieutenants and the fourteen enlisted men. All sixteen of these had been abruptly, and to their own astonishment, detached from regiments on active service against the Indians. They were restless men, inevitably; and the long boredom of their first Arctic night told hard against them.

Greely found jobs for all. The Signal Corps men were well cared for in this respect; hour by hour, always, they were taking and recording their many observations. Greely sent the others out exploring, blazing trails, and establishing caches of food for a hundred miles about, against the day when the Signal Corps observers could begin their field work.

He also organized a school. More informally, he delivered lectures on a variety of subjects. And every Sunday Greely conducted church services; a typical New Englander, tall, spare, and stern, he had a tender conscience and could preach a better sermon, it was said, than the average Army chaplain. For a certainty he was a great talker—at times, it would seem, unmercifully so. But he had worthwhile things to talk about, for Greely was also a great reader of books.

He had brought with him to Lady Franklin Bay a variety of volumes, including all the available records of men who had previously explored that part of the earth. To encourage his men to read, he had brought along books for them too—and that became, in a way, the subject matter of a Congressional investigation.

The investigation was actually centered upon money. Fiercely resented was an expenditure of $181.76 for books of fiction, sent to Point Barrow and Lady Franklin Bay. An angry Congressman cross-examined the comptroller of the War Department on that point:

Q. *Do these books have any relation whatever to the science of meteorology?—A. Not that I am aware of . . .*

Q. *And you know of nothing in* Innocents Abroad, Roughing It, *or the* Leather Stocking Tales *that applies to any purpose of that expedition?—A. No, Sir . . .*

Anyhow, there was at Fort Conger—to enable the men to while away the weeks and months of enforced idleness—somewhat of a library; and more than half the men, those who knew how to read, made use of it when they were kept indoors by the cold.

How cold it could be out-of-doors was indicated by the experience of an Eskimo pup that one day escaped into the open air. In a second or two, as the pup merely paused to get its bearings, its feet froze to the ice-covered ground, and to save its life, men with axes had to go out and chop free a cubic foot or so of ice, and then carry indoors both the dog and the attached ice cube.

On such days, there was reading. There were games of checkers.

96

And there were efforts, often successful, to bring out a weekly newspaper. Above all, there was talking; and, as one of the enlisted men later on remarked: "Nothing lasts like long, loud arguments."

When the weather was less severe there was hunting. Game was plentiful, the men were good shots, and for a time the ration of steaks and chops, fish and fowl, fruit and vegetables was lavishly augmented by Arctic fowl, eider duck, musk-ox, and seal meat. All the while, too, there was Spartan exercise; and so in their first winter in the Arctic the men retained their strength unexpectedly well.

Then, in the spring of 1882, Greely explored the interior of Grinnell Land; and it was he who, pushing westward, discovered Lake Hazen and the Garfield Mountains. He named the lake in honor of the Chief Signal Officer and the mountains in honor of the man he thought to be President of the United States, not knowing that James A. Garfield had meanwhile died of an assassin's bullet. Then, beyond the Garfields, he discovered another chain of mountains which he called the United States Range. And, beyond that again, he discovered the northern coastal plain and seacoast of the island, and this entire region he called, in honor of his wartime commander, Grant Land.

Teams of his command made efforts, meanwhile, to map the edges of the polar ice cap. And the attached infantrymen began a series of major explorations and discoveries toward the east. They endured serious hardships, but they accomplished a great deal. Lieutenant Lockwood, Greely's second in command, was accompanied by Sgt. David L. Brainard and one of the Eskimos, Fred Christiansen, on such an expedition. In fifty-nine days they traveled more than 1,000 miles; they explored more than a hundred miles of the previously undiscovered northern coastline of Greenland; and, incidentally, they drove closer to the North Pole than any man had done before.

It was a matter of concern that the relief ship due in the summer of 1882 never arrived. It was not a disaster, for the party had insured against this possibility by laying in at Fort Conger a two years' supply of food and fuel. But when the ship again failed to arrive in the summer of 1883, the situation became critical.

However, a carefully worked out plan had been prepared to cover this eventuality also. This was the emergency plan. It required Greely to abandon Fort Conger by September 1 at the latest, to load his entire party aboard the steam launch and to proceed to Littleton Island, some two hundred and fifty miles south by open water from Lady Franklin Bay. There, according to the plan, a ship would be

97

waiting; or there—if the closing in of the ice had forced the ship to leave—a rescue party would be established with shelter and supplies for another year. In that case, the rescue party would send out sledges to meet Greely's party and lead them in.

On August 9, 1883 Greely broke camp. He nailed shut the doors of Fort Conger. He emptied on the snow several barrels of provisions for the dogs he would have to abandon. He loaded his equipment and the remaining supplies into small boats which he attached by towlines to the steam launch. And then with his whole party aboard the launch, he started south.

Freezing temperatures had already set in, and the mercury was still dropping rapidly; and of the first ten days of the voyage, five days were spent locked in ice and waiting for the floes to open again. They had forty days' rations when they set out. By stopping along the coast and picking up food from the caches established eighteen months earlier, they were able for a time to keep their supply at the forty-day level. The individual daily ration was one pound of meat and bread, two ounces of beans or potatoes, and occasionally a bit of fruit.

After seventeen days, they arrived at Cape Hawks, the most northerly of three points at which the 1882 relief ship had been scheduled to cache a food and fuel supply. There was no such cache. There was only the cache established by Sir John Franklin's men a generation earlier; and from this were taken an amount of moldy bread and dried potatoes, a keg of pickled onions, and three gallons of rum.

Sailing farther and farther south, Greely and his men hove in sight of Cape Sabine, where the 1882 ship should have established a second cache. Next day, however, a storm set in and their tiny vessel was frozen into the ice floe. After breaking free, they had to avoid still other floes; and so they steamed four hundred miles to make one hundred miles southward.

Then they were caught fast in ice, and—still eighty miles from their destination at Littleton Island—they were confronted by the imminent danger of an inward heave of the floes that would grind their launch to bits. Greely decided to abandon the launch.

They loaded their equipment and supplies on boats and sledges, and began a long trek on foot across the treacherous rubble of badly fragmented ice. There were no dogs. The sledges and boats had to be dragged by the men themselves, and the load exceeded three and a quarter tons. The ice was badly windrowed; it was blue, solid and tough; and in places the tossed-up chunks were frozen together in

98

"Father of the Signal Corps." Brigadier General Albert J. Myer,
Chief Signal Officer.

ALL PHOTOS U.S. ARMY PHOTOGRAPHS

COL. BENJAMIN FRANKLIN FISHER
1864 · 1866

BRIG. GEN. WILLIAM B. HAZEN
1880 · 1887

BRIG. GEN. ADOLPHUS W. GREELY
1887· 1906

THE BEARDSLEE MAGNETO-ELECTRIC TELEGRAPH, 1862-63

The Beardslee Magneto-Electric Telegraph used during 1862-63 in the Civil War.

A signal tower during the Civil War at Jacksonville, Fla. December 1864.

A group of Signal Corps officers during the Civil War.

The Elk Military Signal Station. March 1864.

Below: A painting of the first field telegraph train to be used in combat by an American army, 1862. The horse-drawn vehicle was equipped with a Beardslee telegraph instrument and the wire was strung on lance poles.

The Cobb's Hill Signal Tower near Richmond, Va., 1864.

Rare photo of the Greely Arctic Expedition. Lt. Lockwood, Sgt. Brainard, and Christiansen returning to Conger, June 1, 1882 from the trip on which they reached the highest northern latitude up to that time.

Signal Corps battery wagons, 1898. Field telegraph trains were drawn by four mules. Driver sat on the box.

A Signal Corps photographer sergeant, about 1900.

Below: U.S. Army Signal Corps Airplane No. 1. Pioneering in aviation, the Signal Corps operated the first military airplane at Fort Myer in September 1909. It was purchased from the Wright brothers at a total cost of $30,000. Orville Wright is in the plane.

Later to become famous as a crusader for air power, Captain William ("Billy") Mitchell is shown here when he was on duty with the Signal Corps in Alaska.

Below: Taking meteorological observations at Fort Monmouth, N.J. What was later to become the U.S. Weather Bureau was then a part of the Signal Corps.

walls eighteen and twenty feet high. The men chopped and filled—in effect, built roadways. Even so, the going was so hard that more than once they had to drag their boats and sledges forward separately, trudging and straining five miles in all for every mile of their advance.

Over a drifting ice pack, they labored through violent blizzards and sub-zero temperatures for twelve hours a day. And they kept this up for twenty days. Little by little, they discarded everything they could. But they were all in favor of saving the instruments and the records.

Meanwhile, the ice pack itself had been drifting south; and after thirteen hours' labor on September 15, they found themselves within four miles of land. Exhausted but happy, they at once crawled into their sleeping bags, pausing neither to eat nor to raise a shelter. During the night a gale sprang up. When the day broke the floe was ten miles off shore. What was worse, the gale had spun the floe around so that the southern edge, where they had been the night before, was now the northern edge. They had no choice but to begin again the three weeks' trudge across the floe. . . .

Ten days later they found themselves adrift on a tiny floe, scarcely one fourth of a square mile in area; and since movement was next to impossible, they were now at the mercy of the currents. They chopped out blocks of ice. They built a house. And there without food or water they slept out a forty-mile gale in snow-soaked sleeping bags.

Then, on September 28, their floe was caught between two towering icebergs, was ground to pieces beneath their feet. By fast and desperate efforts, they managed to transfer themselves and their mass of supplies to the larger iceberg.

They were aware that wind and tide were sweeping the iceberg southward; and they slept their first night aboard it expecting to be blown past Littleton Island into Baffin Bay. But they woke to find their berg had jammed immovable against a grounded iceberg. And across that grounded iceberg, they made land.

They had been traveling for fifty-one days. Driven this way and that, they had covered hundreds upon hundreds of miles, and yet they were still ninety miles short of their destination. However, not one man had been lost, nor any of the instruments, nor a single record.

It was September 29 when they got ashore. They were then on Eskimo Point, ninety miles across the sound from Littleton Island and eighty miles or so southwest of Cape Sabine.

On October 1 Greely selected Sergeant Rice and Christiansen the Eskimo, and sent them on foot to Cape Sabine to find the food that should have been cached there in the summer of 1882. They were back eight days later with very bad news. They had found the cache. However, it contained but two hundred and forty rations—fewer than ten meals for each of twenty-five men.

The cache also contained a note addressed to Greely, asserting that two hundred and forty additional rations could be found at the appointed place on Littleton Island and—in effect—that that would be all. The 1882 relief ship, the note went on to say, had established caches at two of the points specified in the emergency plan; had returned south without reaching the third point. Then, in the summer of 1883, the same ship had sailed north again, had been crushed in the ice a hundred miles or more south of Cape Sabine and had sunk. Thereafter a party of survivors had made their way by boat to Cape Sabine, where they had left the note for Greely, plus a few additional rations. The note added that the survivors planned to cross the strait to Littleton Island where they hoped to meet another ship.

One thing was certain: The emergency plan had failed. The two hundred and forty rations at each appointed cache had been based on the assumption that they would suffice to cover a last few days' march to a waiting ship. But now that ship had foundered.

Yet the shipwrecked men who left the note for Greely had said they hoped to meet another ship. That, of course, was not to say there would be another ship. Drowning men, though, clutch even at straws, and Greely seized upon that mere reference to a ship. It gave him hope—and led him, as he grew weaker, to believe implicitly that there was a rescue party established on Littleton Island.

To cross the sound from Eskimo Point, however, was impossible; the winter storms were too wild, the action of the grinding, churning ice was too violent. So Greely moved his party north, from Eskimo Point to Cape Sabine—where the rations were, and where, presumably, the rescue party would come looking for him.

There he established Camp Clay. And there his men built a crude shelter, shaped like an igloo, with inner walls of stone and outer walls of snow and ice. The vertical walls were three feet high and windowless, and the whaleboat, turned upside down, was laid across them to form the roof. Then canvas tents and sails were draped over this to close the gaps till the next heavy fall of snow should complete the job and make the structure weather-tight. The other boats were broken up and burnt for fuel.

Greely's plan was to lead his men on foot to Littleton Island as

100

soon as the strait froze over. But that winter—for the first time in the recorded history of the North—the strait never froze.

Searching through his books and papers, poring over the records of early explorers, Greely found that many years earlier a party of Englishmen had cached meat at Cape Isabella, forty miles to the south of Camp Clay; and toward the middle of November Sergeant Rice volunteered to go in search of it. Three soldiers offered to accompany him.

They struggled doggedly against a bitter gale the whole way along, in temperatures of thirty-five degrees below zero. They pulled and pushed their sledge over a soft snow that treacherously concealed the cracks and ravines of the roughest kind of ice. Their sleeping bags froze solid when not in use, and it took three men to unroll each one before its owner could crawl inside. Their misery was such that on the third day out they threw away half their sleeping bags and all of their cooking utensils, hoping to make better time by traveling light. And later, on that same third day, they found the meat.

They loaded it aboard the sledge and started back. It was hard work, for all four of the men were weak and starving. Against warnings, one of the soldiers, Private Elison, ate snow. Presently he discovered that his hands had frozen; and then, as he stumbled along, in severe pain, he found that his feet also had frozen.

They tried double trips, first carrying Elison a few miles forward, then returning for the meat. But they were not strong enough. They abandoned the meat.

They pushed on till they fell exhausted. Elison begged them to leave him. But two of his comrades got him into a sleeping bag and crawled in with him, hoping to save him by the warmth of their own bodies. Rice left them thus and did his best to dash the remaining seventeen miles back to camp. He made it, and a relief party found all three soldiers still alive, but in a bag so solidly frozen that they had to use an axe to chop it open.

Elison lost both his hands and feet; they were amputated by the surgeon soon after his arrival back at base. For months thereafter his starving comrades nursed him tenderly, giving him extra food. Oddly, Elison survived, but all three of the men who had risked their lives to save him perished one by one.

Greely organized hunting and fishing parties, sent out scouts in search of the expected rescue party, and kept alive the hope that the sound would freeze over in March or April. Hunting and fishing brought small returns. Seals were plentiful, but when they were shot they sank and could hardly ever be recovered. An occasional fox was killed, and then there was rejoicing; even the intestines were eaten.

Normal rations were distributed daily in sixteenths of an ounce. On Sundays, dinner consisted of two dog biscuits made into a pudding with salt water and two cans of oxtail soup made into a goulash by being mixed with moldy bread. Slowly, the men were dying of starvation.

To keep up morale, Greely delivered long lectures in the dark—on politics, history, religion, and science. To hear him the men sat up in their frozen sleeping bags, for fuel was scarce, A fire could be kept for only a few hours daily, and the lamp could be lighted for only one hour. Greely lectured in the cold. He also encouraged the men to talk about their homes, their past lives, and their plans for the future.

So one of the enlisted men spent day after day discussing his plan to establish a colony in Kansas, at a place he would call Independence. After long and thoughtful consideration, Sergeant Jewell, the weather observer, decided to join him and open the first grocery store at Independence. An infantry soldier agreed to go along, but insisted on his right to open a saloon, despite the fact—more probably in ignorance of the fact—that two years earlier the state of Kansas had outlawed both liquor and saloons.

Still another foot soldier unfolded a carefully worked out scheme to open a restaurant in Ann Arbor, Michigan. And on Christmas Day of 1883 Lieutenant Lockwood spoke for several hours, sitting up in his sleeping bag. He spoke only of his family and of the girl he was engaged to marry, and it was later on recalled that, as he spoke, the silence was absolute.

In February, and again in March, efforts were made to cross the strait. But each time the effort failed.

Two soldiers took a burlap bag and made a fishing net of it, but they caught only a few tiny shrimp. A sharpshooter from the infantry brought down birds, and in his kayak, Jens, the second Eskimo, recovered most of those that fell in the water. But they were few and, taken separately, they were small.

On February 18, 1884 Sergeant Cross died. He was an infantry soldier—the biggest man of all and therefore the least capable of living on short rations. He was the first of Greely's command to perish.

In the first week of April, two more men expired.

On April 6 Sergeant Rice, the photographer, accompanied by an infantry soldier, Private Frederick, set out across the Arctic wilderness to recover the meat that Rice had abandoned near Cape Isabella in the previous November. Both of these men had all their lives been small and frail. Now they were showing the marks of long starvation and, witnessing their departure, Sergeant Brainard wrote in his diary: "Before them lie famine, indescribable cold, torture to their minds, and then, perhaps, failure."

They reached Cape Isabella. There they left their sleeping bags and a few extra rations Greely had allowed them, and through a raging blizzard they tramped seven miles across the frozen inlet in search of the meat cache. Five months earlier, Rice had marked it carefully, so that it could be seen for miles. In the storm they could not find it.

The going was hard. Rice began to stumble. Then he fell—exhausted. He tried to get up. He was too weak to stand. A few hours later, on April 9, 1884, sheltered from the wind by a mound of ice, the Signal Corps' first photographer died in Frederick's arms.

On April 13 Frederick arrived back at camp. There was no meat. But Frederick had brought back untouched what remained of Rice's rations.

Lieutenant Lockwood, Greely's second in command had died of starvation four days earlier—on the same day as Rice. And Sergeant Jewell, the weather observer, had died on April 12, the day before Frederick's return. To replace Jewell and Rice, Greely transferred two men to the Signal Corps. One was Sergeant Brainard. The other, a man without hands or feet, became Sergeant Elison.

Meanwhile—just as Jewell lay dying, it would seem—Jens, the Eskimo, had spied a polar bear; and after tracking the animal three miles, one of the soldiers had shot it. They were too weak, however, to drag the carcass back to camp. They could only stagger back and report the exploit. Greely studied the situation long and carefully. He selected nine men, whom he considered the strongest. He fortified their strength—he issued each of them three ounces of bacon. He sent them out with orders to bring back the bear.

But even nine men, as weak as they were, found the task unbelievably hard. Yet, though it took them many hours, they succeeded. They dragged the carcass inside the hut. And then for a little while there was meat.

Toward the close of April, Jens was drowned. While pursuing the carcass of a shot-down bird, he was caught between two ice floes, and his kayak crushed. Nineteen men remained alive.

Each man's ration was increased from ten to twelve ounces a day. But in May it was reduced to eight ounces, except for the invalid Elison and such men as were still capable of hunting birds and game. On May 12, however, each man received twelve ounces of bacon and tallow. Greely told them, as he portioned out the allowances, that he hoped each man could stretch them over two days—for these were the last of the rations.

In the next five days, four men died. Fifteen were still alive.

In June the thaws came, the hut was flooded, and Greely transferred his command to a tent on higher ground. Also in June the sea fowl, which had been wintering farther south, came north again, and there was hope.

On June 5, or thereabouts, by order of Lieutenant Greely, Private Henry was shot—executed—and let lie where he had fallen; no grave for him. He had been caught too many times stealing food. Fourteen men were left.

They cooked their boots and their sealskin coats and pants, or burnt them and ate the ashes. . . .

Private Schneider died. There was nobody strong enough to bury him, so he lay beside the others in his sleeping bag. . . .

A storm piped up and blew for three consecutive days. It blew down the tent, and the men—those that were still alive—stirred in their agony. There had been no food at all now for thirty-six hours. What had been a tent lay like a blanket across them. Nobody was strong enough to do anything about it.

Three days later Sergeant Brainard organized an effort to raise the tent again. It took many hours. But it succeeded.

On June 12 Brainard, too weak to walk, crawled to a rocky headland facing the sea. There he erected a signal flag . . .

Agonizing days went by. The men were eating lichens and the oil-tanned sealskin covers of their sleeping bags. Nobody noticed any longer who died or when. Roll-call on June 21 showed seven to be alive.

That night another storm blew down the tent. It fell like a shroud upon the dead and dying . . .

Above the storm one of the men thought he heard the blast of a steamship's whistle. He spoke of it. Then others listened, and they too thought they heard it. But nobody spoke after that. They had seen too many of their comrades die; and they had noticed that each man, as he was about to die, suffered the delusion that he was being rescued.

Greely roused himself. He selected Private Long, an infantry soldier, told him that he was the strongest, and asked him to crawl to the top of the mound and look for a ship. Brainard followed Long, and for hours the two men lay side by side peering through the Arctic gloom. . . .

Brainard returned—reported that what they had heard was only the distant roar of the wind.

Long stayed on, atop the mound. He caught sight of something moving in the ice-clogged water. It was something dark. It was moving slowly, jerkily, around one obstacle after another. It seemed to be guided by a purpose. It was moving toward the shore. Considering each point slowly, groggily, Long decided it must be a ship's boat.

With a fearful effort he got to his feet and waved. He was too weak to shout. He started forward, collapsed—he pitched head-foremost down the outer face of the rock, almost to the water's edge. He was picked up by sailors of the United States Navy. . . .

Arriving at the tent, the sailors were almost overcome by the stench of emaciated men who for months had been too weak to wash themselves.

Greely received the sailors graciously. He addressed each one by name. He asked about their fathers and mothers, their sisters and brothers. He recalled their boyhood days when he and they had been at school together. He confided that he had since become an Army officer . . . The pitying sailors got him onto a stretcher and carried him down to the launch.

Seven men were still alive when they were lifted aboard the naval vessel sent to rescue them. Sergeant Elison died a few days later. And so, of the twenty-five men who had formed the garrison of Fort Conger in the summer of 1881, six men were brought back alive in the summer of 1884.

And to them it seemed important that they had brought back all their records. These were America's chief contribution to the international effort to unlock what then appeared to be the basic mystery of the weather. And they were, in fact, among the best-kept scientific records history had ever known. They formed an unbroken series of hourly meteorological, tidal, magnetic, and pendulum observations covering a period of two full years.

There was a tremendous uproar in the newspapers over the tragic outcome of the Greely expedition. The American people were stirred to the depths—one minute beside themselves with rage and fury, another minute crushed with sorrow, and a minute after that again exploding with wrath and indignation. . . . Out of it emerged upon the public mind a picture of Greely as among the greatest of our peacetime heroes, a magnificent commander of men who for a long time had looked tragedy in the eye and never once had been appalled.

105

Almost at once Greely was promoted to captain, but many months fled by before he could return to duty. Then, on January 16, 1887, General Hazen died, and Greely became the new Chief Signal Officer. He had been in grade for fourteen years as a first lieutenant, for a little more than two years as a captain. Now, at a single stroke of the pen, he was raised to the rank of brigadier general.

General Greely Turns to Telephone, Aviation, and Radio

✠ DAVID J. MARSHALL, *U.S. Army Signal Center*

Chief Signal Officer Adolphus Greely began his administration by placing a new and heavy emphasis on combat signaling. In words that sound remarkably like the catchcry of the atomic age— "in these days of rapid military movements"—he requested that signal training throughout the Army be placed in the hands of the Signal Corps. But nothing came of his request. In the next two years no adequate signal training was given anywhere, and the reason was sheer lack of equipment, stemming from an appalling lack of funds. Greely's total budget would not have paid for one-fifth of the signal equipment already requested by the combat arms. Yet he was able, in 1890, to equip a few units with the first heliographs ever used in the service of the United States Army.

Also in 1890 a bill to abolish the Signal Corps was introduced in Congress; and when that failed of passage the rumor went around that the Corps would now face a more cruel death—a death "by slow fiscal starvation." But Greely had been in tight spots before.

Now he took a strong line boldly. In the face of jibes, he plunged for telephones, yet knew there was a limit to miracles. He declared: "The use of portable field telephones with an insulated double conductor is a method of field communication which should be perfected . . . But lack of funds prevents expenditures or purchases for that particular purpose, so this office . . . is compelled to confine itself to theoretical rather than extended practical knowledge."

Greely's theoretical knowledge was practical enough, however, to encourage the experiments of Sergeant Eccard, who produced the first Signal Corps field telephone. (The verdict: "Interesting, but too expensive.")

106

Before the close of 1890, however, Greely had succeeded in putting telephones in the Atlantic coast lighthouses and lifesaving stations, and that was a move that enabled him to turn over to the Treasury Department all of the hundreds of miles of telegraph line the Signal Corps had built, rebuilt, and operated for the better part of twenty years. It cut down operating costs by a handsome figure.

Then, in 1892, Greely was able to announce that one-half of all the Army posts in the country had been equipped with telephones. To do this job the Signal Corps had been able to rent a considerable number of instruments and to purchase others. The purchases were made at a moment when the magneto telephone patent had expired, when rival companies had glutted the market with a score of different models, and when prices had fallen to a point even lower, it was said, than panic levels.

In the next two or three years, the Chief Signal Officer installed for the Coast Artillery the first telephone lines ever used for fire-control purposes; and—still pursuing his theoretical knowledge—Greely in 1897 announced the development by Capt. James Allen of a new type of telephone for use in the field.

Previously, in the fall of 1890—having just decided against abolishing it—Congress passed an act to reorganize the Signal Corps and redefine its mission. Under this new law, the Corps was to consist of ten officers and fifty men—including ten first-class sergeants. This was something new; in the United States Army there had never before been a noncommissioned grade above that of sergeant, and the reason for establishing it now was to offer better pay and thus to attract soldiers of a better class to the Signal Corps.

Acting swiftly, Greely requested and obtained a War Department order directing the Army School at Fort Riley, Kansas, to set up courses for training of Signal Corps sergeants. Then, scrutinizing the newly formulated mission of the Corps, he paid particular attention to the specific "duty of collecting and transmitting information . . . by telegraph or otherwise." On the principle that Congress means what it says and says what it means, Greely found in the word *otherwise* all the authority he needed for setting up at once a Photographic Section of the Signal Corps.

In the Arctic, Greely had learned that photography, within proper limits, could be an effective means of collecting and transmitting information; and at very great cost he had brought back from the Arctic the glass-plate negatives of all the photographs taken by Sergeant Rice. At Greely's request a course in photography was added to the Signal Corps curriculum at Fort Riley; and a few years later—in 1896—the Signal Corps' first *Manual of Photography* was published by the Government Printing Office.

The great event of 1891—a direct result of the 1890 reorganization of the Signal Corps—was the transfer of the weather service to the Department of Agriculture. As of June 30 in that year the Signal Corps was operating five hundred observatories, of which twenty-six were stations of the first class, equipped with automatic instruments for the continuous registration of all weather phenomena. The changeover took place on July 1; and what passed out of the hands of the Signal Corps and that day became the United States Weather Bureau, was an established public service of worldwide importance.

In 1893 trouble broke out along the Mexican border, and tactical operations came abruptly to the fore. In this emergency the Army called for the building in two months' time of a telegraph line from Brownsville to Laredo, Texas. Twenty years earlier Greely himself had built such a line, sending to Virginia for the necessary poles. His reply now was that no such line could be constructed in less than six months' time. But in a matter of hours he had a field telegraph train of nine wagons rolling out of Fort Riley, and less than 2 weeks later there was telegraph service between Brownsville and Laredo.

In 1894, to his own delight, bookish General Greely was directed to take charge of the War Department Library. In effect, then, the library became a division of the Office of the Chief Signal Officer. It contained about thirty thousand volumes, including the one that Greely himself had compiled as a second lieutenant of the weather service back in 1872, the "tremendous" bibliography of books on meteorology.

The library also contained a large number of photographs and photographic negatives, including those Greely had brought back from the Arctic; and in 1895 Greely succeeded in acquiring for the library the more than six thousand glass-plate negatives of the Matthew Brady Collection of Civil War photographs.

Meanwhile—as far back as 1891, in fact—Greely had turned his attention to balloons, and in 1896 had already set up at Fort Logan, Colorado, the first balloon company in the history of the Signal Corps. Then, in early January of 1898, he was selected to represent the War Department on a joint Army-Navy board appointed to investigate the military value of the heavier-than-air flying machine— and, more particularly, to inquire into the experiments of Professor Samuel Pierpont Langley, whose steam-powered scale-model flying machine in 1896 had lifted itself off the ground and traveled half a mile through the air.

Langley was at this time the secretary of the Smithsonian Institution; but Greely had known him some twenty years earlier, when he had been a civilian weather specialist in the service of the Signal Corps. Now Greely took up his cause and, on behalf of the joint board, reported that Langley's machine could be expected to carry a man into the air. Therefore he recommended that the Army undertake to build one. The result was a directive that settled for years to come the position of the Signal Corps in respect to aviation.

In 1899 and 1900 General Greely presented to Professor Langley two grants of $25,000 each to finance his researches on behalf of the Army. Greely was responsible also for following the progress of Langley's work and for assuring the Army that its money was well invested. In this way, and to this extent, the Chief Signal Officer was concerned for the first time in history with subsidizing a civilian scientist in his work on a still-to-be-invented something of military value.

In the end, the project was written off as a failure, and shortly thereafter Langley died. But eleven years later an experienced flyer took out Langley's machine and vindicated the old man's memory by flying her. It became clear then that the Langley episode, which had ended in failure, should have ended in success.

Meanwhile, however, there had been the war with Spain. As that war began, Greely had eight hundred dollars cash on hand plus a commitment to provide the fire-control systems needed for the Coast Artillery's new disappearing guns. For the latter purpose, however, Greely talked the Secretary of War into allowing him twenty-four thousand dollars, and then he placed the coastal defenses for the first time in touch by electric telegraph with one another and with the War Department.

For the first two months, or more than half the duration of the war, Greely worked unbelievably long hours, and ran the affairs of his office in total solitude. For there were, after all, only eight commissioned officers in the whole Signal Corps in April of 1898, and they were needed elsewhere.

He leased a cable ship to repair the cables off Cuba; and, suspecting that signal equipment would be crowded out of the regular supply vessels, he used the leased ship to get to Cuba the miles of wire that had to be strung through the jungle. In addition, he took over the job of censoring the traffic that moved over all cables entering the United States and over many of the domestic telegraph lines.

And there is good evidence that he had a friend in the cable office in Havana—for it was Greely who appeared before the Secretary of War on May 19, 1898 and announced that the long-missing Spanish fleet had arrived that morning off Santiago, on the south coast of Cuba. The Navy was unaware of that fact and for several hours was highly skeptical. But Greely's news was the war's most momentous piece of military intelligence.

During the War, he also directed the organization of the Volunteer Signal Corps, which in the end comprised seventeen companies of four officers and fifty-five men each; and—what took the breath away from many an old-time soldier—he equipped each company with a typewriter!

He saw the units into service in Cuba, Puerto Rico, and the Philippines; and after the war he directed the building of telegraph and cable networks running to 3,500 miles in Cuba alone. When the Signal Officer of Seventh Corps first cabled from Manila requesting 100 miles of wire, Greely sent him 1,000 miles, later on decided that he should have sent 10,000, and did in fact, before the Philippine Insurrection ended, send 16,000 miles.

Meanwhile Greely saw the job through in China, during the Boxer Rebellion, when the Signal Corps and the British Royal Engineers together built the telegraph line to Peking; and meanwhile, too, he designed and almost completed the building of the Alaskan telegraph and cable system.

Notably, too, Greely assigned two of his officers, Maj. James Allen and Capt. George O. Squier, to follow the experiments of the Italian scientist Marconi; and before the close of April, 1899 the Signal Corps was operating the first successful wireless-telegraph system ever placed in service in the United States. Signal Corps radio was an established fact even before the Alaska telegraph and cable system was decided upon.

Nor was this all of Greely's work. He purchased the first motor car ever placed in the service of the United States Army. He set up in Washington the famous Signal Corps Laboratory, and he established at Fort Leavenworth the Army Signal School. It was for such things as these that he became known as the father of the modern Signal Corps.

As for the Army Signal School, it was set up with what was more than half admiringly denounced as "Greelyesque abruptness." General Greely, it was solemnly reported, had the idea first at 0900 hours and before noon he had convinced the Secretary of War of its excellence. Next day a War Department order appeared, and the day after that the school was in session.

Everything about the man was Greelyesque—even his abrupt departure from the Corps. In 1906, after serving for nearly nineteen years as Chief Signal Officer, Greely was posted a major general and placed in command of the Department of the Pacific with headquarters at the Presidio of San Francisco.

Throughout history the U.S. Army has made contributions that have greatly benefited the people of the United States. The construction of the Panama Canal by the `Army's Corps of Engineers is a striking example. The construction of the Alaska Communications System by the Signal Corps—though equally as arduous a task—was perhaps less glamorous, but it contributed greatly to making possible the development of Alaska and its entrance into the Union as our forty-ninth state.

The Building of Alaska's Communication System

✠ DAVID J. MARSHALL, *U.S. Army Signal Center*

In the year 1867 the Russian colony of Alaska was purchased from the Czar at two cents an acre. At that price, said some, it was a bargain, but others raised an uproar and spoke of the purchase as "Seward's Folly." In any case, Alaskan affairs for the first ten years were administered directly by the War Department.

In 1877, however, U.S. troops were withdrawn and the few settlers, mostly of Russian birth or descent, were left to look after themselves. Then, almost at once, the Indians began a campaign of terror. In 1879 they moved into Sitka for the avowed purpose of killing every white inhabitant, and it was only the timely arrival of a British warship that saved the situation. . . . Washington was none too happy that the Royal Marines had had to go ashore to protect the lives of American citizens in an American possession.

Accordingly, Washington dispatched a gunboat to patrol Alaskan waters and thus to serve as the representative of law and order, and it was not till 1884 that a civil government was established for what then became the Territory of Alaska. Its value was chiefly strategic. Our owning it kept the Russians off the North American continent.

But in 1896 gold was discovered in the Klondike, and the great gold rush began. Thousands of prospectors and miners poured into Alaska. They were quickly followed by gamblers and gunmen. "Gold was crossed with whiskey," and the combination bred violence and murder. The civil government at Sitka was forced to call upon the Army for help.

The Military Department of Alaska was created in 1899, with headquarters at Fort St. Michael, on the south shore of Norton

Sound. Five garrisons were established—Fort Davis near Nome, Fort Gibbon near Tanana, Fort Egbert near Eagle, Fort Liscum near Faldex, and Fort Seward near Skagway. And the Signal Corps was directed to build telegraph lines connecting the garrisons with headquarters and with one another.

Involved in that project was the construction of hundreds upon hundreds of miles of wire line across a country of which little was known—except that it was wild and dangerous. Very few people knew that vast areas were extremely boggy in the fall; that the winter temperatures ran to seventy-two degrees below zero; that the wet snow was treacherously deep in the spring; and that the summer brought clouds of insects.

On May 26, 1900, Congress appropriated $450,550 to cover the cost, and provided, incidentally, "that commercial business may be done over these military lines." So, in effect, the system was to offer its service to the entire population on much the same basis as a commercial communication company.

Greely was the mastermind who directed all the work. Without leaving his desk at Washington, he decided upon galvanized iron wire to withstand the ice and gales of the Alaskan winter, and he sent to Alaska shiploads of galvanized iron poles for use where timber was not locally available. Perhaps he remembered the pole-line he had built in North Dakota twenty years earlier and the North Dakota blizzard he had lived through. And perhaps he remembered the line he had built across the treeless prairie in Texas in 1873, when he had had to import poles from Virginia. In any case, the steamships were chartered early, and galvanized iron was on its way to Alaska.

Adroitly, Greely paid a private visit, almost a secret visit, to the Canadian Prime Minister at Ottawa. They struck a bargain, and presently teams of men were moving out from Dawson, in the Canadian Klondike, and down the Yukon Valley. The Canadian Telegraph System was pushing across the border into Alaska.

In the spring of 1900, Capt. Frank Greene was Signal Officer, Military Department of Alaska. Two things happened in swift succession: Greene was transferred to the Philippines, and his one and only assistant contracted a serious illness. With these two definitely out of the picture, there remained in all Alaska not one representative of the Signal Corps, commissioned or enlisted. So it came about that Greely himself took off for Alaska to supervise the start of work on the "Washington-Alaska Military Cable and Telegraph System," which for many years to come would be known as WAMCATS.

113

It was the early summer of 1900 when Greely arrived in Alaska. His first move was to order the construction of a telegraph line from Nome, on the north shore of Norton Sound, through Fort Davis at Port Safety, twenty-five miles to the east.

Chosen for this work were men of the Seventh Infantry, stationed at Fort Davis. They were fortunate. The weather was mild, and they erected the iron poles easily on the brown hills overlooking Norton Sound. The line was completed on September 15, 1900, only a few days before the cold winter settled down, transforming that part of Alaska into a world of snow and ice and frigid silence.

But in spite of the shortness of time, Greely turned at once to the task of laying between Fort Safety and Fort St. Michael a submarine cable that would bring department headquarters—Fort St. Michael —into the hookup just completed. For this purpose Greely had already chartered a steamship and filled her hold with one hundred and eighty-seven miles of cable—fifty miles more than the estimated requirement. Instruments and shore end were landed at Fort St. Michael on September 20, 1900, and the ship steamed northward under Greely's command for Port Safety, paying out cable as she moved along.

She had covered only five miles, however, when she ran aground on a reef. Her bottom was ripped open, water poured into her, and she was a total loss.

Greely had to act fast now. He called upon the Alaska Commercial Company for help, and the company sent him a lighter and an oceangoing paddle-steamer. The lighter was brought alongside the wreck, and Greely was able to salvage the one hundred and eighty miles of cable still aboard of her. Slowly, painfully, he hauled it out of her flooded hold. He piled it mountain-high on the deck of the lighter.

And when all that work was done, and the Alaskan winter was inexorably closing in, he resumed the job he had started out to do. In a race against the ice the lighter, towed by the paddle-steamer, paid out close to one hundred and thirty miles of cable. On October 17, 1900 the work was done. Communication was established over a distance of one hundred and fifty-eight miles between Fort St. Michael and Fort Davis via Port Safety.

But the triumph was shortlived. The newly laid cable had been in service for only a week or two when it was crushed by a movement of the polar ice.

According to General Greely's plan, the next step was to connect Fort Egbert, in the Klondike, with Fort Liscum on the seacoast; and

114

An early observation balloon used by the Signal Corps.

Below: This Signal Corps balloon made an ascent at Gas House Field, Washington, D.C. on April 17, 1908. Officers who made ascent (l. to r.) are Lt. Frank P. Lahm, Capt. Chandler, Capt. Van Horn, and Lt. Thomas E. Selfridge.

On August 4, 1908, U.S. Army Signal Corps Dirigible No. 1 made her first flight at Fort Myer. The following year this dirigible was transferred to the balloon center at Fort Omaha where the first aviation training program began with twenty enlisted signalmen.

During the Spanish-American War in the Philippines, a Signal Corps wire and wigwag party advances on the left of the American lines toward Manila. Flags are being displayed to show the Navy their progress. Date is August 13, 1898, a little over four months after Adm. Dewey's victory at Manila Bay.

Painting of a Signal Corps balloon at San Juan Hill, Cuba during the Spanish-American War. Balloon is spotting the strong points of the Spanish positions for the direction of artillery fire.

Manila, Fort Malante, August 1898. Signal Corps soldiers are wigwagging for U.S. Army reserves to advance after the retreat of the Spanish.

A Signal Corps telegraph station at Pasig, Philippine Islands in 1899.

Signal Corps personnel do cable work on the Malecon Drive, Manila, Philippine Islands, in 1902.

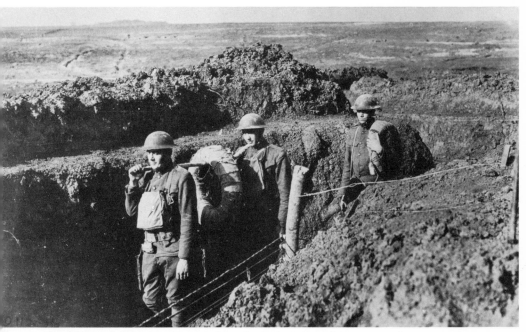

World War I, Soissons, France, March 1918. A Signal Corps Headquarters Company carries wire through the trenches for phones in observation stations at the front.

Crossroads in Argonne Woods, near Montfaucon, Meuse, France, October 1918. A lieutenant of the 32nd Division acts as operator of this important switchboard, vital in the attack since it linked Division, Regimental, and Corps Headquarters.

Mareuilen-Dole, France. A Signal Corps soldier photographs among ruins in August 1918. Note camouflaging on camera. Outfit was a Photo Unit of the 77th Division.

Signal Corps wiring detail tying in a pole line. Twenty kilometers were finished by this small detail in just two days. Tartigny, France, June 1918.

Men of a Field Signal Battalion displaying the Papham panel system of visual airplane signalling. Soldiers are showing white letter "T" — an all-clear sign. Beauval, France, July 1918.

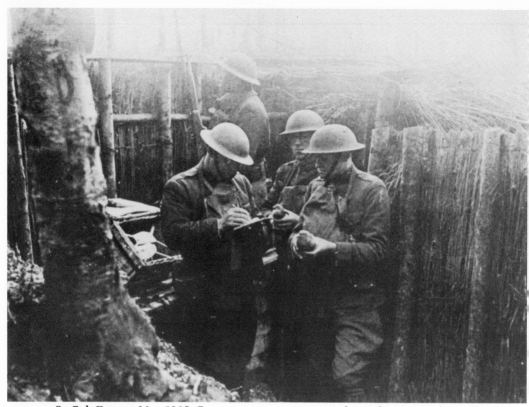

St. Pol, France, May 1918. Preparing pigeons to carry dispatches at Headquarters, 42nd Division.

Paris, France, 1918. Signal Corps electricians installing telephone lines in the study of Prince Murat's mansion, which was to serve as President Wilson's "White House" overseas during the Peace Conference.

Above: President Woodrow Wilson talks to an airplane pilot over wireless telephone. November 21, 1918, Washington, D.C.

Signal battalion's telephone switchboard in operation at Essey, France, September 1918.

Signal Corps soldiers practice the heliograph at Fort Myer, Va.

A Signal Corps radio truck, SCR-108.

Hawaii, 1942. General view of radio communications at the Forward Echelon Headquarters.

During the siege of Corregidor, Army finance personnel shared a part of famous Melinta Tunnel with Message Center Signal Corps personnel. April 1942.

D-Day plus 4. During the Allied invasion of France, members of a communications outfit set up shop in an old shell hole and proceed to direct the fire of naval guns against targets on the beach.

European Theater of Operations, December 1944. Soldier traces a broken field wire for splicing.

Italy, February 1944. Soldiers operate radar in a field in the Nettuno area of Anzio beachhead.

Men of a Signal Corps company reel out wire in the jungles of New Georgia. July 1943.

Radar station on Saipan in 1944.

Left: Radioman with handie-talkie describes advance of men of the 96th Division battling for possession of Big Apple Hill on Okinawa. June 1945.

Korea, January 1951. A Signal Corps soldier on a line pole leans dangerously over a cliff to fasten a jumper as the group rehabilitates lines from Tanyang to Chechon.

Spotter of signals in space, Fort Monmouth, N.J. This giant radar spotting device gives scientists accurate information on satellites' orbital paths.

this work went on in the face of all the unknown terrors of the Alaskan winter. A party of thirteen men of the Seventh Infantry, commanded by Capt. George C. Burnell of the Signal Corps, began building this line in the fall of 1900. Burnell had been ordered back from the Philippines for the assignment. Just out of the tropics, he now faced the Alaska winter.

He and his thirteen men took off from Fort Liscum. They moved northward along the edge of Prince Edward Sound. They passed through the seaport settlement of Valdez. And then turned inland to the Klondike, far to the northeast.

Where there were trees, poles were cut as the party advanced. Iron poles were carried on the backs of mules for use beyond the timber line; and two wagons carried the reels of galvanized wire.

Until the middle of October, it rained incessantly. The two wagons foundered in the mud and had to be abandoned. After that, all the materials and supplies had to be carried by the mules—over trails so rough that the animals could barely cover fifteen miles a day. The rain gave way to snow, and presently the wild Alaskan winter beat down upon them.

The men continued working in overalls and rubber boots. They continued placing pole after pole in the frozen earth of mountain trails. They continued sleeping under canvas at night.

Despite the freeze-up, with temperatures below zero, the glacier streams continued to flow. They changed their courses overnight, sweeping away miles of completed line.

By this time the men were unable to build even two miles of line a month. But they stuck it out, all through that winter and all through the spring of 1901.

When the spring thaws came in June, the Copper River Valley turned into a sea of mud, and all operations came to a halt. Up to that point, only thirty-seven miles of line had been completed. That was a poor showing for ten months' work; but the showing at the opposite end of the line was decidedly worse. According to Greely's plan, a second party should have begun to string wire southwestward from Fort Egbert at the same time Burnell and his men were starting northeastward from Liscum. The plan was that the two parties would meet, and the line would be completed, somewhere along the route. But the party in the north had built no line at all.

Greely worked out a new plan. He had thought he could build the Alaska Telegraph System by using infantry soldiers under the command of signal officers; but before the close of 1900 he was convinced that pole-line work was too exacting for men who had had no prior experience of it. And, anyhow, the Signal Corps had too few officers to work that way. So Greely changed his plan of action and also increased the number of signal officers assigned to Alaska from two to four.

He formed a signal battalion of two companies, and set up battalion headquarters in Seattle, Company C headquarters at Fort Liscum, and Company K headquarters at Fort Gibbon. To command the companies he recalled two lieutenants from the Philippines, and to fill up the companies he ordered signal detachments directly from the Philippines to Alaska.

Meanwhile, before the end of November 1900, he sent Lt. William ("Billy") Mitchell to Fort Egbert to find out what was going on there, and why the pole-line directive had been ignored. Mitchell arrived at Egbert in the middle of January, interviewed the commander, then made his way back to Fort St. Michael. There he told the Commanding General, Department of Alaska, that the fort commander considered the building of a telegraph line up there to be out of the question. It would be too hazardous a job even in the best of weather, and he would not risk the lives of his men to attempt it.

In reply, the General turned over to Mitchell a handful of his own men, and supplied him with wagons, poles, and wire. The later famous Mitchell, just twenty-one years old at the time, equipped his party with snowshoes and heavy winter clothing which he had borrowed from a tribe of Eskimos. He then moved his men directly to Fort Egbert.

In early April of 1901, Mitchell and his party of infantry soldiers arrived at Fort Egbert. All winter long the Canadians had been extending wire down the valley. They had two objectives: Skagway and Fort Egbert. And Mitchell was at Egbert. Inspired by a spirit of rivalry, he began building eleven miles of line eastward from Egbert to meet the Canadians before they could cross the border onto American soil.

He got off to a bad start, however. To steal a march on his rivals, he decided to begin at the mid-point of the route and to work both ways from there. But the steamboat that carried them up the Yukon from Fort Egbert simply dropped them at the midway point, unloaded their materials, and left them stranded, without food or shelter. To save their lives, they had to abandon their materials and break trail by marching four abreast, all the way back to Egbert, through waist-deep snow.

116

There they quickly reorganized and returned, recovered their materials, erected poles, and strung wire. On May 5, 1901, they met the Canadians at the Canadian border; spliced the two lines and Fort Egbert was connected with Skagway and Fort Seward by Canadian wire.

Far to the south of this meeting place, the Canadians had met no Americans working eastward from Skagway. So down there, they had run their wire straight across the border into Alaska. And Skagway, the nearest town to Juneau, had become a wirehead of the Canadian system.

A few months later, on September 4, 1901, the Canadians completed a line seven hundred miles across the mountains of British Columbia; and by this wire the garrisons at Skagway and Fort Egbert were placed in direct touch with the War Department in Washington.

Juneau, which had become the capital in June, was now to be tied into the Canadian wire head at Skagway by a submarine cable one hundred and twenty-four miles long. Greely signed a contract for the laying of such a cable along the inland waterway that connected the two towns, and the company that won the bid found the work easy enough. The job was completed in less than a week and in August of 1901, the cable was placed in operation. So Juneau was expecting momentarily to be placed in touch with Washington.

The cable had been in service for only a few days when it was broken by the tidal currents. Efforts to repair it were suspended by the early arrival of winter, and it was not till June of 1902 that contact with Skagway and Fort Egbert were reestablished. Then the Alaskan capital was brought in direct contact with Washington via Canadian wires.

Except through the Canadian system, Fort Egbert had no link with anything at all in May of 1901. In that month Mitchell began building southwestward from Fort Egbert to Fort Liscum on the seacoast. Five months later, Captain Burnell and his men resumed the push northeastward from the point where they had halted, just thirty-seven miles out from Liscum. And, though it took them fifteen months to do it, Mitchell's men completed the line from Fort Egbert to the Tanana River. There they met Burnell and his party, and the two sections of line were joined. Contact was established between Fort Egbert and Fort Liscum on August 24, 1902.

For the first year of its operation, however, this line was periodically in and out. Where it crossed the coastal range a few miles north of Valdez, high winds and storms in the mountain passes

117

broke the wire almost as soon as the line was in operation. And every once in a while a snowslide tore out wire by the mile.

A serious maintenance problem was solved in 1903 when every section of this line that ran through a canyon or a mountain pass was replaced by a submarine cable.

Greely had worked out his new plan of operations in the last few weeks of 1900, but before he could implement the plan, he had had to send Mitchell to Fort Egbert, and Mitchell had had to follow the original plan of working with infantry soldiers. While this was going on, the two signal companies arrived in Alaska, and the building program was stepped up.

The first project now was to complete a telegraph line from Fort St. Michael to Fort Gibbon on the Tanana River. This line was to be five hundred and twenty-eight miles long, but eighty miles had already been built by men of the Seventh Infantry. Lt. George S. Gibbs of the Signal Corps was sent out to build the remaining four hundred and forty-eight miles.

He began work six months after Mitchell had taken off from Egbert. He finished the job nine months before Mitchell met Russel on the Tanana River.

Gibbs and his party of signalmen took up where the infantry had left off, on the south shore of Norton Sound; and for a time followed the coastline. As the summer began, they struck inland. They were harassed by flies and mosquitoes that rose in black clouds from the soggy earth, buzzing, biting, stinging. Doggedly, the signalmen pushed on with their work, and by the time they descended into the lower valley of the Yukon, their faces and hands were puffed with bites and running sores. Their clothing had been torn to shreds by the brush, and they themselves, sleepless by itch and pain, were exhausted.

In the Yukon Valley there was no brush, and there were no trees. All that lay before them now were the flies and mosquitoes and a vast plain of soggy tundra. It was mucky at the surface, but below the summer thaw line, the tundra was permanently frozen. And across the illimitable wasteland, the harrassed, struggling men dragged the iron poles after them as they continued their advance. They used explosives instead of spades. For every pole they blasted a hole five feet deep in the frozen part of the tundra. They set the pole in this, and packed it in with mud; the mud froze solid in a matter of minutes. Thus the pole was embedded as permanently as in concrete.

When the crew reached the bank of the Yukon at Kaltag, they

followed the river upstream. They had left the tundra behind and were now facing a forest overgrown with vines and thickets, where the silence was broken only by the fierce, whining buzz of the mosquitoes.

The men cut a right-of-way along the riverbank; through miles of heavy thicket, all the way to Nulato, they carved and sliced and hewed a passage between vertical walls of high-growing trees and brush. At Nulato, the line was swung across the mouth of the Koyukuk River, and from there, through many more miles of thicket, it was finally carried up the right bank of the Yukon to Fort Gibbon.

In just about six months' time, Gibbs and his men had built four hundred and forty-eight miles of line. The job was completed, and the line was in service in November of 1901. It placed Fort Gibbon in direct touch with department headquarters at Fort St. Michael, five hundred and twenty-eight miles to the west.

The final link that tied all the principal garrisons into a single network was completed in 1903. This connected Fort Gibbon with Fort Egbert; and when that last section was built, department headquarters at Fort St. Michael was placed in direct touch with Fort Liscum and Fort Egbert and, via Canadian wires, with Fort Seward, Skagway, Juneau, and Washington.

The last of the overland wire lines was built along the valley of the Tanana by two separate parties, one pushing southward from Gibbon, the other working northward from Ketchumstuk.

But the Tanana had up to this time never been explored, so the first job of the Signal Corps was to reconnoiter the valley and produce an accurate map of it. This task was assigned to Lieutenant Mitchell, and many years later the story was told that—to get a bird's-eye view of the place—Mitchell made a kite that carried him a hundred feet into the air.

Lieutenant Gibbs had charge of the construction party that worked southward from Fort Gibbon, beginning in February of 1902; and Mitchell had charge of the party working north and west from Ketchumstuk. The parties met near Salchak on the Tanana River, and the line connecting Fort Gibbon with Fort Egbert and Fort Liscum was completed on June 20, 1903. It was the final section in the construction of a great network of telegraphs and cables.

That, however, was not the end of work for the Signal Corps. Every winter, the Alaskan pole lines were buried by as much as sixty feet of snow. Every spring and fall they were broken apart by sleet storms and high winds. And every summer, without fail, lengths of a hundred miles or more were lost due to forest fires. Floods were still another cause of trouble; they uprooted the poles and washed away the repairmen's cabins.

These cabins were built beside the pole lines, forty miles apart, clear across the wilderness, each of them housing one signalman and two infantrymen. When a line broke, a crew of two men set out from each side of the break, most often by dogsled; and the first to reach the break repaired it, then awaited the arrival of the other crew. From a distance, they exchanged the "all's-well" sign and thereupon both crews returned to their cabins. This procedure was strict, for travel injuries were frequent, and a man even slightly hurt at sixty below zero was doomed unless somebody took care of him.

Even in summer the repair trips were perilous, and the regulations forbade any man at any time to travel alone. In one twelve-month period, of the one hundred and five signalmen in North Alaska, three were killed while repairing the line. In addition, two infantrymen lost their lives, and countless men of both branches were injured.

Every station was stocked with rations and fuel supplies to last for thirteen or fourteen months. Those on the lower Tanana and the lower Yukon could be reached by steamboat for a few weeks every year. But the bulk of supplies—averaging four hundred tons a year—had to be sledded in midwinter and mule-packed in summer, for there were no roads, and wagons could not be used.

Shipments got lost, and one station was without meat for eleven months. In 1905, therefore, the teams were all equipped with shotguns enabling the men to hunt game; and there was a step-up in their allowances of butter, milk, and syrup.

The solitude was all that most men could bear. Not even an Eskimo or an Indian was seen for months at a time, and the only visitor was an occasional inspecting officer. At one station, it was once as long as two years between inspections.

Thirty-three months before the land-line system was completed, General Greely himself, as we have seen, had laid the cable between Fort St. Michael and Port Safety, and that cable had been in service for only a short time when it was crushed and severed by a movement of the ice pack.

It was repaired in the spring of 1901. It was still in service on November 18, the day Lieutenant Gibbs and his party carried the far end of a land wire into Fort Gibbon; and for the next two days, in fact, messages were exchanged between Gibbon and Fort St.

Michael over a cable and telegraph circuit 686 miles long. But then, on November 21, 1901, the cable failed a second time.

It was never repaired; when the ice began to crack up in the spring of 1902, the fast-moving floods carried forty miles of it out to sea. In the summer of 1903—just seven weeks after the Alaskan land-wire system had been completed—it was replaced by a wireless telegraph.

It was one of the notable events of Signal Corps history that General Greely, as far back as 1898, had assigned two of his officers—Capt. James Allen and Lt. George O. Squier—to follow the experiments of a man in England who thought he had found a way to transmit and receive electric telegraphic signals through the "ether," without the use of wires. The man was an Italian by birth, a scientist by profession. His name was Guglielmo Marconi. Greely, in his report for 1898, declared that "a system of wireless telegraphy" was being investigated "with a view to adopting it whenever the progress of invention and the conditions of military service shall warrant . . ."

Allen was well known in the Signal Corps. In 1897 he had developed the buzzer-phone to take the place of Morse telegraphy in the field. Squier was a neat and tidy, bright-eyed man who was, at the age of thirty-three years, both a soldier and a scientist. There was no question of his scientific attainments. He had been graduated from West Point, near the top of his class, in 1887. Six years later he graduated from Johns Hopkins with a doctorate in physics and mathematics. And three years later still, in 1896, he had won the John Scott Legacy Medal, which was awarded annually to the year's most eminent research scientist. When he transferred from the artillery to the Signal Corps toward the close of 1897, Squier had as good a claim as any man alive to the name of scientist.

As a team, Allen and Squier had their own ideas about watching Professor Marconi. They worked together on plans of their own. They carried out experiments endlessly; and as a result of their efforts the Signal Corps, by the end of April, 1899, was operating a wireless telegraph between Fire Island and the Fire Island Lightship, which was anchored twelve miles offshore on the north approach to New York Harbor. This achievement was historic—for the Fire Island telegraph was the first successful wireless system ever placed in service in the Western Hemisphere.

Allen and Squier were quick to repeat their triumph. Almost at once they linked department headquarters on Governors Island with Fort Hamilton at the entrance to Upper New York Bay. And a few

121

months later on, they installed a similar system in San Francisco harbor, linking Fort Mason and the island of Alcatraz.

From all this it followed that the Signal Corps, in the summer of 1903, had had four years' experience of wireless telegraphy, and for almost a year, in fact, had been making effective and reliable use of it between stations fifty miles apart.

Now, faced with a problem of establishing a link between Port Safety and Fort St. Michael in Alaska, General Greely decided to test wireless telegraphy over a distance of one hundred and thirty-three miles. He went to a private contractor for the equipment. The agreement specified that Fessenden equipment was to be used—and that the company would not be paid unless the system continued to operate flawlessly for ten consecutive days. The company went to work at once but problem after problem arose and, after a year, the company, admitting failure, repacked the equipment, picked up its tools, and left, praised but unpaid.

After that, no other company would risk the same contract; and the Signal Corps had to try its own men at the work. The project was assigned to Capt. Edgar Russel, who would have the help of Capt. L. B. Wildman. Commercial equipment was purchased after many types had been tested. Buildings and two-hundred-foot towers were constructed at the station sites: Port Safety, at the north end, and Fort St. Michael, at the south end of Norton Sound.

In each of the two buildings, Russel installed a power plant consisting of a six-horsepower gasoline engine and a three-kilowatt generator. In each building he also installed a transmitting and receiving set which had been developed in the United States by Captain Wildman. Essentially, this was an assembly of items produced by different manufacturers—chiefly Fessenden, De Forest, and Marconi.

The sets were installed; and at 0800 hours on August 7, 1903, the operator at Fort St. Michael sent out a call to Port Safety. Port Safety replied at once; and from that day forward, Alaska's first wireless telegraph continued operating, without an hour's interruption, for more than a year.

At the end of that time, however, three serious breakdowns were averted by only the narrowest of margins—and only because the station affected had been supplied with five or six duplicate sets of equipment. The "close calls" occurred at Port Safety and all within a period of seven weeks in the dead of winter.

First, at 0400 hours on January 25, 1904, a raging blizzard took the roof off the powerhouse. The room filled rapidly with snow, the fire in the potbelly stove was killed, and the inside temperature fell in less than one minute to something like seventy below zero. Before it could be emptied, the gasoline engine's water jacket froze and cracked the cylinder; and that might have been the end of operations for the rest of the winter.

But the reaction was fast. Fighting fiercely against a wind that every now and then rose to hurricane force, the station personnel were able to stretch a tarpaulin across the open top of the building and to batten it down securely. So the building was roofed again, and the fast-accumulating snow added to its protection.

Next, they shoveled their way into the building, dug out the stove, and relit the fire. But then as the place warmed up, the tightly packed snow that still covered the equipment began to melt, and the equipment was flooded. In the end, however, that difficulty too was overcome. A spare engine was running. A dried-out generator was whirring. And, as it had been doing every day for more than a year, the station opened that day at 0900 hours, dead on the minute.

In February, a power-transmission belt broke during the sending hour and lashed about, ripping out pipe connections and putting the engine out of line. Fortunately, no traffic was moving at the moment. Another spare engine was started, and power was restored within two minutes. So the second crisis was met, without interruption of service.

In March the cracking of a sparkplug threw the power plant out of commission again. But this time the experience of the previous month had prepared them. The third spare engine was on the floor ready for service. Power was restored in somewhat less than half a minute.

Captain Wildman was in charge of the station at Fort Safety. He had requested the assignment to study the influence of the Arctic winter on wireless operations generally. He found that the Leyden jars were breaking, and he began a search for substitutes. He constructed a number of air condensers, and before the winter's end, prevented a breakdown of service.

Wildman's ingenuity was matched by that of Sergeant McKenny, who in the course of that first winter at Port Safety invented a key that increased the average operator's sending capacity from fifteen to thirty-five words a minute.

Two thousand words an hour, transmitted and received without error, became standard on the wireless telegraph between Port Safety and Fort St. Michael. And, since commercial traffic was accepted at commercial rates, this Signal Corps facility was the first

123

public wireless telegraph system to operate regularly on the American continent.

On the day of its completion in June of 1903, the Alaska telegraph system had no direct tie to any commercial telegraph in the United States, and all official messages between Juneau and Washington passed over lines of the Canadian Telegraph System. But Congress by the spring of 1903 had appropriated funds for a submarine cable to connect Juneau and Sitka with Seattle, and General Greely had begun work on plans not only to lay the cable, but to have it operating by the first Monday in December, when Congress would again come into session.

The cable would be thirteen hundred miles long—the longest in the Western Hemisphere.

Many problems would have to be solved. The only cable ship—*Burnside*—was in the Philippines. The ocean floor between Juneau and Seattle had never been surveyed. Greely was unable to find a cable engineer willing to work for the Army. Nor could he find as many cable technicians as he needed. Machinery for making and laying gutta-percha-covered cable did not exist in the United States, and foreign manufacturers reported that they could not supply the cable at the time stipulated or at the price Congress was willing to pay.

Greely did his best, however. He ordered the *Burnside* to proceed to Sitka with her trained Filipino cablemen. Instead of imported cable, he decided upon a seamless rubber cable that just then had been developed in the United States. He bargained with a New York manufacturer for all that he needed, and out of the sum appropriated by Congress he had enough money left over to pay for transporting the cable sixteen thousand miles around Cape Horn to Seattle.

In place of a cable engineer, he recruited electrical engineers and trained them as cable specialists; and in four months, he also trained a force of cable technicians. Greely selected Col. James Allen to lay the cable—assisted by Capt. Edgar Russel.

The *Burnside* made a survey of the ocean floor from Sitka to Seattle. At Seattle, she was loaded with cable and on September 22, 1903, she arrived in Juneau. The first cable was to be laid between Juneau and Sitka.

The first day out—with Colonel Allen in command—she laid forty miles of cable. And then she struck the submerged portion of an iceberg. Though shipping water all the way, she got back to port without help; but to lighten her load she had continued to pay out cable. So she laid eighty miles of cable—forty miles out from Juneau and forty miles back again.

After repairs, the *Burnside* again steamed south picking up cable for the first forty miles, and then laying it as she continued down Frederick Sound. From there she moved west into Chatham Strait, pushed ahead to the tip of Baranof Island, and then north to Sitka, where the cable end was landed on October 2, 1903.

General Greely and the Secretary of War, Elihu Root, both cabled their congratulations to Allen, Russel, and their men. They also congratulated each other, for in spite of the *Burnside*'s collision with the ice, the first section of the cable was in operation two months before Congress was to convene.

The *Burnside* lay over only one day at Sitka. On October 3, she shoved off for Seattle, laying cable southward along the west side of the Alexander Archipelago. Within a week, however, she ran into violent storms of snow and ice blowing in across the Bering Sea, and on October 16, after one hundred and forty miles of cable had been laid, Colonel Allen was forced to call a halt. The cable end was then buoyed in six hundred fathoms and the *Burnside* headed for Seattle—and the Philippines.

In May of 1904, however, the *Burnside* was once more in Seattle. Her cable-laying machinery was overhauled, cable newly arrived from New York was taken aboard, and toward the latter part of June she headed northward for the anchor buoy.

But the buoy had disappeared, carried off by the winter storms. A search was made for the cable by dragging the ocean floor, and finally it was found where the storms had dragged it, many miles off its original path. Colonel Allen decided to make a new start from Sitka.

It was summer, and a routine operation was looked for. But from the day she left Sitka to the day she arrived in Seattle, the *Burnside* had to fight against storms and heavy seas. "She pitched, she rolled, she creaked, she groaned," said Colonel Allen. But she paid out the cable just the same, and the cable end was brought ashore at Seattle on August 28, 1904.

Even before this date, Washington had called for direct communication with the military stations in the valleys of the Tanana and the Yukon. To furnish the required service, Sitka would now have to be connected with the Valdez; and that problem was solved —on paper, anyhow—by a cable six hundred and forty miles long.

To eliminate the need for a second trip, the *Burnside* was loaded far in excess of her stated capacity, and on September 18, 1904 she sailed directly for Valdez. There she laid four miles of cable between Fort Liscum and the town itself, and on September 29 she cast off for Sitka.

Steadily and surely, she ploughed southward across the Gulf of Alaska, and four days later, on October 3, she arrived in Sitka, the cable end was drawn ashore, and her job was done.

It was an historic event. By the Signal Corps cable-and-telegraph system, Washington was now in touch with every military outpost in Alaska. And how great that system was, Greely demonstrated quite effectively in his annual report.

He began by calling it "unique in the annals of telegraphic engineering, whether one considers the immense extent of territory, its remoteness from the United States, the winter inaccessibility of the region, the severity of the climate, and the uninhabited and trackless districts, or the adverse physical conditions." Then he declared: "If superimposed upon a map of the United States, it would extend from Wyoming to the Bahamas, off the coast of Florida. The cable would reach from Newfoundland to Ireland, and the land lines from Washington to Texas. Its totality comprises elements not elsewhere combined in a single system—submarine, land, and wireless methods, all worked as one . . . harmonious system."

In siring and nurturing military aviation, the Signal Corps deserves great credit for major contributions to both the preservation of the nation in time of war and the phenomenal growth of its civilian air industry in peacetime. Call military aviation the Air Force today, if you desire, or if you fought in World War II, perhaps you called it the Army Air Corps. But if you were around during World War I or before, you'd know that it was brought to manhood as a branch of the Army Signal Corps.

Offspring of the Signal Corps –
The Balloon, Dirigible, and Airplane

✠ R. K. TIERNEY

The growth of the Signal Corps and the foresight of such officers as Brig. Gen. Adolphus W. Greely and Brig. Gen. James Allen led to the reestablishment of balloon operations, and the incorporation of the dirigible and the airplane within the U.S. Army.

General Greely was Chief Signal Officer from March 3, 1887 until his promotion and transfer, February 9, 1906. He was replaced by General Allen, who carried on the aeronautic policies of his former chief.

A balloon section created in 1892 by General Greely was the beginning of the first all-military aeronautic organization in the U.S. Army.

Signal Corps plans in 1892 called for a balloon section as part of each telegraph train. A balloon secured by Lt. William A. Glassford from the French firm of Lachambre was the first obtained for these plans. The balloon was named *General Myer* in honor of the first chief of the Signal Corps. The *General Myer* was used extensively over the next few years until destroyed by high winds.

Despite early enthusiasm, the years leading up to the Spanish-American War were lean ones for Signal Corps balloonists. At the outbreak of the war the Army had only one available balloon.

Lt. Col. Joseph E. Maxfield, charged with the organization of two balloon companies, was dismayed to find that his only balloon, when inflated, had the somewhat uneven appearance of a "misshapen pumpkin." The only "modern" feature aboard the basket was a telephone, which replaced the telegraph used in Professor Thaddeus Lowe's day.

127

This odd-shaped balloon—destined to be christened the *Santiago* and to participate in the battle of San Juan Hill—was moved to New York to watch for an anticipated invasion of Manhattan by the Spanish.

Realizing such a bold attack would never materialize, General Greely suggested instead that the balloon be used in Cuba. Despite numerous transportation snarls, the balloon finally arrived in Cuba on June 28, 1898.

Heavy rains and intense heat caused the varnished silk envelope to stick together, and the underbrush had torn it in numerous places. Hurriedly patched with surgical adhesive tape, three ascents were made in the balloon on the afternoon of the thirtieth. The third aerial reconnaissance was made at the request of the commanding general, Maj. Gen. William Shafter. The observations provided the Army with valuable information on roads to the front and the location of the Spanish fleet in Santiago Harbor.

On the morning of July 1 the Army prepared to launch an attack on San Juan Hill to destroy the heavily garrisoned blockhouse, the last remaining obstacle on the road to Santiago. Colonel Maxfield was ordered to have his balloon keep pace with the lead units of the Army.

The balloon was sent aloft. According to Colonel Maxfield's observations, it presented a most tempting target as a wagon bore it along with the advancing troops.

A volunteer from New York, Pvt. Charles Johnson Post reported:

We heard yells and cheers from the rear of our columns. An observation balloon came into sight high above the jungle. A four-man ground crew held its trail rope and kept the balloon under control. Signal Corps men followed with coils of the rope, which they payed out or took in according to the directions from the basket of the balloon above. Two heads peered over the rim of the basket and occasionally a little note would flutter down. The trail rope led directly down into the Aguadores Road; it was a beautiful range marker for the Spanish artillery and infantry, and they promptly used it as such.

Lt. Col. John D. Miley, Maj. Gen. William Shafter's aide-de-camp, wrote:

Winding its way among the troops the balloon was soon within a few hundred yards of the Aguadores River. The enemy's musketry fire was already becoming quite spirited, but when the balloon reached this point it was opened upon by a heavy fire from field guns and musketry fire also increased. The third shell or shrapnel fired at the balloon struck it, and the next one tore it so badly that it at once descended. Time enough, however, was afforded Colonel Derby to discover a road leading from the main road to the left and crossing the Aguadores River four or five hundred yards farther down the stream. This was a most opportune discovery as the main road was congested with troops and the fire so heavy as to tend to demoralize the men.

The *Santiago*, too badly damaged to be used again, may have been responsible for heavy casualties from Spanish artillery fire. But it also seems to have been one of the determining factors in the capture of San Juan Hill. General Greely remarked, "This action enabled the deployment of our troops over two roads, and by doubling the force may possibly have been the determining factor in the gallant capture of San Juan Hill."

Army officers like General Greely knew the value of aerial observation—and they knew the inadequacies of available equipment. After the Spanish-American War they watched with envy the increasingly successful use of military dirigible balloons by European powers, and eagerly anticipated the development of a heavier-than-air flying machine.

The Army organized a balloon detachment in May, 1902 at Fort Myer, where the Signal Corps balloon equipment had been stored for two years. Since the equipment had deteriorated beyond use, a new balloon was purchased for maneuvers in Connecticut, and met with limited success after numerous logistical obstacles were overcome.

The Army's balloon activity remained fairly stagnant until the spring of 1907 when the Signal Corps purchased a new balloon—Signal Corps Balloon No. 9 (the ninth balloon obtained since the Civil War). Another larger balloon which had been ordered in 1906 was accepted on June 4, 1907 and became Signal Corps Balloon No. 10.

Under the guidance of General Allen, a balloon house and hydrogen plant was established at Fort Omaha in 1908. However, ballooning in the U.S. Army retrogressed over the next several years. When the United States entered World War I, the Army had only three serviceable free balloons and two captive balloons on hand.

The training program at Fort Omaha was immediately stepped up and newly organized balloon companies were sent to field artillery firing centers and new schools at San Antonio, Texas, Fort Sill,

Oklahoma, Arcadia, California, and Lee Hall, Virginia. Balloon observers received further training at the American School, Camp Souge, France, and at French schools and artillery centers.

By April 15, 1918 the Army had two balloon companies operating against the enemy. By Armistice Day the Army had trained 89 balloon companies and 751 balloon officers in America. Thirty-three companies and 117 officers were sent overseas to join the two balloon companies organized in France. In all, the Army's balloon operations in France totaled 446 officers and 6,365 enlisted men. Of the 265 balloons sent to France, 77 participated in action. The Army employed 252 balloon observers within 23 companies. It lost 48 balloons; official German losses were set at 73.

A captain in the Air Service wrote that observation balloonists noted any changes within five miles back of German lines and reported their findings to ground stations and other balloons by telephone. During actual fighting they watched for new enemy batteries to open up and the appearance of hostile aircraft, which often forced the observers to make parachute jumps. The balloons would ascend as high as 4,500 feet and remain in the air for hours, from two and a half to four and a half miles from enemy lines. The balloonists could see about eight miles in all directions. At the start of battle a large number of balloons would be sent up. Specific duties divided among them included: recording heavy artillery fire, shot by shot; observing demolition behind enemy lines; and watching for reinforcements or traps, the shifting of enemy positions, the assembly of supplies by the enemy, and the forward movement of enemy troops.

In all, the Army's balloon operations in World War I accounted for 1,642 ascensions; 3,111 hours in the air; 316 artillery adjustments; 12,018 shell bursts reported; and numerous other types of intelligence recorded.

After the armistice, numerous lighter-than-air projects were cancelled, and by the summer of 1920, the Army's authorized balloon strength was cut to 29 companies. With the introduction of the fighter plane during the war, the balloon became exceedingly vulnerable and quickly faded from the scene as a useful implement of war.

But, as proved along the Potomac and at San Juan Hill, aerial observation provided invaluable support to the ground commander, both as a source of intelligence and as a means of directing artillery fire. The balloon companies and the airplane operations of World War I convinced many Army officers that aerial observation in support of the ground commanders was essential. This concept would grow among ground commanders, and twenty-four years later it would blossom into our present concept of Army aviation.

Before the Spanish-American War, General Greely began trying to obtain funds for the development of a dirigible, but his pleas went unheeded.

It fell to his successor, General Allen, to find the way. In November, 1907, he obtained $25,000 from the War Department Board of Ordnance and Fortification to procure an experimental nonrigid dirigible balloon for the Signal Corps.

A contract was awarded to the lowest bidder, Thomas Scott Baldwin. His quotation was $6,750.

By August 18, 1908 an airship propelled by a gasoline engine had been built and successfully completed a series of performance trials. Baldwin then taught Lieutenants Frank P. Lahm, Thomas E. Selfridge, and Benjamin D. Foulois to fly the dirigible. On the twenty-second the airship was officially accepted and became U.S. Army Dirigible Balloon No. 1. This airship made several demonstration flights around the United States, but was not used after 1909. In 1912 it was condemned and sold.

The Army did not acquire another airship until 1919 when another nonrigid airship was procured.

Airships were not used by the Army in France during World War I, but by the summer of 1920 the Army had seven nonrigid airships. However the airship, like the balloon, was nudged from the scene by the airplane.

Shortly after the turn of the century Congress appropriated $25,000 for the War Department to "build a flying machine for war purposes." General Greely turned to an old friend, Professor Samuel P. Langley, director of the Smithsonian Institution, for assistance. Dr. Langley had been experimenting in aerodynamics since 1885. In 1896 he built a steam driven model airplane that flew three-fourths of a mile along the Potomac River. He agreed to build a full-sized test machine for $50,000.

On October 7, 1903, Dr. Langley's *Aerodrome A*, as he called his flying machine, was launched from a houseboat in the Potomac River. However, the test was unsuccessful and the *Aerodrome* crashed into the river. Eight weeks later a second attempt to fly the *Aerodrome* also failed.

Reasons given for the failures were that the center of gravity was off, and that the engine was not powerful enough.

As we know, these failures resulted in severe attacks on both

131

Congress and the Army for "squandering money on such an impossible invention." Consequently the project was cancelled.

Meanwhile Wilbur and Orville Wright's aerodynamic experiments reached a successful climax on December 17, 1903 when they made their first airplane flight at Kitty Hawk, North Carolina. However the Army, recalling the abuse it had absorbed over the Langley failure, remained skeptical about the Wrights' success and did not state performance requirements for an airplane until 1907. Consequently the job—and honor—of introducing airplanes to the Army fell to General Allen.

In the history of Army aviation, 1907 was an important year. As noted, a contract was awarded to build U.S. Army Dirigible No. 1; an Aeronautical Division in the office of the Chief Signal Officer was established on August 1; and the United States became the first country to contract for a military airplane when the Signal Corps called for bids in December, 1907.

The Aeronautical Division, responsible for all matters pertaining to military ballooning, air machines and all related subjects, was first headed by Capt. Charles deForest Chandler.

On February 1, 1908 the Army received forty-one bids for a military airplane. Only three bidders met the requirements outlined in the specifications:

Mr. J. F. Scott, Chicago, $1,000, 185 days.

Mr. A. M. Herring, New York City, $20,000, 180 days.

Wright Brothers, Dayton, Ohio, $25,000, 200 days.

All three bids were accepted but only the Wright Brothers' airplane was ever delivered and accepted.

On August 20, 1908, the Wrights brought their plane, a modified version of their 1905 airplane, to Fort Myer, Virginia, for testing.

It was a pusher type, with the motor and prop located behind the pilot and passenger. On September 3 the first flight, lasting 1 minute and 11 seconds, was made. This flight, the first of an airplane on a military installation in America, was followed by a series of test flights that were highlighted on the afternoon of September 9 when Orville remained aloft for 1 hour 2 minutes 15 seconds.

Just as success seemed imminent, tragedy struck at Fort Myer. On September 17, 1908, Orville invited Lt. Thomas E. Selfridge, an official Army observer at the trials, to ride as a passenger on a test flight. On the fourth turn of the field one of the props struck a brace wire attached to the rudder. An eyewitness account reported in the *Washington Post* stated: "The spectators saw a fragment of something fly from the machine and describe an arc in the air.

" 'That's a piece of one of the propellers,' shouted one of the officers. 'I wonder what will happen to—! My God, they're falling!' "
The airplane, twisting and turning, fell 150 feet and hit with tremendous force.

Lieutenant Selfridge died a few hours later in a hospital, the first man to give his life in heavier-than-air powered flight. Only a few months before, Lieutenant Selfridge had become the first Army officer to make a solo flight in a powered airplane, when on May 19, 1908, he flew Alexander Graham Bell's airplane, the *White Wing*. Selfridge's death was a blow to the Signal Corps Aeronautical Division. He had been considered by many "the most widely informed expert on dynamics of the air and mechanical flight."

Orville remained in the hospital several weeks. Upon his release he and his brother continued their work. They returned to Fort Myer on June 20, 1909 with an improved version of their 1908 plane.

After a series of practice flights, the Wrights announced that they were ready for the official trials. On July 27 Orville made the first test flight, carrying Lt. Frank P. Lahm as passenger. Lt. Benjamin D. Foulois flew with Orville on the final test flight on July 30. The tests were successful and the Army accepted the airplane on August 2. It became U.S. Army Aeroplane No. 1.

As part of the contract, the Wrights trained Lt. Frederic E. Humphreys and Lieutenant Lahm to fly the airplane. Instruction began on October 8 and on October 26 the students soloed. Lieutenant Humphreys soloed first and became the first Army aviator.

Lieutenant Foulois reported to College Park, Maryland, on October 20 and received some instruction from Wilbur Wright, Humphreys, and Lahm.

Navy Lieutenant George C. Sweet's visit to observe the operations at College Park on November 3 resulted in two firsts. Lieutenant Sweet became the first Navy officer to fly in a heavier-than-air machine and the first passenger carried by Lieutenant Lahm.

In November, Humphreys and Lahm returned to duty in their respective basic branches, the Engineers and Cavalry. Lieutenant Foulois, who had moved the Army's only airplane to Fort Sam Houston, Texas, for the winter, received flying instructions from the Wrights by mail. The Wrights sent an instructor to help Lieutenant Foulois master the art of landing.

The Army struggled along with one pilot and one plane until 1911 when Congress appropriated $125,000 for Army aviation. General Allen received $25,000 immediately and ordered five planes. The first to be delivered was a Curtiss pusher, which became the Army's second plane.

Three Army lieutenants, Paul W. Beck, G. E. M. Kelly, and John C. Walker, Jr., were trained as pilots by Glenn Curtiss. They joined Lieutenant Foulois at Fort Sam Houston in April, 1911. A month later, on May 10, 1911, Lieutenant Kelly was killed in a crash and became the first flight-training fatality.

In the summer of 1911 the Army had five airplanes, three small balloons, and six officers who held airplane pilot certificates. Having no prescribed test for pilot qualifications, the Army adopted the rules of the Federation Aeronautique International as administered by the Aero Club of America.

By November, 1912, the Army had twelve pilots, thirty-nine enlisted men, and twelve airplanes, including hydroplanes. One hydroplane was the Army's first aircraft with the propeller in the front. The pusher plane, which had accounted for most of the fatalities, was condemned by the Signal Corps in 1914.

The Army first used airplanes for observation and adjustment of field artillery fire in November, 1912. At the request of the Field Artillery Board, two aircraft were sent to Fort Riley, Kansas, for a series of experiments. Portions of a letter from 2d Lt. H. H. Arnold to the Commanding Officer, Signal Corps Aviation School, Washington, D.C., tell the story. It was written at Fort Riley, Kansas, and dated November 6, 1912:

> *The first test in connection with artillery took place on the fourth of November; both machines took part in the test. There was no firing by the battery; the flying was done for the purpose of testing out different kinds of signals. There was a wireless station put up in the immediate vicinity of the battery and No. 10, (one of the aircraft) with Lieutenant Arnold, pilot, Lieutenant Bradley, operator, sent messages down to the battery. No. 11, with Lieutenant Milling, pilot, Lieutenant Sands, observer, was equipped with a smoke signal device made at this place. No. 11 sent signals from this device and also dropped cards. The smoke signal device, although improvised, showed that such a device could be used to signal from the aeroplane to the battery. However, on account of the manner in which it was constructed, the dot and dash system of signals could not be used. A system of dots alone had to be used.*
>
> *On the fifth of November, the aeroplane was used for the first time with the battery actually firing at a target. The target*

134

was about 3200 yards from the battery. It was a dark day, a dark target and a dark background for the target. In spite of this, the target was picked up by the aeroplane very easily. . . .

In August, 1913, a bill in Congress called for an aeronautical branch to be a part of the line of the Army. The majority of the Signal Corps officers opposed such a move at that time; instead, on July 18, 1914 Congress created an Aviation Section within the Signal Corps. The establishment of a separate Army Air Corps was to take place later in May, 1918. Meanwhile, the Aviation Section increased the Army's aviation strength and scope, gave it a definite status, attracted top grade personnel, and gave manufacturers much needed encouragement.

During World War I, the Army had thirty-nine aero squadrons participating in action against the enemy. These included eighteen pursuit, twelve corps observation, three army observation, one night bombardment, and five reconnaissance. Assigned to these units were 1,402 pilots and 769 airplane observers. Employing day bombardment and pursuit airplanes, the Army in 150 organized bombardment missions dropped 275,000 pounds of explosives. Army squadrons engaged in over 2,100 combats, 12,830 pursuit flights, 6,672 observation flights, and 1,174 bombing flights. The enemy was strategically photographed 17,845 times; tens of thousands of rounds were used in ground strafing; and reconnaissance and artillery fire-directing missions were flown on innumerable occasions.

From a point of low ebb just prior to the Spanish-American War, the Signal Corps grew rapidly and greatly expanded its functions in support of the Army. It successfully provided telephone and telegraph wire lines, cable communications, heliograph services, photographic support, and revived aeronautics and the use of balloons. After the war, in both the Caribbean and in the Philippines, it left excellent communications networks which would immeasurably assist civil authorities in building up the two areas.

The Signal Corps in the Spanish-American War

✠ FROM OFFICIAL SOURCES

At the outset of the 1890's the Signal Corps transferred its largest activity, the weather service, to civil authorities—and with it went most of the Corp's budget and personnel. The Chief Signal Officer, Brigadier General Greely, resisting proposals to eliminate the Corps altogether, set about enlarging the support that Signal Corpsmen might provide in addition to such basic signaling services as telegraph, telephone, flags, and heliograph. In 1892, winning the War Department's consent for Signal Corps use of balloons, he purchased the Army's first peacetime gasbag for employment as "a captive balloon, with modern equipment, so that military information may be collected photographically or visually." At the same time he made military photography an unofficial responsibility of the Signal Corps.

Meanwhile, as the nineties wore on, the Army shrank to minimum proportions, the Signal Corps declining to a low of only eight officers and about fifty men. Then suddenly, in 1898, the nation was caught up in a war which, though small, would precipitate the United States into international affairs in a large way, elevating it into a world power with possessions and involvements far from the home shores.

National policy had long favored elimination of European colonialism in the Western Hemisphere. Numerous revolutionary movements had troubled Spanish rule in the West Indies for many years, and the American people sympathized with the aspirations of the insurrectionists.

Both foreign policy and public opinion were far in advance of Army preparation when the tension came to a head with the mysterious sinking of the battleship *Maine* in Havana Harbor on February 15, 1898. On the military side, the Regular Army included approximately 28,000 effectives, backed up on paper by an untrained and poorly equipped militia of about 115,000 men. Nor had plans been made for an expansion of the Army or for the procurement of large quantities of munitions in case of war.

The Regular Army had been concentrated at several points on the Gulf of Mexico for only a short time when the President approved a joint resolution of the Congress on April 19, 1898, demanding that Spain withdraw from Cuba. Spain countered by declaring war on April 24.

The Army had no experience in the tropics or training in amphibious operations, and none of the higher officers had commanded large bodies of troops since the Civil War. Nevertheless, the President ordered a naval blockade of Cuba and issued a call for 125,000 volunteers.

By acts of Congress on May 18 and on July 7, 1898, a voluntary Signal Corps was authorized. Quickly the number of officers and men on signal duty grew to over thirteen hundred, organized into seventeen companies (four officers and fifty-one men each), including one balloon company and one field telegraph train.

Mastery of the sea had to be gained before the Army could be deployed overseas. This was made possible in the Western Pacific by Commodore George Dewey's victory at Manila Bay on May 1, 1898.

In the Atlantic, Commodore William T. Sampson quickly gained control of the Caribbean area and bottled up Spanish Admiral Cervera's fleet at Santiago Harbor. Maj. Gen. William R. Shafter's poorly equipped force of about 17,000 men was then landed at Daiquiri on June 22, 1898. After brushing aside light opposition, the main attack on Santiago began on July 1; the next day El Caney and San Juan were assaulted and captured, completing the investment of the city. Admiral Cervera's fleet was forced to come out of Santiago Harbor and was completely destroyed on July 3, 1898. During the same month Puerto Rico fell to a smaller Army force.

Col. James Allen acted as chief signal officer of the Caribbean expedition. The steamship *Adria* was fitted with cable gear and loaded with forty-five miles of submarine cable, all that could initially be obtained. On arriving off Santiago on June 1, 1898, his first task was to grapple for and cut the cables landing there in order to severely cripple enemy communications. One of these was raised and cut under fire of the Spanish batteries in Morro Castle. For his

137

services on this occasion, Allen was later awarded the Distinguished Service Cross.

With the sailing of the Fifth Army Corps for the reduction of Santiago, on June 14, plans were made for placing the task force in telegraphic communication with Washington. The French cable near Caimanera in Guantánamo Bay was grappled and repaired after a week's work. On June 21, the day before the disembarkation of General Shafter's corps commenced, Colonel Allen landed the cable and opened communication from the Marine camp near Guantánamo, via Haiti to New York. The French cable along the southern coast of Cuba from Siboney to Playa del Este was also repaired, and a Signal Corps cable was also laid between those points.

Col. Frank Greene accompanied the Fifth Corps as chief signal officer. He had been compelled to leave behind at Tampa the telegraph train provided for the expedition. The expedition was therefore forced to depend for wire communication on the equipment and wire already aboard the *Adria*. Major G. W. S. Stevens and thirty-five men were charged with establishing and maintaining communication between the commanding general, his division and brigade commanders, supply depots, and other important points. Visual techniques of communications were almost impossible for the land operation, but were useful between coast stations and the fleet.

This war tested many new Signal Corps efforts. The advance of troops into the Caribbean called for wire lines that were quickly supplied, but this was not easily done because of extreme difficulties in supply. "Lost equipment" lay idle in scores of boxcars jamming the rails into Florida. A notable example of improvisation was a telegraph switchboard which Maj. Samuel Reber fabricated, on the spot, out of a copper kettle. This device successfully switched hundreds of messages through a Signal Corps telegraph office in Ponce, Puerto Rico. It was, moreover, possible to communicate directly from Washington, D.C., to the front lines in Cuba.

The Spanish-American War was the first conflict in which the Army used telephones. The Signal Corps strung wires along the line of advance and nailed hand-cranked telephone boxes to trees right up to the front lines. In this war, too, combat photography made its first appearance.

As we know, the Signal Corps took a balloon to Cuba—its only balloon, which was in poor shape because of damages suffered in shipment. Capt. Joseph E. Maxwell and men of the Signal Corps Balloon Company patched the bag and inflated it for use in the fighting around San Juan Hill. The balloon was meant to be used as an observation post and signal station, and was intended to be elevated far enough back from the front lines to be safe from gunfire. But an Engineer Corps colonel decided to go up in the basket himself, and he ordered that the towline be hauled forward so that he could get a closer view of the fighting. Although this was contrary to the intended purpose of the balloon, and contravened the instructions of the Balloon Company, the colonel, who of course outranked Captain Maxwell, had his way. The balloon was pulled along the trail to Bloody Ford, bobbing some hundreds of feet above the treetops. The troops were bitter because the descent of the rope into the forest roadway clearly marked the American advance and drew accurate enemy fire. And of course the big bag was repeatedly punctured. Leaking gas, it deflated gradually and came to earth at the stream itself, beyond repair. The balloon had served some usefulness for observation purposes, despite its misuse and early loss.

In the attack which took place on July 1, each division commander was assigned suitably equipped signalmen. The telegraph line was extended forward as the troops advanced and on July 3 was carried to San Juan Hill and to the center of the American trenches. From the headquarters of Generals Wheeler and Kent, near San Juan Hill, the line was extended to the headquarters of Generals Lawton and Bates on the right and left, respectively. Telephones were installed at all these headquarters—the instrument installed for Lawton's division being one abandoned by the Spanish at the San Juan blockhouse. The connecting wire was laid largely in forks and tops of small trees in the dense undergrowth.

Soon after the Spanish-American War, Army telegraph and telephone facilities in Cuba and Puerto Rico were turned back to civilian interests on those islands. The Signal Corps greatly increased and improved the commercial lines previously existing there. In Cuba alone, corpsmen erected twenty-five hundred miles of wire, including nine lines running north-south across the island, and one trunk from east to west. They also placed an underwater cable between Siboney and Playa del Este.

In the Pacific phase of the Spanish-American War, an expedition under Maj. Gen. Wesley Merritt landed in the Philippine Islands with a force of about eleven thousand men and attacked the defenses of Manila in conjunction with the fleet and the insurgents. Offering only token resistance, the city quickly fell on August 13, 1898.

During the capture of Manila, Signal Corps units advanced in the forefront of the assault on Forts San Antonio and Malate along the bay just south of the city. While the fleet under Adm. George Dewey fired upon the fortifications ashore, the American attack began early on the morning of August 13. As the First Colorado Regiment took the lead, a signal detachment sloshing waist-deep in the water along the beach advanced on the extreme left flank of the troops. Two men, Sergeants George S. Gibbs (who was to become Chief Signal Officer in 1928) and Henry F. Jurs carried large wigwag flags to communicate with the fleet, correct naval gunfire, and mark the position of the advancing infantry. Other Signal Corps men carried rolls of wire, uncoiling it as they advanced, while still others provided covering fire with their carbines. Sgt. Harry W. Chadwick photographed the battle area.

By mid-morning the Americans had captured Fort Malate. One of the first men to reach it was Sergeant Gibbs who wigwagged the news of the capture to the fleet, then tore down the Spanish flag (which is now exhibited in the Signal Corps Museum at Ft. Monmouth, New Jersey). All through the fighting that day, this unit and several other Signal Corps detachments maintained communications between the different parts of the American Army during the assault and capture of Manila.

Increasing dependence of the Army upon wire lines required that the Signal Corps install them and establish stations, sometimes even in advance of the troops. It also required that the stations and their connecting links be maintained in isolated exposed situations. This placed considerable strain upon Signal Corps men, particularly during the native insurrection which immediately followed the defeat of the Spanish, and which prolonged the fighting in those islands for several years.

During the early months of 1900, Lt. H. W. Stamford and his men, charged with building a line north from Subic Bay, Luzon, fought off repeated attacks. Their cumbersome construction train was conspicuous and exposed. On one occasion the group surprised a party of insurgents, scattered them, and silenced their fire. Lt. Basil O. Lenoir, with a train of sixteen carts and fifty men, was attacked south of Iba on the coast of Luzon. Managing to reach the beach, he sheltered his train behind a row of sand hills and posted a rear guard to hold off the attackers. Since the guerrillas had cut his wire line, he sent two men creeping along the water's edge to summon reinforcements to his rescue.

In other isolated areas of Luzon where wire lines had to be installed, numbers of Signal Corps men were ambushed and killed. Corporal Wilson, with an escort of twenty men, was ambushed by several hundred insurgents on the island of Bohol, near Leyte. Five Americans and nineteen insurgents were killed. Wilson himself, although smitten with nine bolo wounds, from which he died the next day, killed four of the enemy. On Leyte, too, almost within the city limits of Tacloban, a Signal Corps working party lost four men to attacking natives.

Many hundreds of miles of land line and undersea cable were laid and maintained in the Philippines under Colonel Allen—a service which Gen. Arthur MacArthur described as indispensable. Cable-laying to link up the major islands of the archipelago became a large scale responsibility of the Corps. General Greely, as soon as he had won War Department consent for the undertaking, set about the construction of cable and cable gear, the outfitting of a cable ship, and the training of a cable crew. The first such ship to be dispatched, a former Army transport—the *Hooker*—set sail with two hundred miles of cable coiled in special storage tanks, under command of Maj. Joseph E. Maxfield. Though it was wrecked on a reef soon after arriving off Corregidor, enough cable was salvaged to enable Maxfield and his men to link up the islands of Leyte, Cebu, and Samar before the end of 1899.

General Greely, commenting on the hazardous duty of his men in the Philippines, stated that the percentage of Signal Corps war casualties suffered—5.7 per cent—was far higher than that of the Army as a whole in the campaign. Disease took its toll too; Greely noted in his annual report of 1899 that one-fourth of the Signal Corps officers were disabled from Philippine service.

In summary, the part played by the Signal Corps in the Spanish-American War and the Philippine Insurrection, was vastly larger than the restricted role of the Corps' signaling services during the Civil War. The Signal Corps provided telephone and telegraph wire lines and cable communications, as well as visual signals, notably heliograph. And it provided for the first time in war a photographic service, as well as reviving aeronautics and the use of balloons.

A military censorship was exercised by the Chief Signal Officer over all cables from the United States to foreign countries, land lines in Florida, and the foreign-owned cables landing in Cuba. The Western Union Telegraph Company placed its counsel, skill, and aid at the free disposal of the government. And a rich harvest of information was reaped from commercial and personal messages passing over lines controlled by the Signal Corps.

From scant beginnings, and only a handful of personnel, the Signal Corps mushroomed into a formidable, professional force of many thousands. The required expansion of the Corps was assisted immeasurably by the high quality of the leaders from industry who donned the uniform, and by the thousands of competent technicians who came into the Army from civilian life. The Signal Corps had much to learn from its Allies when it first came to France. When it departed, it had much to bequeath.

The Signal Corps in World War I

✠ DAVID J. MARSHALL, *U.S. Army Signal Center*

When he ordered mobilization on March 10, 1916, President Wilson also mobilized the National Guard. In a period of seven or eight weeks, from the early part of May to the close of June, 100,000 guardsmen arrived on the Mexican border. Representing 55 per cent of the total strength of the Guard, they patrolled the American side of the border and took part in gigantic training programs and maneuvers.

Among them were about 2,000 signalmen, poorly organized, poorly equipped, and for the most part very poorly trained. Their training on the border was strict. They received training in the use of the equipment issued them, including flags and heliographs, buzzer phones and wire carts, and field wireless sets. These sets were the same type Pershing had in Mexico: wagon sets and mule-pack sets. Even some Signal Corps officers considered them too heavy, bulky, and unreliable for use in the field. But they were used for training purposes just the same.

The guardsmen remained on the border for about six months. Their training was part of a systematic effort to prepare for the possibility of America's joining in the European war. While wireless training was stressed, the real emphasis was on buzzer-phone telegraphy and heliograph, and above all on flag telegraphy.

All this while, however, other events were taking place which were to have an even greater impact upon the future.

Soon after New Year's Day, John J. Carty delivered a confidential lecture at the Army War College. Carty, the chief engineer of the Bell System, was well known by then. During that past year he had been telling the Secretary of War and the Chief of Staff that modern

142

battles were fought by telephone. At the War College his lectures on "The Organization, Plant, and Personnel of the Bell System" awakened the Army to the importance of the telephone in and out of the combat zone.

In February, before the National Defense Bill was introduced in Congress, the Chief of Staff sent a confidential copy of the Signal Corps proposal to Carty. From this, Carty evolved a plan to fit the entire Bell System into the Signal Corps.

In March, at a Washington banquet honoring Alexander Graham Bell, Carty was in the limelight again. This time, when the long-distance telephone was still so new that the wonder had not yet worn off, he electrified his audience by telephoning, while he stood on the speaker's dais, each of the principal cities of the United States. Then he dramatized the military value of the telephone by inviting General Scott to the dais and placing him—the Army Chief of Staff—in conversation with General Pershing at El Paso, Texas.

The effect of this was to bring cheers from every Army officer present; and all the glowing details were carried in the next day's newspapers.

A few weeks later in 1916, Congress appropriated $500,000 for military aviation. Part of this money was used to buy twelve new planes. Some of it was used to reopen the Balloon School at Fort Omaha and some was used to start a course for field officers at the San Diego Aviation School. The new course in aviation brought forty-five Army officers and two officers of the Marine Corps, all above the grade of captain, to the school.

Also in 1916, the French word for wireless began to creep into Army talk. One year earlier, *radio* had appeared in print for the first time in the United States, and the American people had adopted it; *wireless* was now being called *radio*.

A special headgear for airplane pilots was also introduced in 1916; it enabled a flyer to hear incoming radio signals above the noise of the propeller and the engine.

Also in that year Capt. Joseph Mauborgne was transferred from the Infantry to the Signal Corps. That year, too, radio messages were exchanged between airplanes in flight for the first time, and one air-to-ground message was picked up over a distance of one hundred and forty miles. The aircraft communication problem had not been solved, however. The sets were still too large and too heavy, and they robbed the plane of its maneuverability. But advancements were being made which would lead to greater achievements in the future.

143

General Scriven was the Chief Signal Officer, but with almost forty years' service behind him in 1916, he was nearing the retirement age of sixty-four. In spite of that, it was fortunate for the Army and the Signal Corps that Scriven was able to combine his experience and ability with a vigor that would have been surprising in a man twenty years his junior.

It was fortunate, too, that he had to assist him an officer who was both a soldier and a scientist. This was Lt. Col. George Owen Squier. Graduating from West Point in 1886, Squier took his doctorate degree at Johns Hopkins University seven years later. In time he became a Fellow of the university and a member of the National Academy of Sciences, and for many years he carried on a series of electrical and radio experiments that brought him into close association with Armstrong, de Forest, and Thomas A. Edison.

In 1911 he was appointed military attaché to the American Embassy in London. When the war broke out in Europe in 1914, he was transferred to British headquarters in France, and from this assignment he returned home in the summer of 1916 to become Scriven's chief assistant.

West Point could hardly have turned out two men more different from each other than Scriven and Squier. Scriven was a big, strenuous, out-of-doors man, who had spent a great part of his life in the saddle. But Squier was more like a bright-eyed handsome doctor. The bulky Scriven, in his crumpled-up uniform, was the man among men. Squier—a small, wiry, nervous man—was the scholar and scientist, reserved in manner, trim and fastidious in appearance.

Yet they made a good team, each bringing to the partnership strong, positive qualities of his own. The differences between them gave emphasis to a tremendous change the Signal Corps was passing through. Scriven was the author of that change, but it was Squier who would carry it into effect.

With United States' entry into the war, there were a great many things to be done, and the Signal Corps lost no time in getting started. First was the process of physical expansion. Thousands of men came pouring into the Corps from the commercial telephone and telegraph companies; and thousands of other men—men of no training or experience—were assigned to the Corps, merely on a percentage basis, out of the total number of recruits volunteering for the Regular Army.

In July, the calling out of the National Guard, 180,000 officers and men organized in sixteen divisions, added to the flood. In

144

September the induction of draftees into the National Army—500,000 in a single day—added still more. And that kind of expansion continued month after month; it went on, in fact, until at one point in the war 200,000 officers and men were wearing the crossed flags and torch of the Signal Corps.

In exactly one year, Squier's office force expanded from 124 to 3,547 persons, and spread from a single suite of rooms to entire floors and whole buildings in sixteen different parts of Washington.

On the day the United States entered the war, the Land Section of the Corps consisted of 55 officers and 1,570 enlisted men. On the day the war ended, however, it had 2,712 officers and 53,277 men. In the space of nineteen months, it became almost thirty-five times as large as it had been.

The Aviation Section, on the other hand, began the war with 52 officers and 1,100 men and became, in little more than thirteen months, 142 times as large as it had been; at final count, it consisted of 16,084 officers and 147,932 men. That final count was taken on May 20, 1918—the day on which the section was separated from the Signal Corps to become, first, the Aviation Department, then the Army Air Corps, and finally the United States Air Force.

The expansion of the Signal Corps in World War I marked a dividing point in its history. Up to that point, the Corps had retained a pioneering quality; it was forever investigating something new, and it was so small that every mission became the personal adventure of a handful of men. It was to a large extent a band of individual experimenters: they had gained their knowledge through personal experience and personal discovery, and they hadn't had time to solidify their experience and call it doctrine.

But the expansion from 2,700 to 200,000 officers and men in less than a year produced effects that, for better or worse, could never be undone. Henceforth the Signal Corps would be a large organization; and while it reaped the benefits, it also paid the price of bigness. It shed the character of individuality, and took on a corporate existence of its own matched by corporate control. Doctrine became a force to be reckoned with, and every new exploit and accomplishment of the Signal Corps was the outcome of organized effort.

The great expansion of the World War I period also had the effect of introducing the Signal Corps to the methods, practices, and terminology of the civilian telegraph and telephone companies. The influx of civilians was overwhelming; inevitably Army customs gave way to civilian customs, and Army talk was pushed out of the way by civilian talk. The very word *signal*—meaning a letter, a flag, or wire telegram, or any other kind of message—was driven out of the language of the Signal Corps itself. The civilian word "communication" took its place, and the various signal systems became *communications*.

The problem of supply was of the same magnitude as the training problem; and the Air Section, when it was separated from the Signal Corps in May, 1918, took with it the entire Procurement Division of the Office of the Chief Signal Officer.

Nobody was surprised though, for the aircraft and aircraft supplies jobs had loaded the division with work and everything else had been secondary. In July, 1917, the Signal Corps had a $685,000,000 appropriation of which $45,000,000 was for the Ground Section and $640,000,000 for the Aviation Section. This was almost 94 per cent of the whole appropriation; and the Procurement Division gave 94 per cent of its attention to aviation matters.

The problem was that this separation came just as the American expeditionary Forces in France were calling for more and more signal supplies. The Signal Corps was therefore forced to build up a whole new procurement service.

With $45,000,000 in hand for the purchase of all kinds of materials and supplies, the Land Division began a carefully worked out program. The program called for the use of standard American equipment for the telephone and telegraph systems to be installed in France and on combat signal equipment if it "could be made to marry up well with French and British equipment," and for the purchase of French and British equipment as a means of insuring signal uniformity in the combat zone.

The principal purchases were significant. Of the $45,000,000 authorized, a total of $5,300,000 went for storage batteries alone. Ten thousand pigeons and more than 100,000 pairs of field glasses were shipped to France. The pigeons cost about $20,000, but the field glasses were loaned as the result of an appeal to the American people.

On the whole, outpost wire was the most-needed material and the item that was purchased in greatest quantities. It was also extremely difficult to procure because of the priorities imposed by the War Industries Board on copper and rubber. By the summer of 1918, however, such wire was being manufactured for the Signal Corps at the rate of 20,000 miles a month.

Gen. John J. Pershing sailed for Europe on May 28, 1917, two weeks after he had been selected for the top command of the American Expeditionary Forces. He took with him a number of aides, including Col. Edgar Russel, who was to be the Chief Signal Officer of the American Expeditionary Forces.

His job was not easy. When he opened up in Paris what was officially the Office of the Chief Signal Officer, AEF, Russel was confronted by hundreds of problems, and all of them were difficult. Some he could tackle at once, but others he could hardly touch.

As matters stood in July, 1917, General Pershing had arrived in France expecting to command an American offensive. But the Allies had never agreed to turn over any portion of the front to the American Army. The French and British were decidedly unwilling, and they said so pointedly. They had asked only for men—millions of men to fill up holes in the badly shattered French and British divisions. Pershing demanded a separate section of the front where the Americans would fight under their own commanders and under the American flag; and for months to come, Pershing's Chief Signal Officer would have to meet his problems day by day, while that question of a separate American front continued to be unresolved.

But if some of Russel's problems would have to wait, there were many that could be attended to at once. One of the first and most pressing of these was due to the fact that the Americans were an expeditionary force. They were in a foreign land—and Russel's job was to establish communications between France and the War Department in Washington. For a time, he would have to rely upon the transatlantic cables, the mails, and a system of messengers and couriers carrying the same communications by different routes and different ships in order to elude the German submarine packs.

But it was obvious that the Germans would like to cut the cables. There were stories of U-boats grappling for them, or placing time bombs on the Channel floor in the hope of blasting them apart; and there was always the chance that some day they might succeed. It was this possibility, plus the insufficiency of the cables themselves, that led Russel to decide upon radio. And out of that decision came Radio Lafayette.

This took a relatively long time to build. It was erected close to the port of Bordeaux; all the work was done by the Signal Corps, and the job was finished in the spring of 1918. Radio Lafayette was then the most powerful station ever built and it placed the AEF in instant touch with Washington.

But Radio Lafayette had barely been decided upon when Russel was at work establishing four new organizations within the Land

147

Section of the Signal Corps. First, there was combat photography. Pershing said he would want a permanent photographic record of the fighting; and his directive assigning that job to the Signal Corps was of historic interest. Though photography had been a Corps activity since 1881, it was only now that the photographic mission was, by Pershing's order, officially assigned to the Corps. Pershing also called for motion pictures to be made of men and units in combat for the first time in history.

Second on Pershing's list was pigeons. They had proved of little value in Mexico; but the soldiers who had handled the birds there had not been trained for the job. In France the British had a remarkably effective pigeon service, and the success of the German "pigeoneers" was phenomenal.

So Russel set up a Pigeon Service and passed on to Squier the problem of finding the men and the equipment. In the United States, two pigeon experts were commissioned; a search through the Army reception centers yielded twelve experienced pigeoneers, and from that point on it was routine. In November, 1917, two detachments of pigeoneers arrived in France with birds and mobile lofts. To complete their education, Russel sent the officers to the British front and, after that, to the French front.

The primary mission of the Pigeon Service was to establish and maintain a frontline communication service. Its secondary mission was to train large numbers of combat troops in the art of pigeoneering. Eventually, the Service included roughly one hundred and fifty officers and men.

Pershing's third requirement concerned meteorology; in France, the weather was a carefully considered factor of every combat plan. Accordingly, Russel set up a Meteorological Service—and here was still another case of an old activity being made official overseas. Ever since the old Weather Service was transferred to the Department of Agriculture, the Signal Corps forecasted weather conditions just for the Army; but this was done by order of the Chief Signal Officer, by reason of necessity, and without benefit of any formal directive. Now, in France, the weather mission was for the first time officially assigned to the Signal Corps.

The Meteorological Service was small, for in France only a few weather stations would be needed and they would have the cooperation of the French and British stations. The officers and men of the new Weather Service were all trained in France.

Fourth and last on Pershing's list was radio intelligence; and this assignment was wholly new to the Signal Corps. Like those of the

Weather Service, the officers and men of the Radio Intelligence Section, established in July, 1917, were all trained in France. At first they were only responsible for locating enemy transmitters. Later on, however, they were also responsible for the monitoring of Allied transmissions, for the interception and decoding of enemy transmissions, and for breaking the enemy's code.

Meanwhile, with observers posted everywhere along the front, Pershing's staff was at work on a study of the tactical situation to determine the lines along which that situation was developing and would continue to develop in the foreseeable future. Russel participated in most of the studies. His task was closely intertwined with Pershing's, for his work too would be dictated by the situation inherent in the tactical problem. So Russel had observers in the frontline trenches also, and he himself kept in immediate touch with his opposite numbers at French and British headquarters. His first objective was to root out information on German strength and weakness in the field of signaling.

These investigations gave a clue to some of the things Russel had still to think about. All our experience of combat signaling had been in support of fast-moving, far-ranging units; the special pride of our signalmen had been their ability to send and receive over great distances. But in France, the two opposing forces lay in trenches face to face, and separated by a no-man's-land that was sometimes less than a hundred feet wide. The soldiers' ordinary conversation often carried across to the enemy; and the rolling of a pebble, the crackling of a twig, was enough to concentrate heavy rifle fire upon the immediate vicinity of the disturbance. Flags were useless in a place like that.

On the other hand, the Germans were well supplied with field glasses and, on a clear day, their observers could read our visual signals at a distance of twenty miles. It followed, therefore, that all means of visual signaling—flags, lamps, heliographs—would have to be mostly confined to areas far back of the lines; they would not be of much use in the combat zone.

Russel could not expect much of the existing American field wireless sets. They had failed in Mexico and the objection to their use in France was that they were not good enough. The experience in radio had centered round an open spark gap and a crystal detector; and these were all right in America. The open-gap transmitter sprayed its output over a wide range of frequencies, and the crystal-type receiver could pick up anything that happened to be in the air.

149

Under America's wide-open skies, there was no particular need of close tuning. But in the tightly concentrated combat zone of France, the air was nearly always packed with scores of transmissions, and the one thing necessary was fine tuning. That was not possible with any of our radio sets.

Russel was also warned against the buzzer phone, of which the Signal Corps was especially proud, and upon which the Corps had mainly relied in Mexico. The Germans were so close to the Allied front in France that, with crystal-set radio receivers they could pick up the traffic passing over Allied telegraph and telephone wires through electrical induction. For this reason, the British had outlawed the use of the ground-return circuits and were using two wires for each of their telegraph and telephone lines.

Pershing continued to defend his position that the Americans in France were going to fight on a front of their own. He had defended that position since June—and he finally prevailed. At once he organized and established his line of communications; and it was a week or so after he had done this that he transferred his headquarters to Chaumont, which lay at a central point just back of the proposed American sector.

Once the line of communications was established, Russel's task was clear. Before the promised American offensive could begin, there would have to be installed and operating a regular network of telegraph and telephone wires extending from the seacoast to the front. No planning was involved. All Russel did was apply a plan worked out in advance of hostilities in conjunction with the engineering department of the Pennsylvania Bell Telephone Company; and it was almost perfect. There were a handful of minor deviations, but these called for little more than taking in a mile or two of wire here, letting out a mile or two of wire there.

From the port of St. Nazaire, the line ran eastward—following the main highway up the valley of the Loire—through Nantes, Tours, Nevers, and Dijon into Chaumont, and from Chaumont to Neufchâteau and Gondrecourt. Tours was to be the base of the Services of Supply, and auxiliary wire lines were subsequently worked into the system connecting Tours with Paris and with two additional seaports, Le Havre on the north coast and Bordeaux on the south coast.

Building was begun at three different points along the line, and three different battalions were joined in a race, each one attempting to outdo the others. The race was watched closely at Russel's headquarters, for it pitted the Second Field Signal Battalion, a Regular

Army outfit, against the two "professional" battalions formed of Pennsylvania Bell and New York Bell telephone company personnel. When all the differences of terrain were taken into account, the Regular Army Signalmen "stood second in a three-way tie."

However, it was not until September 3, 1918 that the last of the American units left the trenches of the French and British armies and joined the parade which was to bring them to the great rendezvous at Saint-Mihiel. On their arrival, the concentration was completed, and the hour was at hand for the creation of the long-awaited American front.

Much work had been done before this. The American First Army was formed and set up its headquarters at Le Ferte-sur-Jouarre, southwest of Vaux. The 411th Telegraph Battalion and the 319th Field Signal Battalion arrived there in the last week of July and, upon arrival, began installing telephones and stringing trunk lines. On August 3, a telegraph trailer arrived and its crew handled thirty thousand words the first day, nearly forty thousand the second day. Such performance exceeded all expectations, and five additional trailers were called for at once.

On August 10, the First Army took over a sector previously held by the French sixth army. The First Army had almost everything then, including pigeons, telephones, radios, and multiplex printers. Notably, there was a Signal Corps Section of women telephone operators who had been recruited in the United States. They were among the first women ever to wear the American Army uniform. For the most part, they were college girls and recent high school graduates, accepted for service overseas by reason of their ability to speak French.

The First Army had the largest switchboard in France, but the traffic soon overtaxed it, and arrangements were made to double the number of operators on duty for the night of September 12 when the first American offensive was to begin.

The Signal Corps had been under orders to complete the gigantic wire system, reaching from the seaports to the American battle zone, by July, 1919. But now with an all-out effort, these lines were brought to completion, and local lines were laid throughout the American combat zone. A day or two before the first American offensive began, the wire system was completed.

Including the few lines leased from France, the system consisted of ninety thousand miles of lines. Embraced within the system was a multiplex printing telegraph net connecting Tours, Chaumont, Paris, and London; but, mainly, the system was composed of telephone lines. It was the outstanding characteristic of the American signal system that the American advance and rear zones both depended upon the telephone.

Similarly, before the first attack was launched from the new American front, preparations were completed to run the wires forward of the front lines as fast as the Infantry went forward. For this purpose, light bronze wire was strung on light poles; and mile after mile of twisted pair was strung on poles or trees, laid across underbrush and bushes, or simply laid upon the ground.

Preparations for the offensive had been going on for about three weeks when, abruptly, the mission of the American Expeditionary Forces was expanded, and a new strategic plan was formulated at Allied headquarters. This change occurred on August 30. Marshal Foch called at American headquarters to confer with Pershing. In the previous week, he reported, the situation had changed completely, as a result of new victories of the British and the French. All the objectives the Allies had looked forward to hopefully on August 9 had now been won. The foundation for the following year's offensive had been laid.

But this was no time to stop. The German line was crumbling so rapidly, said Foch, that the summer offensive ought to be pushed for all it was worth. And Pershing agreed.

At Foch's headquarters on September 2, three new objectives were agreed upon—one for the French, one for the British, and one for the Americans. The Americans were to establish a frontline of ninety-three miles, extending from Port-sur-Seille, east of the Moselle, westward to include the Argonne Forest. Along this front they were to wipe out the Saint-Mihiel salient and then launch an offensive against the entire region extending from the Meuse to the western edge of the Argonne. The war would soon be over.

The primary mission of the Pigeon Service established by the Signal Corps during World War I was to maintain a frontline communication service. The following story is about one of the most valiant members of that service who, despite numerous wounds, got the message through.

John Silver:
Signal Corps Airman Extraordinary

✠ LT. COL. C. V. GLINES

A revival of interest in World War I aviation in recent years has resulted in several books and articles about air heroes of yesteryear whose feats have become legendary, but none of these stories includes the saga of one of the most famous flyers of his day: John Silver.

Silver had no rank, yet he flew many important missions over the front lines for the Allied forces. He received no pay, yet he served in the Army for almost eighteen years. He never received formal flight training, yet he was respected throughout the aviation world for his extraordinary feats of airmanship. He lost a leg while on a vital mission over enemy lines, yet received no compensation or awards and was never even fitted for an artificial leg. When he died, he received no military funeral, yet he has been permanently memorialized by his flying brothers whose sky he shared.

The United States Government isn't ungrateful in the case of John Silver. It just has never quite known what to do about a fellow like him. You see, he was the Army's most famous homing pigeon.

According to official Army records, John Silver was hatched in January, 1918, in a Signal Corps pigeon loft behind the lines in France. He spent his first weeks learning the art of day flying and homing. He learned to carry a small canister strapped to his leg and to fly unerringly back to his loft in spite of the noise of gunfire and bad weather. Upon "graduation" he was assigned to a frontline infantry unit for courier duty. His first messages were relatively unimportant so that if he became confused and fell into enemy hands, no vital information was lost. When his signal company commander was satisfied that John was reliable, he was given more important messages.

153

From the first, his exceptional skill at dodging artillery barrages was noted. Time after time, when the shelling was especially heavy and a message had to be sent rearward, John got through. On several occasions, he was the only one of several pigeons released that survived the mission.

It was on October 21, 1918, at exactly 2:35 P.M. that John Silver was released from a frontline trench near Grandpré. The now famous Meuse-Argonne drive had just begun and the rear headquarters at Rampont, 40 kilometers away, had to be notified of the rapidly changing battle situation. The Germans were laying down an intense artillery barrage before an attack, and the unit needed help.

When the canister was strapped on his leg and John was released, the tense soldiers watched anxiously because their very lives might depend on his getting through. John fluttered briefly along the ground, started toward the enemy lines for a few feet, then turned toward the rear as he leveled off at tree-top height. The men below shouted their encouragement, but suddenly gasped when they saw a shell explode near him.

The blast threw the pitifully small body upward for a hundred feet amid a shower of earth and feathers. John plunged earthward momentarily, then flapped his wings wildly to gain back his balance and continued on his way. But the men felt sure that he had been badly hurt and would never make it back to headquarters.

Less than a half hour later, John flopped onto his loft landing, more dead than alive. A machine-gun bullet had pierced his breast, bits of shrapnel had ripped mercilessly into the tiny body and his right leg was missing. The message tube, however, was dangling from what was left of his torn leg. He had successfully completed his mission in spite of his wounds.

The men of John's Signal Company nursed him back to health. The stump of his right leg healed and he could still fly. His gallantry was contagious and the men refused to let him be destroyed or retired. Instead, he became an inspiration and acquired the name of "John Silver," after the one-legged pirate in *Treasure Island*.

After the war, John was assigned to the Eleventh Signal Company stationed at Schofield Barracks in Hawaii where he became the special charge of Pigeon Sergeant Clifford A. Poutre, who is now a retired colonel.

"We kept John Silver in comfortable retirement in his later years," says retired Col. John A. Ballard, then a major and Signal Company commander of the Hawaiian Division. "He was one of

240 pigeons we had in our lofts there at the time but we didn't give him any 'duties' and didn't let him fly. I couldn't say positively, but I think he was an inspiration to the other pigeons and gave them encouragement when we were pioneering in the training of night flying birds."

John Silver stayed in Hawaii until his death on December 6, 1935 at the age of 17 years, 11 months—a remarkably old age for a pigeon.

"I know how an old cavalryman felt when his horse died," Colonel Ballard said, "because losing John was like losing an old service buddy. There wasn't a dry eye in the company when the news got around, because we loved the old gentleman more than we realized."

Colonel Ballard immediately ordered that he be preserved and on January 1, 1936, signed a company order which is still being carried out today. The order said, " . . . The courage and devotion to duty displayed by John Silver, and above all, his will to accomplish his mission and reach his objective, are attributes worthy of emulation by every soldier of this company.

"Hereafter on each organization day of the Eleventh Signal Company, this order will be read and the name of John Silver will be added to the roll call. When his name is called, the senior non-commissioned officer present will respond, 'Died of wounds received in battle in the service of his country.' "

A few months after the order was published, a visiting Congressman was so impressed with John's war record and the tribute paid him by his comrades that he had the company order inserted in the Congressional Record.

The official files do not reveal what happened to John during the war years but in 1946 he was found stored away with World War I aviation mementos. When Gen. Henry H. "Hap" Arnold ordered the establishment of a permanent museum for the newly created Air Force, John was among the first items put on public display.

Today this gallant airman stands proud and erect in the Hall of Fame at the Air Force Museum located at Wright-Patterson Air Force Base, Ohio. Each year over 350,000 visitors to the world's largest military aviation museum read the citation telling of John's heroic deeds.

"But there's one thing I want to correct as far as the record of John Silver is concerned," Colonel Ballard said. "I notice that he is referred to as 'Stumpy' John Silver in the citation. The dignified mien of the old gentleman was certainly not conducive to calling him that. We never referred to him by that sobriquet and I feel sure that if a visitor to the lofts had ever addressed him as that, he would have been summarily thrown out of the area!"

The record is now straight. The name of John Silver means something more than a character out of a Robert Louis Stevenson classic. Who can deny that *this* John Silver has earned a permanent place for himself on the roster of America's aviation greats?

Prior to World War I, the use of radio was limited almost exclusively to "wireless" telegraph. But under the impetus of the war, great technical strides were made by the Signal Corps in developing radios that could carry the voice. This progress not only presaged the importance that radio would later assume militarily, but laid much of the groundwork for the tremendous advances soon to be made in the utilization of commercial radio for civil communications and also by the radio industry for entertainment purposes.

Radio Comes of Age in World War I

✠ DR. GEORGE RAYNOR THOMPSON

Radio transmission before World War I was largely limited to Morse code, first accomplished by means of spark transmitters, and then by CW (continuous wave) oscillations generated by early triode tubes, such as De Forest audions.

The first spark sets in military use were heavy and awkward. When the U.S. Army went to war in 1917, the Signal Corps was providing only two radio types for field use. Both were large high-power quenched-spark transmitters. These were the so-called pack radio sets (SCR-49), which could be broken down into several components for transport by two or three Army mules, and a still larger motor truck, or tractor, set (SCR-50).

Our European Allies had done better with their combat radios. Under compulsion of combat needs since 1914, the British and French, the latter especially, produced improved sets—CW [Morse code] radiotelegraph types which used tubes altogether. These new tube radios had largely replaced the older spark equipment in the European armies by the time America entered the conflict. Several small types were in production and use by our Allies. Some were even mounted in airplanes. Consequently, all the field radio equipment which the U.S. Army employed in France during its first year of fighting were the superior sets which were obtained from the British and the French.

All of this equipment was radiotelegraph. All the transmission passed in dots and dashes. Military radiotelephone awaited upon mass production of better tubes, upon better methods of evacuating air from the glass envelope so that the electron stream between

157

the electrodes might move more freely. Only then could voice modulated signals be well amplified, without serious distortion.

Before 1917, Signal Corps leaders had recognized that in tubes lay the key to better military radio. Looking to tube development, the Chief Signal Officer during World War I, Maj. Gen. George O. Squier, himself a doctor of electrical engineering, cooperated with industries such as General Electric and Western Electric. Some of their best technical men he commissioned directly into the Signal Corps, for example, Lt. Col. Nugent H. Slaughter of Western Electric. These officers tackled the problems of tubes for Army radio, coordinating this military effort with their former colleagues in the industrial labs and in the factories that would mass-produce the new tubes.

Within six months after the start of the military tube program in the United States, standardized radio tubes began to flow out of the factories: standardized, interchangeable, and more rugged than any tubes built hitherto. Further, the new triodes, vacuum tubes VT-1 and VT-2, the first in a long series of subsequent VT types, were better evacuated of air, or gas. Thanks to their more perfect vacuum, they could amplify better, voice as well as CW code signals.

Before the new improved tubes became available in quantity, General Squier turned to the development of radically new radio equipment for the Army. He pressed the effort with energy beginning early in 1917, now that war provided the stimulus and, most importantly, the money. To strengthen the small laboratory and engineering activities which the Corps had maintained for some years, and to aid the handful of able technical minded officers in the Corps (notably Lt. Col. Joseph O. Mauborgne, who had pioneered in Army radio), General Squier enlisted the help of American industrial engineers and university scientists.

Commissioning a renowned physicist, Dr. Robert A. Millikan of the University of Chicago, to assist him (Squier made him Chief of his Science and Research Division in Washington), the Chief Signal Officer built up the Corps' radio effort from a few workers as of 1917 to several hundred persons by 1918. Since the small laboratory facilities which the Corps had maintained for some time at the Bureau of Standards and at 1710 Pennsylvania Avenue were insufficient, Squier created a major laboratory at Camp Alfred Vail, Little Silver, New Jersey. The officers, scientists, and technicians in the radio activity in Washington engineered copies of Allied radios and, more importantly, designed entirely new sets and provided drawings and specifications to the manufacturers. The big laboratory at Vail (which subsequently became Ft. Monmouth) provided all the technical facilities needed for the development of ground and air radio, such as research and test equipment, drafting rooms, a model shop, and a flying field for testing the radio equipment which aircraft badly needed. Among the technically minded officers whom Squier obtained from industry and university sources were Col. John J. Carty, chief engineer of American Telephone and Telegraph Company, and Capt. Ralph Bown, commissioned from the physics department of Cornell University. Bown was placed in command of the technical department of the radio laboratory at Camp Vail.

While thus building up Army R&D (Research and Development) of new radios at home, General Squier also promoted this effort overseas. He organized and sent to France an aggregation of remarkable young men to constitute the Research and Inspection (R&I) Division of the Signal Corps, American Expeditionary Forces. The men were remarkable for what they were soon to accomplish in the future of radio. Such a one was a young radio engineer from Columbia University named Edwin Howard Armstrong. Many came from industry, such as radio operator and Western Electric employee, William A. MacDonald. Another from the same company was Fred R. Lack. Still others from Western Electric were Edwin H. Colpitts (who served as a civilian inspector), Maj. O. E. Buckley, Maj. E. B. Craft, Lt. C. L. Howk, Lt. Col. Frank B. Jewett, Maj. Maurice K. McGrath, and Lt. Col. H. E. Shreeve.

Lack and MacDonald entered service as enlisted men. Having originally enlisted in a Signal Field Battalion, they expected to go overseas to fight. But because of their experience and skills, they and others were pulled out of the ranks for radio work. They sailed on Friday, October 13, 1917, a lucky day it turned out for them, as they headed for the R&I Division in Paris, where they were later to receive commissions as Signal Corps officers. The R&I Division, Signal Corps, AEF, set up for business late in 1917 under Lieutenant Colonel Shreeve in a mansion that had been confiscated from former German occupants, at 140 Montparnasse Boulevard. The Research Section was placed under Major Buckley, the Inspection Section under Major McGrath. The officers and men studied and analyzed Allied sets and their operation, wrote manuals, and descriptive bulletins, inspected and tested new equipment.

Sergeant MacDonald kept a notebook of his own throughout 1918—a technical or laboratory notebook in which he drew the circuit layouts of the sets he worked over, and in which he maintained records of test readings, antenna current, maintenance problems, and so on. He included some of his own ideas on how to improve the equipment—the antennas for example. He drew plans and made experimental installations toward the replacement of the awkward and hazardous trailing wire (used on aircraft) with a fixed antenna strung in a triangular configuration between the two wing tips and the tail.

Many of the test readings which MacDonald entered and dated in the notebook related to antenna current and to operating frequencies, the latter in terms of wave length in meters. Control of meter length output of the transmitter was essential, if transmitters and receivers were to keep on frequency, for dependable intercommunication. The antenna length affected the frequency in these early sets since the wire reacted electrically upon the oscillator within the transmitter. The radio operator aloft had to take care that he let out just enough antenna wire from the reel in the cockpit beside him. He had to know just how many turns to make in the unreeling— 50 turns to let out enough wire to obtain a 400-meter wave, 75 turns for 430 meters, and so on. These rather crude technical details had to be determined and this MacDonald did, as well as determining the procedures for optimum operation and teaching them to the pilot and observer who constituted the crew of American De Haviland bombers, DH-4's. One of the details of operation which the observer had to remember was to crank in the antenna before the pilot landed the craft. Otherwise, the long trailing wire and the "fish" or metal weight at the end could cause some embarrassing complications.

Meanwhile, the radios used by all the Allies in France continued into 1918 to be radio*telegraph* sets only. These had improved a great deal, to be sure, during the war by full employment of vacuum tubes. But they remained limited to communication by the keying of dots and dashes, until the U.S. Army Signal Corps pioneered the development of small aircraft radio*telephones*. Foremost among these pioneer sets, begun in 1917—sets which would remove the telegraph limitation and give radio the flexible facile universality of voice or telephone operation—was the SCR-68, an airborne radiotelephone (its companion set on the ground was the SCR-67).

In mid-1918, SCR's-67 and -68 and related equipment from America began arriving in France. They constituted a revolutionary advance in radio, which General Squier exclaimed "will undoubtedly materially change the system of Army communication." He exulted that radiotelephone would permit the "voice commanded air squadron" and would enormously increase the military value of aircraft formations—prophetic words in World War I.

160

To go back a bit, General Squier had foreseen the potential value of radiotelephone in airplanes for use in voice command and in reporting observations, especially of artillery fire, by voice. He had therefore, early in 1917, called to his aid (among others) Capt. Clarence C. Culver, a Signal Corps officer and aviator, and Maj. Frank B. Jewett, chief engineer of Western Electric, whom the Signal Corps had commissioned into the Army. In May, 1917, these officers worked out the requirements for an airborne radiotelephone. Western Electric then developed a model—Jewett, Craft, Colpitts, and numerous others working on it. Their first experimental model they called a soapbox (the ultimate SCR-68 did indeed resemble a small box, of wood, bakelite, and brass mountings, measuring 16 inches by 11 inches by 6 inches). By the end of June, the model was ready for testing. It worked, the radiotelephone or voice signals carrying over distances up to three miles between airplanes in flight, and between planes and ground. These first successful tests were run off at Langley Field, Virginia, during late June and early July, 1917.

After some further development work, the set underwent more extensive tests in December at Dayton, Ohio, and astounded skeptical observers. Then one day in 1918, President and Mrs. Wilson stepped out of the White House to try for themselves the mysterious telephone circuit, via radio, between people on the ground and aviators whizzing aloft. A photograph of the occasion shows their amazement and pleasure, standing on the White House lawn, amid a gleeful group of officers and civilians.

The development of the SCR-68 was pressed by Western Electric under supervision of the radio section (Lieutenant Colonel Slaughter) of the Office of the Chief Signal Officer's Research and Engineering Division, of which Lt. Col. J. O. Mauborgne was chief. The sets were designed for two-seater planes, and included interphone connections. The problems were many. One was the power supply. Since storage batteries were too heavy to burden the craft, the Signal Corps sought to develop a fan-driven generator attached to the exterior, driven by a small fan or propeller that whirled in the slip stream.

When by mid-1918 the sets began to arrive in France, Sergeant MacDonald was among those in the Paris laboratory who were sent to Orly Field to install the new radiotelephones on De Haviland two-seater planes, to maintain the sets, and instruct the air crew in their use. These and related sets had their defects. Maintenance and repair were considerable, and depended largely upon "by guess and by gosh" methods. Design and redesign depended heavily upon cut and try techniques, just as did the development of the flying machines themselves.

Sometimes the consequences were humorous (at other times they could be tragic). Consider, for instance, a French radio telegraph set on which MacDonald worked. He found that it flashed a 220-volt jolt through the pilot's head when he switched the radio from receive to transmit. Not a fatal shock since the current was low, but doubtless enough to discourage skeptical aviators in these new fangled aircraft radios. The trouble was a slight error in wiring, so MacDonald discovered and recorded in his notebook on July 17, 1918: ". . . considerable shock was given by the headband of the receiver when the switch was thrown to transmit. On measuring this it was found to be 220 volts. After considerable testing it was found that the ground lead instead of going to the bottom of the B inductance went to the opposite side of the key binding post. This would consequently allow a small plate current to pass which would go through the common point in the receiving battery and through it to the phones. The set of course would function okay, the objectionable point being the shock."

Each set of SCR-68 received individual attention. MacDonald recorded many case histories in the summer and autumn of 1918. SCR-68 set number 8, for example, tested out well, both the transmitter and the receiver. But after installation in an airplane, troubles began. To quote some of his entries (two of them dated in August):

Installed in a Liberty. A feedback hooked on receiver. Oscillates well, at lower points on the condenser, but not higher up.
Transmitter bad. Although it oscillates okay, get a negative reading on grid. Trouble located in change over switch. August 26, 1918.

Set gone bad. Plus B-choke probably broken down. August 27, 1918.
After carefully going over this set, can find nothing wrong with it. The trouble seems to be in the kenatron where the filament shorted on the plate.
Located trouble in receiver in variable tuning condenser. The handle turned and blades did not.

Sometimes the SCR-68 stood up surprisingly well. Set number 14 survived an airplane crash. It had been installed on October 16,

1918 in a DH-4. On October 28, MacDonald jotted "machine crashed and completely wrecked. Apparatus salvaged but condition uncertain at present." His next entry, on October 30, reads, "set tested okay after crash."

When he tested set number 17 on October 18, MacDonald noted "something wrong with transmitter. Get low antenna current (about .2) and low plate current with no grid current. Receiver works but seems rather weak." Five days later he found the trouble, repaired it, and jotted in his notebook, "on taking set apart, found grid leak broken in half. Put in a new one and set worked okay."

Following the Armistice on November 11, 1918, Sergeant MacDonald concluded his labors with these airborne radiotelephones. His last note on the subject bears the date of November 25, 1918 and reads as follows:

A brief summary of the troubles in the complete SCR-68 sets are:

Cabinet:	*Poor inspection in America which passes sets which will not operate;*
	Faulty and poorly soldered connections;
	Poorly designed grid leaks which break mechanically when used in a plane;
	Poor connection plugs which fall out after continued use.
Filter:	*No trouble.*
Generator:	*Regulator tube poorly designed so that filament shorts on plate;*
	Broken connections after continued use.

The new American voice radios were obviously far from perfect. But they promised better things to come. The Navy tried them in seaplanes and subchaser vessels, altering and improving them for their particular needs. The commanders of subchasers noted that they could keep in touch with each other more readily than before, increasing the effectiveness of the operation of the vessels in groups. Obviously, the promise far outweighed the fact that the first sets were not entirely dependable, which was no wonder at that infant state of the art and in view of their development—designed in 1917, built and delivered in 1918. The brilliance of this United States concept and effort in radiotelephone, or voice radio, was a bright light which shone out of the murk of World War I and illuminated the path of radio developments to come.

In addition to the work on SCR-68 and related voice sets, some other very important accomplishments in radio were carried out at the Signal Corps R&I Division in Paris—accomplishments which would greatly speed the arrival of better radios. Two examples were first, the development of MOPA, the master-oscillator power amplifier circuit, and secondly, work done on the superheterodyne circuit by Capt. E. H. Armstrong.

Capt. Harold W. Webb, who, like Armstrong, the Signal Corps had drawn from the physics department of Columbia University, worked on tank radios. Antenna troubles on tanks were severe, for obvious reasons. It was a trailing wire, and was often broken, often cut by shell fire. When thus reduced in length, it affected the oscillations of the transmitter within the tank, throwing the set off its original frequency and so out of communications. Armstrong suggested to Webb a design which would free the transmitter oscillator circuit from the effects of variation in antenna length. This became the MOPA circuit, which had the further value of increasing the power output of the transmitter. A radio incorporating MOPA was built in the summer of 1918 by Lt. A. D. Silva and Sergeant Pressley and installed in a Renault tank. It operated with notable success.

Impetus for the superheterodyne circuit came from the need for more sensitive and more stable receivers. It was thought that a receiver might be designed with sufficient sensitivity and amplification to detect the radiations from the spark plugs of an approaching airplane at a sufficient distance to provide effective warning. MacDonald contributed to the superhet development. "About June 10–18, Captain Armstrong proposed the following circuit," MacDonald jotted in his notebook, and he sketched a schematic of the superhet design.

As Armstrong pursued this monumental effort in the second half of 1918, he needed the help of experienced laboratory assistants. He specifically desired MacDonald's aid. But whereas Armstrong had remained in the R&I Division laboratory at 140 Montparnasse Boulevard in Paris, MacDonald had transferred earlier in 1918 to Orly Airfield outside the city. Furthermore, work at the airfield kept MacDonald busy six days a week. But not on Sunday, because World War I combat pilots would not fly on Sundays. Would MacDonald contribute his free time that day to work on the superhet? He would indeed! Consequently, throughout the summer of 1918, Armstrong sent out a motorcycle driver and sidecar every Sunday to Orly Field to fetch MacDonald to the Paris laboratory to assist him. In paragraph after paragraph of his notebook, MacDonald recorded this effort, setting down circuit designs, test measurements, and comments. Some of the comments read like this one: "Comparative tests with this circuit showed it enormously better . . . tests against seven stages British HF [high frequency] amplifier also show it greatly superior."

Toward the end of the summer of 1918, Sergeant MacDonald ceased working on Captain Armstrong's superhet project. His notes read "being unable (meaning himself) to continue with the work, Sergeant Lewis was left to finish it." Sgt. Harold M. Lewis, together with Sgt. Harry W. Houck, continued to assist Armstrong in this most important development, completing tests and readying this first superheterodyne receiver just as the Armistice came. The superhet arrived too late for use in World War I, but its contribution to future radio was of course immense.

Other radio advances sprang from the pressure which World War I put upon this communications medium. One was the RF [radio frequency] amplifier stage inserted in the front end of receivers. MacDonald had experimented with this one, too, using a French IF [intermediate frequency] stage in the superhet design to isolate the input antenna. The effect of course was to remove receiver circuits from interaction with the receiving antenna. This stabilized and improved receiver performance, much as MOPA improved the operation of transmitters. All these and other advances in radio circuitry and "know-how" added up to a progress of large proportions, a World War I development of immeasurable significance for the future.

The radiotelephone, voice radio, the airborne SCR-68 and ground component SCR-67, constituted the outstanding Signal Corps contribution to radio in World War I. By November, 1918, at the war's end, sufficient SCR-67's and -68's had been received and put to use in France to demonstrate the potential superiority of voice radio, pointing to the revolution in military communications which General Squier had prophesied. The sets came into greatest demand, despite their defects. Both the British and the French lauded them. Colonel Slaughter wrote soon after the war, with pardonable pride, "Development of the airplane radio telephone set has been considered the most spectacular accomplishment of the Signal Corps."

Far more SCR-68's and related equipment, intended for aircraft use, were manufactured than any other Signal Corps World War I radio type, about 3,000 combined transmitting and receiving sets and about 6,500 receivers.

Thus the radiotelephone arrived in 1918, thanks to the U.S. military and industrial effort under new military communication demands. And most importantly the Signal Corps had developed a sizable group of young American officers and men possessed of new skills. They had learned from the French and British. They had gone further than their Allied friends with innovations of their own. Not all had progressed or would continue to progress in radio as brilliantly as young Armstrong. But many of them had advanced the new radio art a great deal and would continue to do so in postwar years. These men constituted a concentration of communications technicians and scientists such as had never been gathered together before in the infant business of radio. From their pooled effort, from their accumulated knowledge and from the experience which they gained in the war, backed by U.S. industrial production of components and sets, would soon grow the postwar radio and entertainment industry in the United States.

These Signal Corps radio officers and men further enlarged their experience and knowledge after the Armistice in an unexpected manner. There was not enough shipping for all the millions of American troops in France to sail merrily home at once. Many would have to wait months for their turn. But this proved no problem, no idle loss for a group of men who were going places. The scientists and technicians in the R&I Division of the Signal Corps, AEF, all went to school to study radio in that greatest of French universities, the Sorbonne in Paris.

Their relations all through the war had been close with French radio experts and with French army signalmen, thanks to the generous welcome of General Ferrie, chief of the Établissement Central du Matériel de la Radiotelegraphic Militaire. And the French signal experts had themselves worked closely with physicists and radio engineers in the Sorbonne. Now they suggested that while the officers and men of the Signal Corps awaited transport home, they might all profit from some advance study in the Sorbonne itself.

Thus it was that through the first half of 1919, from March to July, they constituted an Allied Radio Engineering Class at the university. On June 27, 1919 the Americans and their French comrades sat for a class picture under the Eiffel Tower. The fifty or so young Americans in this group would, as soon as they returned to the United States after mid-1919, spark the radio broadcast industry and the radio entertainment business for the next decade. The knowledge and experience they garnered in the American military effort, especially in new voice radio techniques, helped introduce a new era into the art and the business of communications.

It is indeed noteworthy that communications and electronics played a critical role in the dramatic beginning of World War II. Had the authorities acted on the warning given them by our "newfangled" radar, the teeth would have been removed from the initial Japanese air attack.

"This Is Not a Drill"

✠ DR. GEORGE RAYNOR THOMPSON, DIXIE R. HARRIS, PAULINE M. OAKES, and DULANY TERRETT

At four o'clock on the morning of December 7, 1941, two U.S. Army signalmen switched on the radar at their station near the northernmost point of Oahu. They would be on duty until seven, when a truck would call to take them back to the post for breakfast. The rest of the day would be theirs, for it was Sunday, and the big SCR-270 radar would be closed down until the next early-morning shift. Together with five other mobile stations spotted around the perimeter of the island until the permanent sites could be made ready, the Opana radar was intended to operate for two hours before dawn and one afterward, according to the latest operating schedule agreed upon under the past week's alert.

Throughout the Hawaiian Department the alert had been ordered rather suddenly on Thanksgiving Day, and instructed all troops to be on guard against acts of sabotage. The *Honolulu Advertiser* had printed a story on the Saturday after Thanksgiving that had carried the headline "Japanese May Strike over Weekend," and certainly it was difficult not to see how ominous the international situation was; yet nothing had happened after all, and the round-the-clock operating schedule which the alert had brought about had been relaxed. Another week of menacing headlines had reached a climax just the day before, on December 6, with a warning, "Japanese Navy Moving South," on the first page of the *Advertiser*. Many persons felt that it would be well, in view of the large population of Japanese origin in the Hawaiian Islands, to prepare for the possibility that a Japanese power drive into the rich Asiatic Indies might be accompanied by trouble stirred up locally.

The officers charged with aircraft warning saw no reason to anticipate trouble beyond that possibility. The operation of the radars and the control of the Signal Aircraft Warning Company,

167

Hawaii (13 officers and 348 enlisted men) were currently responsibilities of the signal officer of the Hawaiian Department, although when the training phase was completed they were to be turned over to the Air Forces, which controlled the information center and the other elements comprising the aircraft warning system.

The alert which the commanding general, Lt. Gen. Walter C. Short, had ordered into effect upon receipt of secret messages from his superiors in the War Department was the lowest of three grades, an alert against sabotage. Accordingly, in order not to risk burning out the radars, for which there were few spare parts, the acting signal officer of the Hawaiian Department (in the absence of the signal officer, who was on a trip to the United States) had instituted a short but intensive schedule calling for radar search during the three hours considered to be the most dangerous each day. Moreover, the platoon lieutenant of the Signal Aircraft Warning Company, Hawaii, who had the Opana crew under his responsibility, had agreed that two men would be enough for the Sunday operation and had let the third, normally on the roster for that duty, off with a pass to Honolulu. Pvt. Joseph L. Lockard and Pvt. George A. Elliott drew the duty, went up to the station Saturday afternoon, and woke themselves up at four to begin their stint.

The radio aircraft-detection device, the SCR-270, was very new and very secret. It generated a powerful pulse of electricity which its antenna threw out into the surrounding sky, and it caught upon the luminous face of its oscilloscope the reflection of the interrupted electric beams in case anything got in the way. Some of these echoes were steadfast, caused by nearby cliffs and hills beyond which the radar was blind. Others were temporary—and these were the ones to watch for. They indicated and tracked airplanes in the sky reflecting the invisible beams of the radar transmitter.

For the entire three hours of their scheduled watch, Privates Lockard and Elliott saw nothing out of the ordinary. Elliott was new to the device, but it was as apparent to him as to Lockard that the oscilloscope showed a normal early dawn sky, with an occasional airplane from one of the military or naval fields on the island.

At 0700 they prepared to close down. The truck was late. The radar hut was warmer than the out-of-doors and there were places to sit down, so Elliott urged that they keep the equipment on while they were waiting. He could then take advantage of a good opportunity to practice with it under Lockard's supervision. At 0702 an echo appeared on their oscilloscope such as neither of them had ever seen before. It was very large and luminous. They reasoned that something must be wrong with the equipment. Lockard checked it, found it in good working order, and observed that the echo was as large as ever. He took over the dial controls, and Elliott moved over to the plotting board. By their calculations, a large flight of airplanes was 132 miles off Kahuku Point and approaching at a speed of three miles a minute.

Because such a large formation was so unusual, Private Elliott suggested that they report it to the information center. After some discussion, Lockard agreed, and Elliott made the call at 0720. At the information center at Fort Shafter, atop a small concrete building used as a signal warehouse, only Pvt. Joseph P. McDonald, 580th Aircraft Warning Company, Oahu, and a young Air Corps lieutenant, Kermit Tyler, were present in the building. The plotters had left at 0700 to enjoy their first off-duty day in a month. McDonald had been on duty at the private branch exchange switchboard since 1700 the previous evening, and was waiting out the last ten minutes until he, too, would leave at 0730. So far as he knew at the moment he was alone in the building. There was no one at the Navy position—no one had been appointed. Tyler would not have been in the center, either, except that he was new, and the air control officer had thought it a good idea for him to take a four-hour tour of duty to become acquainted with the routine. Thus it was only an accident that Lockard and Elliott happened to be on hand at the detector station after 0700, and part of no formal schedule that McDonald and Tyler happened to be on hand after that time at the information center.

When McDonald answered Elliott's call, Elliott told him that a large number of planes was coming in from the north, three points east, and asked him to get in touch with somebody who could do something about it. McDonald agreed, hung up, looked around and saw Lieutenant Tyler sitting at the plotting board. McDonald gave him the message. Tyler showed no interest. McDonald then called back the Opana unit, and got Lockard on the wire. By this time Lockard was excited, too. McDonald, leaving Lockard on the wire, went back and asked Tyler if he wouldn't please talk to the Opana men. Tyler did, spoke to Lockard, and said, in effect, "Forget it." Tyler had heard that a flight of Army bombers was coming in from the mainland that morning, and he had heard Hawaiian music played through the night over the radio, a common practice for providing a guide beam to incoming pilots flying in from the mainland. He assumed that the airplanes the radar was reporting were either the B-17's expected from the west coast, or bombers from Hickam Field, or Navy patrol planes.

Back at the Opana station after talking with Tyler, Lockard

169

wanted to shut the unit down, but Elliott insisted on following the flight. They followed its reflection to within twenty miles, where it was lost in a permanent echo created by the surrounding mountains. By then it was 0739. A little later the truck came, and they started back to the camp at Lawailoa for breakfast. On the way, they met a truck headed away from camp, bearing the rest of the crew with all their field equipment. The driver for Lockard and Elliott blew the horn to signal the other truck to stop, but the driver paid no attention and kept on going.

The Japanese air attack on Pearl Harbor began at 0755, with almost simultaneous strikes at the Naval Air Station at Ford Island and at Hickam Field, followed by attacks on strategic points all over the island of Oahu. The residents of Oahu were accustomed to the sight and sound of bombs used in military practice maneuvers; they did not realize immediately that this time it was no practice drill. Some of the Signal Corps officers on the island were on duty; others were alerted by the first wave of bombings; still others knew nothing of it until notified officially.

Lt. Col. Carroll A. Powell, the Hawaiian Department signal officer, had just returned from a trip to the mainland. Lt. Col. Maurice P. Chadwick had been appointed only a month before as signal officer of the Twenty-fifth Infantry Division, which was charged with the defense of the beaches, the harbor, and the city of Honolulu. He was in his quarters at Hickam Field when the first bomb dropped on the battleships in the harbor. A few minutes later Japanese planes winged in low over his house as they attacked the nearby hangars. Hastily the colonel piled mattresses around a steel dining table and gathered his children under its shelter. Then he hurried off to direct the communication activities of the signal company as the troops moved into position.

The officer in charge of the wire construction section of the department signal office, 1st Lt. William Scandrett, was responsible for installing and maintaining all permanent wire communication systems throughout the islands—command and fire control cables, post base distribution facilities, and the trunking circuits from major installations. By one of the quirks of fate that determine the course of events, the Engineers had been remodeling the tunnels at the battle command post, and the Signal Corps had removed the switchboard and distribution cables to preserve them from the blasting and construction. Thus the command post was virtually without telephone communication when the Japanese struck. At once Scandrett's Signal Corps crews rushed to the command post and restored the switchboard and cables in record time.

170

At Schofield Barracks, men from the communications section of the Ninety-eighth Antiaircraft Regiment were frantically setting up switchboards and connecting telephones at the regimental command post at Wahiawa for the gun positions around Wheeler Field and Schofield Barracks. The communications lines had been strung to each gun position, and at the command post itself all the wires were in and tagged. But under the November alert the telephones and switchboards remained in the supply room at Schofield Barracks as a precaution against theft and sabotage. About 0830 2d Lt. Stephen G. Saltzman and S. Sgt. Lowell V. Klatt saw two pursuit planes pull out of a dive over Wheeler Field and head directly toward them. Each of the men seized an automatic rifle and began firing. One of the two planes, trapped by high tension wires, crashed on the far side of the command post building. Running around to look at it, the men felt worried—to use Saltzman's words—at seeing an American engine, an American propeller, and an American parachute. "And, well, that's about all there was to it"—except that Air Corps Intelligence later decided that the plane was Japanese—"and we went back and finished setting up our communications." Within twenty-five minutes the equipment was connected. In fact, communications were set up hours before the guns were in place and ready to fire, in late afternoon.

Within a half hour after the first bombs fell in Hawaii, the Signal Aircraft Warning Company, Hawaii, had manned all six radar stations and the information center. About 1000 a bomb blast cut the telephone wires leading from the Waianae radar to the information center. The Waianae station commander at once sent a detail of his men to the nearest town where they confiscated a small forty-watt transmitter and antenna, together with the Japanese operator, who was prevailed upon to help install the set in the station. By 1100 the Waianae radar station was communicating with the information center by radio, thus establishing the first radio link in what became within the next few weeks an extensive aircraft warning radio net covering both Oahu and the principal islands nearby.

The attacking Japanese planes withdrew to the northwest, the earliest returning to the carriers by 1030, the latest by 1330. The Opana station, reopened after the first wave of Japanese planes attacked, tracked that flight or some other flight back from Oahu in the same northerly direction from 1002 to 1039. In the confusion and turmoil, amid numerous false reports from both civilian and military sources, the Navy sent its ships and planes out to search for the Japanese carriers, centering the search to the southwest. The

Air Corps also sent planes in that direction. There was much bitterness afterward over the question of why there was no search to the north, and why the radar information of the outgoing flights, apparently headed back to rendezvous, was not given to the searchers at the time. The reasons for this failure are much the same as those that underlay other mishaps of that day: the information center, and indeed the entire aircraft warning system, was still in a training status, and if any one in authority saw the radar plot, he was too inexperienced to realize its possible significance at the time.

Except for one major cable put out of commission at Hickam Field, the Japanese attack did little damage to signal installations. Soldiers and civilians working through the second phase of the bombings quickly patched all the important circuits in the Hickam cable. Two hours before midnight a third of the damaged Hickam Field circuits was back in the original route, and by two o'clock on the morning of December 8 the whole cable was restored.

Word of the attack reached the Navy communications center in Washington at 1350 Sunday, Washington time, over the direct Boehme circuit from the Pearl Harbor radio station. In an action message over the name of Adm. Husband E. Kimmel, the commander in chief of the Pacific Fleet, the broadcaster was saying "Air attack on Pearl Harbor. This is not drill." Thus he was correcting the first incredulous reaction to the falling bombs.

As word spread through the military establishment in Washington, Gen. George C. Marshall, the Chief of Staff, wanted to know why the warning message he had sought to send that morning had not arrived in time to avert disaster. Atmospheric disturbances in the vicinities of San Francisco and Honolulu that morning had rendered the Army radio circuits unusable. For that reason, Lt. Col. Edward F. French, the Signal Corps officer in charge of the War Department Message Center, had turned to the commercial facilities of Western Union and the Radio Corporation of America (RCA). When he had sent Marshall's message from the Center (at 0647 Hawaiian time) he had told Western Union that he desired an immediate report on its delivery. Now he perspired at the telephone trying to get it. "I was very much concerned; General Marshall was very much concerned; we wanted to know whose hands it got into. This went on late into the night; I personally talked to the signal office over there." French was not able to talk to Colonel Powell, the Hawaiian Department signal officer, who was busy in the field, but he did talk to the Hawaiian operator, and told him that it was imperative to be able to tell Marshall who got that message.

It was not until the following day that Washington received a definite answer, and learned that the RCA office in Honolulu had delivered the message to the signal center at Fort Shafter in a routine manner. The warning message had arrived in Honolulu at 0733, twenty-two minutes before the attack, and a messenger boy on a motorcycle was carrying it out to the Army post when the bombs started falling. The boy delivered the message at Fort Shafter at 1145, long after the main attacking groups of Japanese planes had retired. About an hour was spent in decoding it; it had to be processed through the cipher machine and then played back to make sure of its accuracy. At 1458 it was placed in the hands of the adjutant general of the department, who delivered it to General Short's aide, who gave it to Short at 1500. The warning was in Short's hands, then, eight hours and thirteen minutes after it had left the War Department Message Center, seven hours and five minutes after the attack had begun.

173

Technology and logistics came to the forefront in World War II in a manner undreamed of before in all of military history. Together with the exploding advances made in technology, there came an almost insuperable necessity to train competent people who could make the new machines work. Nowhere was this challenge more keenly felt than by the officers and men of the Army Signal Corps. And in no other army were better communications provided!

The Signal Corps in World War II

✠ DR. GEORGE RAYNOR THOMPSON

World War I had been a one-theater conflict, whose communications needs the Signal Corps met with sudden growth from fewer than 2,000 officers and men to over 60,000. The magnitude of the second world war was much greater. The Corps mushroomed from a strength of 27,000 at the outset to about 350,000 men who supported the U.S. Army in theaters all around the globe. Great as this expansion in manpower was, greater yet were the new equipment developments and the mass production of wire and cable, radio radar, and all the increasingly complex components of modern communications-electronics.

More than any conflict before it, World War II became a war of materials and machines, of tanks and vehicles of all sorts, and of the equipment that goes with motorized land operations, with aircraft and their specialized needs, and with all the communications equipment required to coordinate the men and their machines.

These circumstances demanded enormous quantities and elaborations of communications-electronics components, requiring large development laboratories (chiefly at Fort Monmouth, New Jersey, and Dayton, Ohio), huge procurement and supply organizations, not to mention a manyfold expansion of the nation's electric manufacturing plants. World War II also placed upon the Signal Corps enormous training requirements for unheard-of numbers of skilled soldier operators of communications-electronics (C-E) equipment, as well as for troops to supply and distribute the equipment, to install it, and then to attend to its maintenance and repair. All of these tasks in the Army were the responsibility of the Signal Corps. Such was the magnitude of the need and the responsibility.

Yet, during the depression decade of the 1930's, the Army's com-

174

munications equipment and techniques had fallen behind the new requirements of mobility, range, and reliability required to meet the growing needs of motorized infantry, artillery and armor—not to mention the pressing demands of air-to-air and air-to-ground communications and of radar.

But the leaders of the Signal Corps were aware of the needs. Maj. Gen. Joseph Mauborgne, a research-minded Chief Signal Officer during the years 1937–41, gave strong support to Army radar, which Col. William Blair, Director of the Army Signal Corps laboratories at Fort Monmouth had initiated (Blair received a basic patent for the first Army radar that was demonstrated in May, 1937). Mass production of two radar sets, the SCR-268 (designed to direct searchlight beams upon aircraft), and the SCR-270 (a mobile long-range aircraft detector, or early warning set) had begun before the nation entered the war. It was an SCR-270 on the island of Oahu which detected the approach of Japanese aircraft on the morning of December 7, 1941—picking up the echoes from the planes when they were one hundred and thirty miles away and giving the warning which no one would believe.

Months before Pearl Harbor, radar developments, especially for the Army air forces, began to press the Signal Corps. Development and production of superior microwave radars was made possible by the British cavity magnetron transmitter tube, which our Allies brought over to us in greatest secrecy in 1940, seeking engineering and manufacturing assistance of microwave radars in quantity. This led to the expansion of radar research and development facilities in the military services, in universities, and in industry. Dozens of Army ground and airborne radar types were developed and produced under Signal Corps supervision. Outstanding among the ground sets was the microwave SCR-584, a superlatively accurate gun director. It was first used in combat at Anzio, Italy, in 1944 where antiaircraft artillery, directed by the SCR-584, devastated German air attacks. A little later, this radar was the decisive element in smothering the buzz-bomb attacks on England, where accurate SCR-584 controlled gunfire destroyed most of the V-1's in the sky.

Army radar, though it became a billion-dollar baby, constituted but a part of Signal Corps equipment tasks. Communications, wire and radio, stood foremost. Communications—that is reliable heavy-duty message and voice traffic—had previously meant telegraph, teletype, and telephone transmission over wire or cable circuits. But now mobile warfare, requiring communications links to every moving tank, command car and airplane, meant that radio circuits must also be heavily relied on. Hitherto, radio usage had not compared well with wire either in reliability or in clarity. Fortunately, the solutions to problems in tactical radio for ground vehicles had been worked out in the 1930's by the renowned electronics scientist, Maj. Edwin H. Armstrong, when he invented FM (frequency modulation) radio. Major Armstrong of course had served the Signal Corps brilliantly in France during World War I where, among other contributions, he had developed the first superheterodyne receiving sets.

Late in the 1930's, the Signal Corps labs, under Col. Roger Colton working with Armstrong, developed the first pushbutton crystal-controlled FM tactical radios (Armstrong donating his time, his radio equipment, and his patents voluntarily). Crystal control of every channel eliminated fussy dial tuning, so that unskilled harried soldiers could talk over these voice radios simply by pushing a button. This control, however, meant the mining of great quantities of rare quartz crystal, and the production of millions of precisely-cut crystal frequency-control units. The radio industry had heretofore never imagined possible the production of more than a few thousand hand-fabricated units a year. The Signal Corps risked the chance that enough crystal units could be produced. More than a hundred manufacturing companies, with the Army's aid, attacked and solved the intricate task of mass producing the crystals and the highly complex pushbutton radios.

FM crystal-controlled sets elevated radio usage, making it the equivalent of wire telephone communications—reliable, easy to use, usually easy to understand. Then, upon the application of FM radio to radio relay techniques the inherently short range of very high-frequency FM was extended, in thirty-mile hops, to whatever distance the circuits might be desired. This was accomplished by relays of truck-mounted equipment, able to provide in a matter of hours long distance highly reliable multi-channel circuits—much faster, much easier, and less costly than the erection of miles of wire lines. Furthermore, all this superlative radio communications could be, and eventually was, interconnected into wire-line systems. As a result, wire and radio became married; their circuits were integrated, providing high-quality communications irrespective of whether the signals traveled by wire, or by radio, and alternatively over links of each.

The tactical FM radio of American armies became the envy of all nations in the combat of World War II—in tank warfare and in amphibious assaults, too, wherein the Navy and Marines eagerly

176

sought the FM sets and relay, and also for ship-to-shore use. FM radio relay, AN/TRC-1, -3 and -4 (commonly called "antrac" in Europe, and "VHF" in the Pacific), alone kept communications operating all the way forward during General Patton's Third Army dash deep into France in 1944 after the Saint-Lô breakout. The fast long-distance penetrations of the tank forces operated on a shoe-string for days—the shoestring was the slender but vital radio relay circuits which Brig. Gen. E. F. Hammond, Patton's signal officer, provided by employing twenty-eight radio-relay truck units. These antracs and their operators kept Patton's headquarters, "Lucky Forward," in complete communications throughout the daily giant strides of Third Army combat forces.

In tactical combat, Armored Force and Artillery operators (also infantrymen using the walkie-talkie SCR-300) could talk and clearly hear over their FM sets which remained free of the static and interference that bedeviled the AM (amplitude modulation) radios of other combatants. One American veteran of Siegfried Line combat wrote, "I know the fighting would have lasted longer if we hadn't had FM on our side. We were able to shoot fast and effectively because we could get information quickly and accurately by voice, on FM." He added, "FM saved lives and won battles because it speeded our communications and enabled us to move more quickly than the Germans, who had to depend upon AM."

Likewise Col. Grant Williams, signal officer of the First U.S. Army, commented, "I feel that every soldier who lived through the war with an armored unit owes a debt he does not even realize to General Colton." For it was Colton who had made the risky decision to commit Army tactical radio to FM and crystal control at a time when there was uncertainty if effective FM radio could be mass produced, if quartz crystal could be found in sufficient quantity, and if precise fabrication of the frequency-control crystal units could be converted to mass production.

As in tactical radio, so too in worldwide strategic communications of the Army there occurred tremendous equipment innovations and expansions. Before World War II a modest number of radio and wire circuits for military command and administrative communications had been extended over continental United States, and beyond, to a few outlying headquarters locations. The radio circuits were mostly hand-keyed, transmitting Morse code. Some employed higher speed Boehme telegraph equipment. Messages had to be hand enciphered and deciphered before and after transmission for security purposes. But these facilities and these methods were totally

177

inadequate for the worldwide nets that the Army and Army air forces required at once after Pearl Harbor—long-range, transoceanic, multichannel circuits, channeling massive flows of communications traffic around the clock, day after day.

The Army Communications Service, operating from the Office of the Chief Signal Officer in Washington, went to work at once in cooperation with the nation's commercial communications companies and quickly developed single sideband radio facilities, spiral four-field cable, and complexes of carrier equipment which could be applied either to radio or wire lines and which permitted the transmission of several telephone or teletype communications simultaneously over a single circuit. Fast teletypewriter techniques were applied to radio usage, replacing the older, much slower hand-keyed or Boehme operations. Above all, the Signal Corps developed new enciphering and deciphering machines which did their work automatically, synchronized with the teletypewriters at both ends of the circuits. The elimination of slow hand ciphering or coding methods chalked up a major advance in World War II strategic communications.

Beginning in 1942 the Army Communications Service rapidly built up a huge semiautomatic global system called ACAN—Army Command and Administrative Net—which centered in station WAR in the Pentagon. The Service simultaneously built up a second global net serving solely the Army Air Forces. This was called the AACS, or Army Airways Communications System.

Major ACAN stations were established—eastward in London, Algiers, Cairo, later in Caserta, Italy, in Paris, and by mid-1945 in Frankfurt, Germany. Other stations moved westward with the progress of the war—from Hawaii to Nouméa in New Caledonia, to Brisbane in Australia, to New Delhi in India, to Hollandia in New Guinea, and by 1945 to Manila, Okinawa, and finally to Tokyo at the war's end. Between these eastward and westward ACAN links a major tie-in was established early in the war at Asmara in East Africa. The Asmara station, like a keystone in an arch, caught up and firmly bonded the other links into a global belt line of powerful long-range multichannel radioteletypewriter circuits. It was called the belt line since the radio links that composed it girdled the earth in latitudes near the equator. Signal Corps operators found that high-frequency radio was much more dependable in tropical areas —freer from ionospheric interference and able to operate with a minimum of circuit outage (interference became progressively worse in latitudes farther north, worst of all in polar regions).

178

All these massive ACAN facilities—plus the air ferry communications of the AACS guiding aircraft across the North and South Atlantic, across Africa and the Near East, across the Pacific to the Far East—all constituted a system of communications—the likes of which had never existed, or scarcely even been imagined possible before. Maj. Gen. Frank E. Stoner, Chief of the Army Communications Service, enjoyed reminding the Army that the commodity sent overseas in World War II was words, not bullets. He figured the proportion at eight words to every bullet. By 1945, ACAN capacity was 100,000,000 words a day. The average daily load amounted to about 50 million words.

The equipment, the facilities, comprised only one face, one side, of the Signal Corps coin. The other was the human side, the 350,000 officers and men, and Women's Army Corps personnel. Training them by the tens of thousands constituted a staggering task. Sources of men with some C-E familiarity, or electrical experience in industry, radio-repair shops, schools, and colleges, in radio amateur organizations were soon exhausted. The majority had to be trained by the Army, generally from scratch. The Signal Corps struggled to get as large a portion as possible of the more promising draftees, for rapid mastery of C-E skills could not be accomplished by those who stood low in AGCT's (Army General Classification Test).

The established Signal Corps Specialist Schools and the Replacement Training Center at Fort Monmouth were bolstered by huge new camps such as Camp Murphy in Florida (for radar training), Camp Crowder in Missouri, and Camp Kohler in California, for all types of C-E training. Under the Enlisted Reserve Program of the Signal Corps, students were enrolled in C-E courses at numerous colleges and institutions across the country.

Altogether more than 30,000 officers were graduated in some fifty different types of courses during the war. Enlisted men trained in C-E amounted to nearly 400,000. Many of the officers and men went into units serving the Army Air Forces. Further training was conducted in the overseas theaters of the war, notably in the Mediterranean area under Brig. Gen. R. B. Moran, Signal Officer of the Fifth Army, and under Brig. Gen. F. B. Ankenbrandt, Signal Officer in the South Pacific area.

Signal units by the hundreds were activated—companies and battalions for operations and construction as in former wars, and also new and previously unheard of types, such as aircraft-warning companies and battalions (for radar-warning services to the Army Air Forces), and radio-intelligence companies, and SIAM (Signal

179

Intelligence and Monitoring) companies to support the Signal Corps large radio security and intelligence responsibilities. Then there were JASCO's, Joint Assault Signal Companies, created to meet the amphibious assault communications needs of joint Army/Navy operations.

Unit requirements were so pressing, and often arose so suddenly, that students were taken out of the schools, their course work incomplete, to fill requirements in signal companies and battalions. These units were trained further in huge unit training centers, especially at Camp Crowder, or they continued training in assignments overseas, on the job. Really skilled specialists were in highest demand. Specialist units were split time and time again to establish cadres, hard cores of completely competent men to serve as nuclei for new combat units or for instruction at training schools.

A major aid in the mass training of the millions of America's unskilled soldiery drawn from the peaceful pursuits of civilian life, was the training film—motion pictures provided by the Signal Corps Photographic Service centered at Astoria, Long Island. Hollywood producers lent much assistance, contributing, for example, animation techniques to enliven and lighten the heavy doses of instruction of thousands of reels of film. Many persons in civilian studios took commissions as Signal Corps officers, for example, Col. Darryl Zanuck and Maj. Frank Capra, contributed their know-how to the organization and operation of Signal Photographic companies that served in every theater of combat. Combat photography (not a few lost their lives in this work) was in much demand for the information and intelligence needs of the Army.

Signal logistics, the production, storage, and distribution of C-E equipment, occupied great numbers of military and civilian personnel. First among the major tasks was contracting with industry for the production of massive quantities of communication end items, components, and spare parts. To bolster and expand the industry, they helped with the labor supply; they helped provide critical raw materials; and they helped build up plant facilities and new factories.

They received the equipment as it poured off assembly lines, moving it to depots for temporary storage. They received requisitions from Army users, filling the requisitions from the depots, shipping and distributing the equipment the world over—not to mention administering payment for it all.

Before World War II the Signal Corps budget had been small. For example, the preliminary budget (drawn up in 1939) for fiscal year 1941 totaled but 9 million dollars. But, as a result of one war crisis after another in these emergency years, the funds which Congress actually made available to the Corps added up to 256 million dollars. But within six months after Pearl Harbor, by mid-1942, the Signal Corps had placed over two and a half billion dollars worth of production contracts. A year later the Corps budget stood at over five billion, about one twentieth of the total Army-Navy costs.

Signal Corps supply centered in the Philadelphia Procurement District and the huge Philadelphia Signal Depot. Other major Signal depots in the United States were located in Boston, Baltimore, Dayton, Chicago, Sacramento, and in Lexington, Kentucky. In the theaters of operations, massive supply bases everywhere backed up the combat fronts—in England and North Africa, in Hawaii and the islands of the far Pacific. Theater signal officers enjoyed direct control over their own supply, giving them an advantage in providing to the combat forces a fast responsive signal support that was the envy of our allies.

Under Maj. Gen. H. C. Ingles, Chief Signal Officer from 1943 to 1947, the U.S. Army Signal Corps came through World War II larger—with wider activities and more responsibilities—than ever before. This was true despite the loss to the Army Air Forces late in 1944 of all responsibility for aviation communications-electronics, and also despite the loss in late summer of 1945 of all radio-intelligence activity. Radio intelligence and security had grown greatly during the war in consequence of the expansion of radio and radar usage, and of radio and radar countermeasures. The activity had required a large Signal Corps organization and dozens of radio-intelligence companies in all the theaters of combat. The entire activity was transferred in September, 1945 to the Army Security Agency. Although these transfers stripped the Signal Corps of half its men and activities as of late World War II, yet almost within months after VJ Day the acquisition of important new missions in the explosively expanding sphere of military C-E, not only restored but in fact further enlarged the Corps' stature within the U.S. Army.

In summary, the Signal Corps had entered World War II with relatively few officers and men, with utterly inadequate stores of equipment, with a skeletal training organization, and with insufficient industrial backing (the nation's electronic producers had little experience in mass production of intricate military radio, almost none in radar). Yet the Corps succeeded in the course of the war in creating a vast organization of skilled men, mountains of equipment, and worldwide communications systems.

181

Signal Corps leaders "were walking on uncharted ground," in the words of Maj. Gen. James A. Code, the Assistant Signal Officer in the Washington headquarters. The job to be done seemed impossible, he added, saying, "We had no pattern to follow either in organization or in demands—we needed more equipment than the entire industry had ever turned out, more trained men than were available, or could be trained in the time allowed us, and we had to fill demands for weapons unheard of." Yet all this was done. "A truly fantastic and wonderful job," Code concluded at the end of World War II.

Thus the Signal Corps developed, supplied, installed, and maintained communications-electronics for all the ground forces of the Army, and for that fast growing youngest Army element, the Army Air Forces. Practically all Air Forces' C-E equipment throughout the war came from the Signal Corps, since the separation of the airmen's electronics from the Corps did not become accomplished till the very last months of the war. Besides supplying all the airmen's C-E, the Corps also met their voracious requirements for aircraft-warning troops and for great numbers of officers and men trained in every sort of communications specialty.

American ground-forces radio equipment was unsurpassed— their handie-talkies (SCR-536), their walkie-talkies (SCR-300), and their larger long-range truck-mounted mobile SCR-299's and -399's. Above all, the short-range vehicular FM radios in the SCR-508 and -608 series (for Armored Force and Artillery, respectively) gave our soldiers in combat a tactical voice communications facility that excelled any equipment possessed by either the enemy or the Allied nations.

Signal Corps achievements in World War II were not confined to meeting its primary mission, assuring the communications which every commander had to have in order to control his forces. The Corps also contributed much to civil progress in postwar years. The war effort and its outpouring of funds, helped boost the relatively small prewar electronic industry to a foremost place in the nation's economy. The Signal Corps contributed thousands of new developments and inventions to the nation's communications-electronics technology. And the Corps returned into civilian employment after the war tens of thousands of the men and women it had trained in the new technologies of radar, radioteletype, radio relay, FM vehicular radio, and in other important areas. Thousands of these people continued to apply their advanced knowledge and skills to the nation's benefit and future progress for many years.

182

Technology, supply, distribution, training—these concepts were all important factors during World War II. But it is men, not concepts, which win a war. Here is a true story of signalmen who courageously performed their duty during a tight spot in battle by keeping vital communications flowing over their radio relay (VHF) station. And right under the very noses of the Germans!

The Inconspicuous Relay

✠ COL. KENNETH E. SHIFLET

"Despite the vast distances that often separated units across the front, at no time was any command farther away than the instrument on my field desk."—An inspiring tribute by General Omar Bradley to Army Signal Corps men in July, 1944. Before the Ardennes breakthrough and Christmas, in the deep Belgian snows and biting weather, with Patton's unbelievable nearly forty-five-degree reorientation of some nineteen combat divisions of his Third Army, the signalmen would earn it.

In this crucial reaction to the sudden German thrust, control of forces was paramount. The ability to re-align, amass, and move units immediately was synonomous with survival. Tactical communications meant the difference between defeat and successful counterattack.

Bradley made the point of the inimitable telephone and radio link even more graphically clear in his *A Soldier's Story:*

> *Those orders, in turn, were transmitted easily over the most valued accessory of all; the elaborate telephone system we carried with us into the field. From my desk in Luxembourg I was never more than thirty seconds by phone from any of the armies. If necessary, I could have called every division on the line. Signal Corps officers like to remind us that "although Congress can make a general, it takes communications to make him a commander." The maxim was never more brilliantly evidenced than in this battle for the Ardennes.*

The connecting system between the telephones was especially important in the fighting for the Ardennes. Radio relay was in-

183

creasingly the means in the Allied reaction to the German's sudden offensive, and it is one of those many vital radio relays that this story concerns.

General Bradley commanded the Twelfth Army Group, which bore the weight of the attack when the Nazis came boiling out in ordered desperation through the Ardennes forests. Bradley reportedly said his drive across France into Nazi Germany depended on the radio link operated by the 980th Signal Service Company. This dependence on radio relay communications became graphically true in the Ardennes fighting.

Many lines were cut in the German breakthrough and penetration. Others stayed in. These were mainly the VHF (very high frequency) radio relay operated over the heads of the attacking enemy forces, giving commanders on the ground the mobility and control to defeat the Hitler-ordered offensive.

American C.O.'s used the telephone to relay orders and coordinate actions. It gave them an instant human medium of influencing what their troops or units did, and a means of getting the subordinate's intelligence and rationale on the spot—at a time when it counted.

The wide-scale radio and wire integrated communications which were put in and defended by signalmen enabled General Patton to dispatch his forces northward with incredible speed, moving at right angles to their previous frontal posture. These communications provided General Bradley positive command control of the Armies under him when containment of the German offensive and counterattack were at stake.

The radio relays—TRAC-3's and -4's—which tied the telephones and teletypewriters together, were directly in the path of the onrushing Nazis. Many relay stations had to be taken down in a firefight, loaded quickly and reprofiled into the communications system by their crews. The December weather of the Ardennes did not make the combat re-sitings under fire any easier.

In one critical instance there were eight Army Signal Corps soldiers from the Twelfth Army Group's Signal Section, helped by twelve guards from the 825th Tank Destroyer Battalion, who fought to defend their radio relay sites and to keep them operating.

Their last location, two relays on Hill 651 near Jemelle, Belgium, was overrun by the Germans on the day before Christmas. They did their best—as small isolated groups must do—but were driven back on Christmas Eve.

One of the signalmen finished guying the VHF's antenna in the new site. He glanced toward the enemy. "Here it is," he said, "the day before and all. It doesn't seem like He's on our side very much."

A crewman who had just finished opening his C rations wtih the tiny hand opener and was testing them with his field spoon, moved the cold cornbeef hash around in his mouth. He swallowed and sighed.

"Come on, Joe, Merry Christmas. You got to know that every time you ask a prayer you don't always get a 'yes' answer. Sometimes it's 'no,' or no answer at all. Maybe He's testing us to see if we want to stay with it. You gotta go on until you get to the yes part." He tried a sample of his hash again. "Know what I mean?"

"Yeah, maybe. Somebody better hurry because the Jerries are setting up something that looks like ack-ack over there. They don't seem like they're getting ready to leave real soon."

"He's right. Look at 'em," somebody with the glasses said.

The others looked where he pointed some five hundred yards away from their relay location. The Germans were siting antiair-craft guns, their thin muzzles showing high on the spread stands as ant-figures moved around them. It seemed unrealistic, as if the Germans were in one world and they were in another. Fortunately, the Nazi troops seemed more concerned with Allied air tactics. Their eyes on the sky, they failed to notice the American radio-relay station no more than a third of a mile away from them.

The signalmen operating the VHF set took advantage of it. They kept operating the relay, passing vital combat traffic that was order-ing and moving forces to drive the Germans back.

The noisy power generators supporting the VHF relay had to be scheduled because they were so close to the enemy. During the day, when troop sounds and battle noises were the loudest, the Signal Corps men ran the gasoline generators that kept their relay on the air. In the comparative quiet of night and slacker com-munication periods, the possibility of discovery by the Germans and loss of the relay made them shut down the power units.

Because of the careful day and night scheduling, the forgotten radio relay continued to operate and pass a heavy volume of traffic under the noses of the Germans.

It was important traffic to the American forces. The incon-spicuous relay was the only communications channel between the Twelfth Army Group TAC and the Ninth Army at Maastrict, and between Twelfth Group and the First Army at Spa.

Certainly, one would have thought, the Germans could hardly miss the station in their searching binoculars. Yet somehow, with

185

the war all around them, the relay kept passing vital traffic. At night they shut down and spelled each other off on guard. There was no real formality to it, just someone crouching awake with his carbine and watching to yell if the enemy tried to take the station.

Even before the fighting they knew was coming, the cold Belgian nights and the concern about the German breakthrough had their own effect on the chilled signalmen and the antitankers who lay in holes around the station.

Probably few general officers, relaying their commands and instructions, knew that a small isolated group of signalmen on a hill now only two football fields from the advancing enemy, were part of the link.

It was late afternoon when the Germans started moving directly toward the radio relay. There were more enemy troops coming toward them than the small eight-man complement of the station, with their tank destroyer companions, could handle. No one bolted for the next hill. They talked about it among themselves, often bringing the twelve soldiers from the tank destroyer unit into it.

"They're moving right at us. I never saw so many Germans. Where the hell did they get them all? I thought they were about done."

Off in the distance, they could hear the crunching snow as the enemy moved up.

"On a big map," one of the signalmen said, "they wouldn't make a little arrow. That doesn't help us, though. We'll knock 'em back, but we got to keep our guys talking with this relay to do it. I'm for staying until they just push us off this hill."

Several soldiers in the defensive forward holes looked at each other along their small line.

"Me, too," one said. "They kicked us off a hill two days ago. Let 'em get up it to knock us off this one."

The sun broke through the cloud layer as it had been doing all day, splintering its light temporarily. Below them, fellow signalmen of the 101st Airborne were using another relay that they had mounted in a truck (the trailer had been destroyed by German fire) to give them two radiotelephone and one radioteletypewriter circuits out of the isolated town of Bastogne.

The Germans came on, advancing straight toward the relay station. The first long-range shots sounded ahead of them. The antenna. The enemy had seen it. The price of their communications on the hill was also the sign of their identification.

Their carbine fire kept off the leading German soldiers for a while. The signalmen and the tank destroyers kept down and shot at the approaching Germans, buying the relay added minutes of command telephone conversation and teletypewriter transmission.

They began withdrawing toward the radio relay set.

"Knock it down," a soldier shouted. "Let's get out of here and move back before they run over us."

They had kept on to hold their communications too long. The advancing Germans were so close that it was hard to dismantle the equipment and move it back with them. The forest was less at their backs, where they could lose themselves in the snow-shrouded trees and thick stands. But the signalmen couldn't withdraw with just their rifles and what they carried on their backs. They had their trade equipment—the antrac—to take with them.

They raced about, loosening antenna guys and dropping the antenna, closing up the carrying cases to get their station out. The wind whipped up thin silts of snow. The mottled round helmets of the Germans thickened below them and the fire became heavy on the hill. The tank destroyer soldiers helped cover them as the Army Signal troops closed their station and began moving it back toward the woods behind them.

Of the twenty men who manned the radio relay, seventeen of them reached their own lines. The remaining three, signalmen who stayed with their gear to keep the essential communications working, were lost. One was taken prisoner by the advancing Germans and the other two were not heard from again.

These men, particularly those who were lost, were undoubtedly part of what General Bradley meant in saying, "this maxim of communications was never more brilliantly evidenced than in this battle for the Ardennes."

187

With respect to signal commmunications, the Korean conflict was not strikingly different from World War II, except for the reduced size and scope of the effort. By and large, the equipment used and the type of communications installed bore a resemblance to that of the last war— though unique problems did exist which had to be solved. One aspect of signaling during the Korean War did assume increasing importance: the frequent necessity for signalmen to fight as infantry in order to preserve their communications—and their lives. The story of "Communications Hill" is but one instance.

"Communications Hill" in Korea

✠ COL. KENNETH E. SHIFLET

The place was the Chosin Reservoir, circa 1950. The "Tenth" Corps had hammered and shelled and fire-fought its way northward along the Wonsan-Hamhung axis. Each mile, each foot, had been paid for in wounded and killed in action. The Corps' forward elements were an arrowpoint on the United Nations' maps, fighting to keep a foothold in Hagaru-ri, a tiny village whose name most of the Americans couldn't pronounce. For some, it was merely a set of map coordinates.

Few men in the Corps' advance command post thought much about Thanksgiving. The November wind whipped up along the southern part of the reservoir and the Virginia turkeys and the New Hampshire framehouse and the family holiday in Tucson seemed far away. The unfamiliar rice paddies with their frozen slivers of trench and the whitened mountain remoteness were all around them.

A part of the Corps' arrowpoint into North Korea, one of the Fourth Signal Battalion's radiomen, blew on his hands.

"Thanksgiving?" he addressed a question to no one in particular. "Sure, I'm thankful. I'm thankful I'm not one of those four guys who was wounded or the one who was killed the last four days trying to keep this Corps' radio in. But," he blew on his hands again and pulled on the insert gloves, "we're going to keep it in."

A mortar started up and he slid into a hole beside the radio relay that worked back to Army. "They must have heard me," he said, shrugging.

He was important. Through the month of October, radio and

188

radio relay teams of his battalion had been trucked and airlifted almost like postage parcels to support the Corps' northward advance.

A relay station of the Fourth's 581st Radio Relay Company at Kujang-ri was the only communications available to the Corps at Hamhung on the last day of October, 1950. Four days later, an SCR-399 high-frequency radio set with Hq and Hq Battery, 196th Field Artillery Battalion, was seriously damaged by enemy artillery. With the wiremen moving up, the Fourth Signal Battalion lost two more men killed and eight wounded in Communist ambushes along Wonsan-Hamhung main supply route.

The signalmen were paying to move the messages back and forth from the arrowpoint of the Corps. Command-control during the critical advance did not come cheaply.

Radio communications were established at Hagaru-ri on the Chosin Reservoir on November 28. The radiomen were under constant attack and only intermittent transmission was possible. They kept the Corps talking. Two days earlier, telephone installation and operation men of the Fourth Signal Battalion's advance team joined them at Hagaru-ni to put in landlines for the Corps' advance.

One of the relaymen threw a quick look at the antenna's outline against the metal blue of the Korean sky and turned at the muffled sound of a bugle.

"What's that crazy call? It's not one of ours."

"The Reds," his sergeant said. "The Chinese Communist volunteers of Mousey Dung." He wasn't excited about it, it was simply an explanation of the sound.

The other radioman had only finished his course at the Signal School a few months before coming to Korea. He came over and squatted down beside the sergeant.

"They use bugles?"

"It's supposed to get you upset." *And it means they're coming in an attack, too, the sergeant thought, but why get this new man all worried. He'll know about it, soon enough.* "You upset?"

"Nah," the new soldier said.

A worn private first class telephone installer with a plier and screwdriver kit and winds of field wire hanging from his belt hurried toward them. He could be either twenty or fifty years old, from the way he looked. The sound of an automatic weapon made him break into a run.

"Here they come again!" he yelled as he approached the radiomen.

He dropped into an empty hole for which there was no rent and they all grabbed their carbines level in their foxholes as the Red Chinese troops came up the hill in successive waves.

"Hope the Gyrenes hold," someone said.

"Hope *we* do, you mean!"

The Chinese advanced up the slopes, attempting to overrun the Corps' command post and the Marine positions toward the left. The signalmen with the advance Corps elements lay in their holes and shot with the others to hold the command post and keep their communications in.

"You get a profiled contact in and the Corps talking and some lousy Commie wants to louse it up," the Signal School graduate thought.

The reservoir seemed to be seeded with crawling or running Chinese Reds. The Fourth's advance team of some ninety men fought desperately to protect the Corps communications. But the bundled and padded Communist figures were always there.

Then someone passed the word to withdraw to the ridge behind them and try to stop the attack.

"We've got to move the radio," the Fourth's new man said. "Some of you guys give me a hand."

"Better keep your head down when you do. Confucius say that bullet make a clean hole that lets life out, air in."

While they dismantled their equipment for the move, they helped all night to throw back Communist attacks. The Fourth Signal picked up more entries on the casualty reports with their brother soldiers-in-arms.

The inexhaustible waves of oncoming Chinese forced them back to the ridge and they carried as much of their communications gear with them as they could. It became a contest to save the equipment they needed to give the Corps' commander a way to communicate. The shortage of power repairmen made the cost of generators precious. Several signalmen tried to lug or manhandle power generators back with them to the ridge.

The next morning they finished withdrawing to a hill where a Marine company was entrenched to consolidate their force against the Red Chinese. Nine days they fought beside the Marines to hold their terrain and guard the Corps' communications. They were northwest of Hungnam, and together with the U.S. Marines, the men of the Fourth Signal Battalion held a knoll in the lower part of the reservoir, fighting as infantrymen.

The Marines and the Army Signal soldiers became a unit, fighting together. The crossed flag-wearers showed a bravery in protecting the vital Corps communications that even the Marines, schooled in fighting, acknowledged.

190

In being forced back from the command post site by overwhelming enemy strength, they gave each yard of ground as unyieldingly as any combat soldier, withdrawing and protecting their communications equipment as well as they could with their small number.

"Hey, Army keypounder," one of the Marines would yell, "here they come on your side!"

The Red Chinese were too much for the outnumbered Army Signal Corps and Marine troops. Still they clung to their positions, forcing back attack after attack, stopping the massed waves often in the first two or three lines of foxholes.

The complete forward element of the Fourth's signalmen was committed in the fighting. On December 1, four more were wounded in preventing the Chinese from encircling them in the reservoir and overrunning their communications.

Task Force Dog finally fought its way up to the Marines and signalmen to relieve them. As the Marines pulled off the knoll they had held with the Army Signal Corps troops, one remarked that the ground should be called "Communications Hill," in tribute to the fighting men of the Fourth Signal Battalion. The small, probably unknown knoll has been known as such from that particular day.

The Marine's comment was perhaps a fair one for the signalmen of the Fourth. In the following year of Korean fighting, its men earned in April, 1951 alone one Silver Star, three Bronze Stars with the "V" device, twenty-one Purple Hearts, and a Commendation with Pendant.

After the action was stabilized, the men of the "Fighting Fourth," as the Marines called them, had their share of casualties from mines and booby traps, experienced especially by the lonely linemen.

The Fourth Signal Battalion, together with several sister Signal battalions, including the Fifty-first, from which it drew teams in 1950 and which now supports I Corps Group in Korea, is still standing ready in South Korea to protect freedom again and to "keep the communications in."

That seems to fit the infantryman's remark during a particularly heavy firefight: "Here they are shooting all over, and those crazy Signal Joes are going on laying lines like nothin's happening."

191

The Signal Corps scientists and engineers of today are proud of the quality of their own work and of that work in which they collaborate with others in our industrial and educational institutions. Let us take the period from 1946 down to 1961, and let us glance at the milestones that mark off its fifteen years.

Modern Signal Research

✠ DAVID J. MARSHALL, *U.S. Army Signal Center*

The first big scientific breakthrough of the postwar period—the one that heralded the dawn of the Space Age—came in 1946 when a radar signal was bounced off the moon and received back on earth some seconds later. Through this pioneering effort, man acquired for the first time a method of probing, actively, into all that lies beyond his earthly confines.

Later that same year fifty Signal Corps scientists, engineers, and military personnel moved into Bikini for the first of the postwar atomic bomb tests. During Able and Baker—the first two blasts—a series of research projects was begun, and these have been continued through all subsequent tests. The findings are embodied in today's remarkable devices for the long-range detection of nuclear explosions, for measuring the absorption rate of radiation, for tracking radioactive clouds, for reducing the vulnerability of electronic equipment to highly radioactive environments, and for doing other things of major importance.

Also in 1946 Signal Corps scientists began growing synthetic mica, and out of that has come the solution of one more critical materials problem. By 1957, one American concern had reached a production rate of one thousand tons of synthetic mica per annum.

In 1947 "nearer space" provided the excitement, as Project Cirrus began its sensational career of pushing the clouds around and—when all the conditions were right—of changing nature's precipitation habits. The last word has yet to be written on this subject; it would still seem possible that man may some day place his order for the kind of weather he desires. Before that day arrives, however, a great deal remains to us of hard work, patience, and what can be described only as scientific brilliance.

The big news in 1948 was still the atmosphere, as new radar

equipment at Fort Monmouth observed a rain storm at 185 miles and then tracked the disturbance to zero range, giving accurate precipitation forecasts for various areas down to the minute—a bit unusual to say the least. This equipment, some of it modified perhaps, is now in wide use by the military services and by the U.S. Weather Bureau.

During this excitement, the Signal Corps weather experts also began looking higher. Using rockets, they started probing for temperatures, wind direction, and wind velocity at altitudes up to 250,000 feet. The rockets were equipped with grenades, and these were exploded in a predetermined sequence. Then, by measuring the time for each individual sound wave to reach the earth, many data could be extracted from the medium through which the acoustic signals passed. Frequently the same rockets also carried flasks in which samples of the atmosphere were captured at various heights for later analysis on earth. And finally, a new-fashioned weather balloon was sent, in that same year 1948, to a world's record height of 140,000 feet.

But 1948 was also the year in which the transistor made its appearance. This was not a Signal Corps development, but many Signal Corps developments resulted from it. It took its place overnight, side by side with electron tubes, resistors, condensers, and inductors, high on the list of things vital to signal research and development. Signal Corps contracts and in-house research efforts were expanded to accelerate work in the now more-important-than-ever field of the solid state, and to hurry the task of making transistors available for experimentation. Industrial preparedness funds were fortunately available, and their use quickly established U.S. world leadership in producing this new and highly important electronic device.

Some photographic research was carried on during World War II, but many real advances were made after 1946. Signal Corps firsts in photography include optical image assessment, rapid processing of photographic films and papers by stabilization chemistry, long-range ground-to-ground photography with very long lenses, photography on light-sensitive plastics, designs of unusual photographic lenses, ion-exchange treatments for purification of photographic solution and wash-water, and comprehensive studies of materials and methods particularly well suited for Army photography. One of the latter studies pertained to the recording of photographic images on the electrically charged surface of a layer of photoconducting insulator. On the other hand, work begun in 1948—both in the Signal lab and under outside study contract—has done much to bring the art of xerography to its present high state.

In 1949 came the introduction of what is known today as the autosembly of printed circuits, a technique now widely used in the fabrication of miniaturized circuits; and for their contributions to this development, two of our Signal laboratory engineers shared an incentive award of $10,000—thereby establishing another laboratory record. Their great achievement was to take the new-born transistor and various other miniature components, and to work them into systems having a parts density of the order of 50,000 to the cubic foot. Scientists today envisage potentials of 250,000 parts to the cubic foot and more.

In 1950 the now-famous surface-wave transmission line, invented by a Signal Laboratory scientist, came into being. This invention owes much to the very early and slightly overlooked computations of Sommerfield. In the light of those findings, a radio wave was found to be transmissable on the surface of a single wire with little attenuation; and so a handy way was discovered to feed a microwave antenna on top of a high tower or to get TV signals to and from the top of a mountain.

Also in 1950 work on crossed-field amplifiers was first suggested and this led to the discovery of the carcinotron principle. Shortly thereafter, then, came the high-power voltage-tunable oscillator, which represented one of the most important steps forward in electron-tube development since the multicavity magnetron.

In 1951 the laboratory scored a quite sensational success in growing large quartz crystals; they ranged in weight from 300 to 400 grams each. In short order, after that, pilot plants were producing crystals in lots of more than one ton a year.

History was made at the Nevada Test Site in 1952 by a radio-controlled weasel with TV eyes. A few minutes after an underground atomic explosion, the weasel moved into the affected area under remote control, took samples of the highly radioactive soil, and then returned with the samples at high speed, thus making possible a quick analysis of the soil while it was still "hot." This was a memorable exploit, duly celebrated by newspapers and magazines throughout the land. Also memorable, perhaps, was the "exploit" of one member of the laboratory task force who shielded his personal film dosimeter with heavy lead wrapping, for fear that his exposure, if properly measured, would cause him to be disqualified for certain other experiments he had in mind.

In the ten-year period from 1945 to 1955, communications history was made as the laboratory, together with industry, developed

194

the concept of a completely integrated series of FM field radio equipment. This period also witnessed the completion of the first model of a fully automatic sferics system, which proved capable of pinpointing thousands-of-miles-distant lightning flashes. In this period, too, the MASER—that extremely useful device that produces m-a-s-e-r, or microwave amplification by stimulated emission of radiation—was developed under contract at Columbia University. And in 1956 the laboratory received delivery of the first commercial sealed-off cesium-beam-frequency standard, which had been developed under contract at M.I.T.

During 1957 as many as one hundred of the laboratory personnel rediscovered that one can do almost twice as much work in an eighty- as in a forty-hour week—but not quite. This was one of the unforeseen and unintended consequences of the orbiting of the first two sputniks, Alpha and Beta. A major effort was begun to track, and to learn as much as possible about, these two excellent and highly mobile transmitters which the Soviets had provided at no cost to our research program.

Also in 1957 we placed our first experimental millimeter radar in operation, and after years of research the Missile Master was made operational. This latter system electronically stores and analyzes data on both friendly and hostile aircraft and presents it, in simplified form, on a TV-like picture tube at the fire control center for a Nike-defended area.

Cross-continent proving extended, in 1957, our newly developed multichannel single-sideband techniques. While riding down the main street of Phoenix, Arizona, in a jeep one sunny day that year, a civilian chief of the laboratory called his office at Fort Monmouth, two thousand miles away, over a wire-radio net, and found no perceptible degradation in voice quality.

As the new year 1958 began, the powerful Diana radar at Fort Monmouth was spraying its energy, via the moon, to the International Geophysical Year (IGY) minitrack stations for calibration purposes. Just a few weeks later, on March 17, Vanguard I, the Navy's IGY "grapefruit" satellite, was launched, carrying solar cells the application and fabrication of which had been engineered by the Signal laboratory. In the ensuing years during which it has continued to send signals back to the earth, the tiny satellite has made major contributions to science. Even today its signals are received each time it passes over Fort Monmouth, though its orbits approach the 15,000 mark and its total travel comes close to 400 million miles.

In other parts of the laboratory, 1958 saw what is probably the world's most unusual antenna come into being—the tapered aperture horn antenna (TAHA), 944 feet long, 560 feet wide and 285 feet high, and, as the saying goes, capable of burning a hole in the atmosphere that lies between the transmitting and receiving sites.

The year was coming to a close with experimental models of a radiac dosimeter (semirad), which uses secondary electrons as a measure of neutron and gamma doses delivered at extremely high rates and in extremely short times. But just before the close, and just before Christmas, on December 18, 1958, an Air Force Atlas placed in orbit our Project Score transmitter. Then the President of the United States, from a vantage point between the moon and the earth, sent greetings to all the inhabitants of our world—and, possibly, to those of other worlds.

About this time, many Signal scientists turned gypsy, packed their bags, and strolled off down the Romany road of the International Geophysical Year—to the Antarctic, the Arctic, and the South Pacific, and to Western Europe, Australia, Japan, and Canada. Rocket soundings producing new atmospheric data were made on a global scale; electromagnetic propagation data were obtained through the fantastically pure ice formations surrounding the North and South Poles; and at Thule, a weasel equipped with a downward-looking radar, while in motion, measured ice thicknesses in minutes as compared to the weeks required by normal seismic techniques in obtaining ground contours.

The year 1959 began with the University of Illinois and the Evans Area people exploring the total content of electrons in the atmosphere by studying moon returns on the Fort Monmouth-Moon-Urbana circuit. From these data, we learned that the ionosphere extends much farther into space than had recently been assumed, and that there are three times as many electrons above the maximum density layer as below it. And within the confines of the laboratory, a 100,000-joule condenser charge was used to produce dense plasma which makes possible the simulation of ionspheric hydromagnetic phenomena, enabling us to learn more of communications problems associated with missiles and satellites.

Then, in a sensational global coverage experiment, using an Argus high-altitude atomic burst as a source of radiation, our scientists discovered two new ductlike mechanisms for the propagation of hydromagnetic waves. These waves appear to be generated when the atomic blast completely annihilates the magnetic field at that point. Hydromagnetic waves are generated as the magnetic balance is reestablished and these travel at several thousand miles

196

a second in a layer of plasma some fifteen hundred miles high, the waves spreading around the earth, like ripples in a magnetic pond.

In an entirely different area, practical cold cathode tubes were demonstrated while the micromodule people talked about, and demonstrated, compact electronic units undreamed of just a few years past. For example, an entire six-transistor radio circuit smaller than a sugar lump was demonstrated, and eager eyes looked forward to millions of parts to the cubic foot as solid-state circuitry techniques came rapidly into being.

As components grew smaller, the communications imagination continued to expand. The laboratory, with industrial assistance, moved into a study of an all-purpose military commuincations system dubbed UNICOM. On a different front, caring not over what circuits it would be asked to perform, a high-speed teleprinter charmed all viewers as it printed from 750 to 3000 words a minute and literally sang while "the lazy dog jumped."

The year ended as our materials people went high up in pressure and temperature, "calibrating" their equipment by synthesizing one of nature's invariants, crystallized cubic carbon—known better as diamonds. The Signal program in this area is now to move forward into an even more creative environment and to produce exotic substances as yet unknown to man: substances with electronic applications that cannot be realized by anything nature has produced on earth.

In 1960, delivery was made of the first Mobidic—the field computer that talks faster, reacts faster, does everything faster, than any general with a Ph.D. entourage. Time alone will tell how man and machine will divide the decision process. The machine suggests a vast untapped potential, but we must learn more of its language before we can even start to effectively use the millions of small components available—in a mobile field trailer today, in a jeep tomorrow.

On the first of April, 1960 the launching of Tiros ushered in a new age in meteorology. A total of almost 23,000 superb photographs of global cloud coverage was obtained in the lifetime of this satellite, all the instruments of which were developed, designed, and constructed under the guidance and control of the Signal lab.

As part of this new scientific crescendo, a high-performance turbojet surveillance drone made its first flight in May of 1960, when unmanned, it streaked high over Arizona, all the while sending back information of tactical value. It was then directed to its recovery area and commanded to parachute to earth.

197

Shortly after 1545 hours on October 4, 1960, a very unusual radio receiver in Puerto Rico, fed by a massive dish antenna pointing skyward, heard a message from the President of the United States: ". . . Taking advantage of the opportunity of this first flight of an advanced communications satellite, specifically designed to transmit a teletyped message from one part of the world to another, I should like to convey a special greeting to the peoples of the United Nations . . ."

That same day the station at Fort Monmouth heard, loud and clear, the voice of the Secretary of the Army: ". . . With these words the United States Army Signal Corps begins a series of communications tests using satellite Courier as a relay station."

By its simultaneous transmission and reception of different messages at the rate of 68,000 words a minute—while rolling through space at the rate of 16,000 miles an hour—Courier made a tremendous impression upon the American people; and even the Fort Monmouth engineers had to readjust their imaginations every time they stopped to think about it. By one scientist the launching was hailed as "a dramatic instance . . . of this country's ability to turn new concepts to practical use."

It was revealed, not only that Courier itself was the precursor of a future permanently established satellite communications system, but that the Courier nerve center, responsive only to command and message impulses of the authorized user, would be difficult to capture and probably just as difficult to jam.

Engineers were impressed by the ground-station equipment. Each of the two stations, it was revealed, "listens to Courier broadcasts on the equivalent of four separate receiving systems . . . Signals are detected, filtered, combined, and amplified into one termination that benefits from the best characteristics of each."

But the public was impressed by that vastly more dramatic picture of the total content of the Bible transmitted and received in the few minutes elapsing from the moment when Courier vaulted the horizon, breaking into radio range of one of the ground stations, to the moment when it bent back over the opposite horizon on its way to the other ground station.

In this long view back, we have touched only upon the highlights of a fifteen-year period of Signal research and development, and we have omitted altogether those many achievements that are classified. Scientifically fascinating and militarily impressive, they must be kept, possibly for a long time yet, under wraps of closest secrecy.

PART TWO

The Signal Corps Today

*The growing importance of communications-electronics to the command
and control of our modern Army has recently dictated major changes in
the communications-electronics organizational structure by which Army
forces are supported worldwide.*

*Effective March 1, 1964, the staff responsibilities of the Chief Signal
Officer were broadened and strengthened while most of his command
functions were transferred elsewhere, and his position was redesignated
as Chief of Communications-Electronics.*

*The decision to separate staff and command functions was based
upon a special study of Signal activities during the summer of 1963 by
a General Officer Board of Review. The Board had recommended to the
Secretary of the Army that the Chief Signal Officer be relieved of his
responsibilities as a commander to enable him to concentrate, across-
the-board, on tactical as well as strategic communications-electronics
staff activities.*

*The Chief of Communications-Electronics provides a focal point at
the departmental level for staff advice and coordination of all communications matters, both tactical and strategic as well as communications security considerations. He is under the General Staff supervision
of the Deputy Chief of Staff for Military Operations.*

*He has primary Army-wide staff responsibility for radio-frequency
and call-sign management and utilization; Army representation on the
U.S. Military Communications-Electronics Board, and other joint, combined, national and international boards, committees and groups concerned with C-E matters; joint actions pertaining to C-E and the
preparation or review of the C-E annexes of Army and joint plans. He
provides a focal point for staff advice and coordination for communications, including communications security and staff supervision of the
U.S. Army Strategic Communications Command (STRATCOM). In
addition, he advises the General Staff on technical C-E aspects of missile
systems, audio-visual functions, aviation electronics, electronic warfare,
fire coordination, combat surveillance and target acquisition, meteorology and Automatic Data Processing Systems. He also commands the
Army Photographic Agency located in the Pentagon.*

*Described below is the Army's new C-E organization, as viewed by
the first Chief of Communications-Electronics.*

The Army's New Communications–
Electronics Organization

✠ MAJ. GEN. DAVID PARKER GIBBS

When the Army was reorganized in 1962, the missions of the
Chiefs of Technical Services were largely reassigned. The research
and development, procurement, supply, and maintenance functions

of the former technical services were reassigned to the Army Materiel Command. Training functions became the responsibility of the Commanding General, U.S. Continental Army Command. Development of Army combat doctrine went to the Combat Developments Command, and the personnel assignment and career management missions were made the responsibility of the Office of Personnel Operations. These changes thus eliminated three of the Chiefs of Technical Services: Ordnance, Quartermaster, and Chemical—and many functions of the remaining four: Engineers, Surgeon General, Transportation and Signal Corps.

In the case of the Chief Signal Officer there remained certain operating functions in communications which necessitated his retention, as both a staff officer and commander, within the Department of the Army. Because of the across-the-board elimination of some Services and many Technical Services functions, the mission of the Chief Signal Officer was not fully developed in the reorganization study of 1962 and his functions were not too well understood at any level. This lack of clarity led to many misunderstandings, both within and without the Army. Some regarded the Chief Signal Officer as head of the Signal Corps branch, with all the responsibilities that such a title would imply. At the other extreme there were those who regarded him as simply the operator of the Army Strategic Communications System. The first reason for the change, then, was to clarify the responsibilities of the Chief Signal Officer.

During the period of the Department of the Army reorganization, the Defense Communications Agency was expanding its activities and becoming a paramount factor in the worldwide nontactical communications operations. The Agency had assumed operational control of most of the Army long-haul facilities, including certain intra-theater facilities overseas which have traditionally remained a part of the Theater Army Commander's domain. This Command arrangement of the Army created a somewhat cumbersome channel of control for the Commander of the Defense Communications Agency in those cases where he had to work with both the Department of the Army Staff and the Theater Army Commanders in the operational direction of their long-haul systems. Concurrently, national requirements for communications were increasing and it became the responsibility of the Army, as one of the agencies responsive to the Defense Communications Agency, to install and operate communications within certain overseas theaters on short notice. Timely execution of these missions has required increased centralized control from Department of the Army level in both the installation and operational phases. The second major reason for the communications-electronics changes, then, was to realign Army long-haul communications to improve responsiveness to both the Defense Communications Agency and national requirements.

Recognizing these problems, the Chief of Staff, Army, in the summer of 1963 directed that a study be prepared looking into Signal activities, including missions and organizations. Out of this study came numerous changes.

Let me review these changes briefly. First, the staff functions of the Chief Signal Officer were broadened and, at the same time clarified for both the military and the public. Because all of these functions were not generally associated with the 1962 version of the Office of the Chief Signal Officer the board considered that a change in name was needed to denote this broader mission. Consequently the title was changed to the Office of the Chief of Communications-Electronics. The Office of the Chief of Communications-Electronics has thus become the focal point within the Department of the Army Staff for the coordination of all communications matters, both tactical and strategic, as well as communications security considerations which, of course, are really indivisible from communications itself. This Office also is required to provide technical advice across-the-board on electronic matters which are associated with other activities such as Air Defense, Combat Surveillance, Target Acquisition, Electronic Warfare, Avionics, Special Warfare, Automatic Data Processing, and Audio-Visual Communications which includes photography. The new charter continues the Office of the Chief of Communications-Electronics as the responsible Department of the Army Staff element for specific functions of Communications-Electronics planning and Frequency Management.

The second major change resulting from the special study of Signal activities was the separation of staff and command functions of the Office of the Chief Signal Officer. This separation was accomplished by the establishment of the Army Strategic Communications Command as a separate major command under the Chief of Staff of the U.S. Army. This command assumed the responsibility for the Army strategic communications function and in addition picked up missions formerly performed by separate elements commanded by the Chief Signal Officer. The most important of these was the operation of joint military and civil communications facilities, known to some of you as the Joint Communications Agency and the Army Inter-Agency Communications Agency; the Army Communications Security Agency—not to be confused with ASA

203

—and the Radio Propagation Agency. The new command is being expanded to include certain long lines facilities heretofore a part of the overseas Army commanders' domain which are under the operational direction of the Defense Communications Agency. The command, within the first year, will have approximately eleven thousand personnel with an annual operating budget of about 100 million dollars. Finally, to complete the job of separating the command from the staff functions of the Chief Signal Officer, the Army Pictorial Center in Long Island was transferred to the Army Materiel Command. However, the Army Photographic Agency, which provides services at the Pentagon, remained under the control of the Chief of Communications-Electronics.

Up to this point I have related to you what happened and why. Now let's look into the policies and objectives that were necessary to carry out these missions. It is important at the outset to emphasize that the Chief of Communications-Electronics was not intended to duplicate the jobs performed by the Army General Staff. That is, to summarize them briefly, the Chief of Research and Development had complete staff responsibility for the research and development of materiel; Deputy Chief of Staff for Logistics for procurement, and other logistic matters; Deputy Chief of Staff for Personnel for the staff planning and supervision of the personnel program, including communications-electronics personnel; Assistant Chief of Staff for Force Development for establishment of doctrine, concept, and organization changes as well as for training; and, finally, Deputy Chief of Staff for Operations for overall planning and operational matters.

By retaining a staff of specialists the Chief of Communications-Electronics is able to assist all of the General Staff in the detailed communications-electronics aspects of their work. A major effort is the job of the Office of the Chief of Communications-Electronics, as the focal point on the staff, to achieve coherence in the total communications-electronics program. This program concerns itself with all hardware aspects, from the Qualitative Materiel Requirement, or QMR, through research and development, production and issue to troops. The program is equally concerned with personnel, the training and utilization of communications-electronics specialists, and with communications doctrine, organizational concepts and operational considerations. It is the task of the Office of the Chief of Communications-Electronics, in coordination with the General Staff, to assure that new tactical communications doctrine and concepts are compatible with equipment under development and that, as new equipment is produced, the training of operating and maintenance personnel proceeds at a pace so that trained personnel and materiel reach units concurrently for field employment. Another area for which the Chief of Communications-Electronics has primary staff responsibility concerns the growing problem of electromagnetic compatibility. This coordination must insure consideration of compatibility at all stages—the research and development of new equipment, the organizational and operational concept for the new equipment and its actual employment. Another effort requiring special coordination concerns communications security and the development of security equipment and procedures in step with the new communications systems.

In all these matters I am emphasizing the improvement of tactical communications-electronics. By this I do not intend to place tactical communications on a level of importance above strategic communications. However, the demands on tactical communications have grown exceptionally fast. The job of planning, training, and operating in the tactical communications arena far exceeds that of strategic communications in complexity and challenge. Tactical command and control in particular is a critical element in the field capability of the Army, and, if not a weak link, it has been one of the limiting factors in many field tests of new organizations and concepts. To achieve this emphasis, the newly organized Office of the Chief of Communications-Electronics has established a Directorate for Tactical Communications.

As to strategic communications, the Office of the Chief of Communications-Electronics is responsible for the overall planning, policy, and programming for the Army. The Chief of Communications-Electronics has staff supervision of the Strategic Communications Command and provides that command overall policy and program guidance and monitors its activities. The policy of the Chief of Communications-Electronics is to provide maximum responsiveness to the Defense Communications Agency as well as the overseas theater commanders. Special effort has been continued to give the Army a capability for rapid buildup of long-haul communications terminals in remote areas for response to cold war emergencies.

In both tactical and strategic communications-electronics matters the Chief of Communications-Electronics is the spokesman and representative for the Department of the Army Staff on boards and committees at higher and adjacent levels within the military and with our allies. Of continuing importance is his responsibility to maintain a close relationship with the communcations-electronics sector of our industry.

Now, as I mentioned earlier, the commander of the Strategic Communications Command reports directly to the Secretary of the Army and Chief of Staff as do other major Army commanders. He is under staff supervision of the Chief of Communications-Electronics for his major mission area, but works directly with other Army staff elements on all other matters. In executing his communications mission he is given the broadest latitude. He is responsible for systems engineering, engineering review, and supervision of fixed plant communications installations and preparation of the Army long-lines communications program for submission to the Army Staff. As a customer, the Strategic Communications Command works directly with the Army Materiel Command for production and procurement of strategic communications materiel. He also prepares Qualitative Materiel Development Objectives and Qualitative Materiel Requirements and works directly with the Army Combat Development Command for their publication. He develops concept and doctrine for strategic communications. He has an electronic data processing element for engineering both switching systems as well as electronic data processing systems for command and control purposes. By assuming the communications security and radio propagation forecasting missions the Strategic Communications Command is given the resources for an enhanced capability to meet communications requirements as they arise. In carrying out his cryptologistics mission the commander is charged with the responsibility for assuring compatability between communications per se and related communications security capabilities. In his broader mission he is responsible for maintaining a communications security program and a radio propagation prediction program which are properly balanced to serve the needs of both tactical and strategic communications. On operational matters the Strategic Communications Command works directly with the Defense Communications Agency on all aspects of the operation of the Defense Communications Agency systems, the National Military Command and Control System, and the National Communications System.

One of the most important aspects of the new organization is the incorporation into the Army Strategic Communications Command of a portion of the overseas Army commander's long-lines network. The need for this was brought about by the expansion of the control of the Defense Communications Agency over many of the systems

206

which, in the Army, have been the property of the theater commander. To respond in a more timely and efficient manner to Defense Communications Agency directives, then, the Army has decided to extend the depth of operation of the Strategic Communications Command to match the Defense Communications System. As a result the Defense Communications Agency will eventually have only a single element in the Army with which it must work on operational problems. However, it will then devolve upon the commander of the Strategic Communications Command to be equally responsive to the needs of the theater commander in the operation of the system. As a matter of fact, the theater should gain by the changes being made. The considerable engineering and operational capabilities of the Strategic Communications Command, can be quickly brought to bear on theater problems as they arise. Under the previous system, these capabilities were not directly available to the theater's use. The effectiveness of the new arrangement largely rests upon the ability of the commander of the Strategic Communications Command to see himself as serving several masters: the Defense Communications Agency, the Department of the Army, and the overseas theater commanders.

I firmly believe these changes in the management of Communications and Electronics in the Army to be a step in the proper direction. It has clarified many of those gray areas surrounding our previous organization involving the responsibilities of the Chief Signal Officer, and the alignment of the Army long-haul communications functions.

Let me reiterate that this change has in no way eliminated the close relationship between my office and the communications-electronics industry. We place a high value on the friendship and assistance which industry gives to the Army and we look forward to continued industry support.

An event in Vietnam demands that the Pentagon be alerted—

An emergency redistribution of supplies to overseas areas becomes necessary—

A United States embassy needs to send an urgent message—

A Red Cross official in Korea must get in touch with a soldier's family back home—

These are but a few examples of the many messages that are flashed daily from the far corners of the world. It's a small world, and getting smaller, but to effectively communicate to all parts of it is still a big job.

Stratcom—The Army's Global Communications

✠ COL. WALLACE M. LAUTERBACH

It has been said that a society or a nation can develop and progress only as fast as it can perfect its means of communication. This axiom is certainly true in the development of the United States Army, of its progress in efficient worldwide organization and action, of its mobility, firepower, and command control. The Army is truly a worldwide force, and strategic communications must satisfy what Gen. Omar Bradley implied by his famous remark about tactical communications in Europe: ". . . at no time was any command farther away than the instrument on my field desk."

The Army's strategic communications must provide timely and authoritative direction of its major field commands. The communications for these forces come generally from portions of the Defense Communications System, of which Army strategic communicators operate assigned elements, or they may be provided as special communications to Army forces operating under executive responsibilities assigned by the Joint Chiefs of Staff.

The Army has always recognized the need for long-distance communications between its major force commands, as evidenced over a hundred years ago by the use of "flying telegraph" in the Civil War. But in recent years, radically altered concepts concerning both the control of these communications and the nature of the equipment and means by which they are provided have emerged.

The Army has centralized command of its global communications in a major new command—the United States Army Strategic Communications Command (STRATCOM). STRATCOM is the youngest major field command among those directly under the Chief of Staff.

208

The command's formation was a companion move to the reorganization of the Army's Office of the Chief Signal Officer as the new Office of the Chief of Communications-Electronics.

At the outset of the 1960's, Army strategic communications were integrated into the ever-growing facilities of all the military services. The total network was designated the Defense Communications System (DCS). The Secretary of Defense established the Defense Communications Agency (DCA) to integrate, coordinate, and centrally control these combined long-distance communications of the Army, Navy, and Air Force. Strategic Army Communications (STARCOM) identified the Army component, or the Army-operated elements of DCS.

Message traffic over strategic systems does not diminish when the shooting stops. The present communications load over STARCOM exceeds the World War II averages. As long as military forces are maintained anywhere, large communications loads must be moved, dealing not only with current operations but with support and administrative actions that go into sustaining Army forces in the field.

During the Cuban crisis, a round-the-clock communications operations center was set up. Within a few weeks, more than two hundred new strategic circuits of all types were put in by the Army and commercial carriers for the combat and support forces being staged.

A highlight of this operation was the rapid deployment and positioning of a hundred-mile tropospheric-scatter radio system for extension to tactical forces if needed, providing twenty-four voice channels and up to sixteen teletypewriter channels. A complete long-range transportable radio team and its equipment were also readied by the CONUS regional command of STRATCOM for on-call air-loading with the advance headquarters of the combat forces. The strategic high-frequency radio of this team was one of a single sideband series of radios designed and developed by the Army to provide a selective communications response over varying distances and conditions in objective areas. This equipment series generally provides four voice channels, one of which can be used to derive from four to sixteen teletypewriter channels for classified and unclassified message traffic. It can be airlifted in C-124 or C-130 aircraft and made operational within hours.

To insure an even more immediate interim radio entry for the force commander from the objective area to DCS, a team was also prepared with small, "suitcase" single sideband radios. The team

209

was to carry its equipment in with the first combat elements and establish initial command control.

Almost concurrently STRATCOM was executing a similar type mission for a different purpose. In an accelerated program, the first of several new strategic Army communications stations was being installed in La Paz, Bolivia. Since it would require some forty-five days to construct the permanent fixed station, quickly establishing an interim communications capability there, a transportable long-range radio was airlifted from Fort Bragg to La Paz. The team and its equipment established communications contact with the Army station in the Canal Zone and DCS entry within fourteen hours after being air landed in La Paz. Valuable experience was gained in rapidly flying this type of equipment and personnel over considerable distance and in air-landing the station and setting it up in a mountainous, high-altitude environment.

These operations illustrate something of the wide range of missions and responsibilities the new worldwide STRATCOM will perform on a greatly expanded scale. Another unique example is the strategic communications support for Army troops employed in civil disturbance operations such as those which occurred in Mississippi and Alabama. In domestic emergencies of this nature, where the Army is designated to act as executive agent for JCS, STRATCOM provides a combination of automatically switched, priority voice circuits, short- and intermediate-range radios in the operational area, long-range transportable radio backup, and classified and public information links from the operational area to the Department of the Army. These diverse communications give the commander on the scene direct hot-line voice and teletypewriter connection to the DA Operations Center and also lateral and coordinating communications with other government agencies.

Since maximum use is made of commercial circuits in these CONUS situations, the civilian common carriers are called on to provide circuits and facilities on a quick reaction basis. It should be said that the Bell System and Western Union, among others, have always responded cooperatively and with timeliness. An illustration of the close coordination developed between the Army and these companies is the development of the portable voice terminal package which can be quickly moved to an operational area by air or vehicle and connected into the switched automatic voice network (SCAN). This terminal provides touch-tone telephone handsets whose push buttons generate different tones for each numerical digit, completing the number much faster and simpler than the finger-turned dial on conventional telephones.

The SCAN system with which these terminal sets are used is another strategic development in which Army communicators now assigned to the new STRATCOM made important contributions. The Army needed a fast and more private communications net that would give its users greater efficiency and flexibility than the old toll-call and tie-line method. The Army Signal Corps worked out with the Bell Telephone Laboratories and the Long Lines Department of American Telephone and Telegraph the system that was first called SCAN, abbreviated from switched circuit automatic network. Switching locations were built in quiet locations remote from industrial areas that might become targets in wartime. Each switching center was connected by long distance trunk lines that permitted alternate routing and considerable redundancy. Users, who are connected by leased circuits to the switch nearest them, can automatically reach any other subscriber in the network by the touch-tone dialing mentioned previously. Similarly, they can use this method to establish a data communications circuit.

When activated at the beginning of this decade, SCAN included these data circuits as well as voice channels, and within the following week, Navy data users were taken into the system. The Air Force's first subscribers joined the network in June of 1962 when data terminals were opened at Andrews and McClellan Air Force bases. Data communications increased rapidly in the network to meet the expanding Army requirements and those of other service or governmental users. This means of communications is used especially for the rapid handling of logistic and personnel information, although it is being broadened to many other military fields. As a measure of its growth, Army data communications cards transmitted rose from a combined total of about 20 million cards in 1957 to 124 million in 1963.

SCAN voice transmission increased even more rapidly in the short period following its introduction by the Army. In mid-1962 the trunks in the network between the switching centers numbered 115 and the subscribers' circuits 650. Today there are some 300 trunks and 1,650 subscriber tributary circuits in the system, which is no longer known as SCAN but as the first-generation Automatic Voice Network (AUTOVON). As a result of this designation by DCA, the network is evolving into two networks, in order to separate voice and data users. The data portion is gradually being transferred to the DCS system known as Automatic Digital Network (AUTODIN), which is intended in the future years to accommodate all digital-type communications.

The voice portion of the former SCAN will remain as the nucleus of the growing AUTOVON. It will shortly incorporate advanced in-and-out dialing for those installations not having the touch-tone sets, automatic preemption and conferencing, call registration, and other advanced voice communications.

In 1963 the Army extended AUTOVON circuits to Alaska and Hawaii. The first voice or AUTOVON communication circuit to Europe made contact with Commander in Chief, Europe, last January. By mid-February circuits were extended to Corozal, Panama, giving Army headquarters in Washington instant telephone connections to the Caribbean. This is the inauguration of AUTOVON extension to all U.S. military commanders around the world, linking them by dependable, secure voice communication with their headquarters and the Department of Defense in Washington, or elsewhere in the system. The Army can be proud of its pioneering with industry in the development of this strategic automatically-switched network, initially for its own service members, later extended to all the military services, and now part of the DCS as AUTOVON. STRATCOM is also directly involved in the Army responsibilities for AUTODIN, on which members of its staff are working with DCA and the other military departments.

The constant enlargement and improvement of Army strategic communications and its tasks in the DCS are continuing priority objectives of STRATCOM. One current project is the further automation of the large automatic teletype relay stations at Fort Detrick, Fort Leavenworth, and Camp Davis, California, which form the backbone of the CONUS system of the Army's portion of the DCS here. At these relay stations, teletypewriter messages are automatically scanned on arrival, ultimate addressee noted, and the message automatically transmitted over an outgoing line to that addressee —all within a few seconds and without human intervention. The computer complex being installed at the East Coast Relay at Fort Detrick as a prototype will automate many peripheral in-station functions now performed manually.

For continued improvement in transportable, long-range equipment, STRATCOM has developed a new radio, the TSC-38, which has many advantages not found in the earlier equipments. It has greater power in a comparable shelter, providing a ten-kilowatt and a one-KW transmitter, and a reduction in the size of components through modular and miniaturized design. Engineering and field tests, the latter in which CONARC participated, have been extremely successful. This new transportable radio will provide three voice and sixteen teletypewriter channels through the second and smaller transmitter, both of which can be operated simultaneously.

In longer range perspective, STRATCOM is amassing considerable experience and individual skills in the operation of the first military satellite communications ground stations in New Jersey and California. Currently, the command operates these stations in support of the Army Satellite Communications Agency during the research and development phase of the Defense Satellite Communications Program. When the complex of these stations becomes operationally part of the DCS, STRATCOM will operate the fixed and transportable satellite stations assigned to the Army in the same relationship as it now does the conventional stations. The two existing stations have already conducted numerous operational tests during the pre-planned periods when the SYNCOM satellite was released to Army communicators for such evaluative tests. Multichannel teletypewriter, data, facsimile, and voice are some of the communication modes which have been successfully transmitted and received via the satellite and these ground stations.

STRATCOM looks eagerly and appreciatively to its historic beginning as the first central voice for strategic communications operations in the Army. Its work force includes some twelve thoussand military and civilian communicators around the world. Incorporated in its parent headquarters in the Washington area will be operational, engineering, planning, computer and equipment applications, logistical, communications security, comptroller and personnel and training staff elements, with Joint Communications, Inter-Agency Communications, Radio Propagation, Installation and Construction, and Flight Information and Navaids special field activities of the command.

Principal communications facilities and systems of the new command will include some eight hundred and fifty teletypewriter and data transceiver stations employing military radio and leased wire and cable, the automatic communications relays previously mentioned, extensive microwave and scatter radio systems, and ground satellite communications stations.

As its primary quick reaction resource for emergency strategic communications entry or extension supporting Army commanders, Chief of Staff- or JCS-assigned missions, STRATCOM has the recently formed Eleventh Signal Group. This specially tailored and mobile organization is scheduled eventually to have three large strategic communications companies, equipped with a variety of the latest long distance, intra-country and intermediate-range communications gear. The long-range high-frequency transportables, tropospheric-scatter terminals, and vehicular-mounted special radios for inter-site control of the Eleventh Group are ready on a moment's notice to move rapidly by airlift or other means to discharge Army communications responsibilities in global contingency operations supporting task forces or commanders anywhere in the world.

This relatively new unit is in the early phases of extensive training and selective cross-training to make its troops capable of meeting the many situations that may arise. Its communications teams have already made local practice air sorties, loading and unloading their equipment to develop the highest skills in rapid air movement. For practical communications training, teams of the Eleventh have also been in the field with STRICOM on Exercise Desert Strike and with the Eighteenth Airborne Corps on Quickkick IV and V, in which they installed and operated hundred-mile tropo radio systems to improve their field and technical proficiency. In one exercise the teams and their equipment were airlifted from Fort Lewis, Washington, to Fort Bragg, where they unloaded and moved one system terminal overland to Camp Lejeune. Every effort is being made to expedite the remaining new equipment for the Eleventh Group.

With all of these total worldwide assets, the Army Strategic Communications Command undertakes the global communications tasks dealing with the operation of current systems and the engineering, testing, installation, operation, and maintenance of new equipment and systems for Army components and for assigned DCS responsibilities.

Atomic weapons have forced the Signal Corps to abandon the Single Axis Communications System formerly used on the battlefield. The old system was simply too vulnerable to atomic attack, as destruction of any signal center on the axis would cut communications both fore and aft. The new "Area Communications System" checkerboards the combat area with many signal centers tied together in such a manner that alternate routing is possible despite the destruction of one or more signal centers. This is how it is done.

Getting the Message Through

✠ COL. G. D. GRAY

If you were there, perhaps you will remember those ragtag wires hanging on shot-up poles along the Main Supply Route from Pusan through Seoul to Uijongbu.

Considering the rough ride and the miserable weather, you may not have paid much attention to them or given them any particular thought. However, those lines were the backbone of the Single Axis Communications System that gave you whatever chance you had at living and performing your combat mission.

Those wires were further backed up by radio relay in the hills and by the old Mukden cable under the road, but they all followed the same single axis over which went the High Command's orders, requests for replacements, ammo, rations—you name it.

Knock out one link in that system, and things slowed to a trickle until signalmen got it operating again. Communications didn't stop, of course; there was alternate routing, because in Signal operations, as in the rest of the Army, you make contact with the man or outfit on your flank, one way or another. Usually, however, there was a limited means of getting the message through.

With the coming of nuclear and unconventional warfare, it was soon recognized that events in future combat operations would move too swiftly to tolerate a "trickle of information" capability. Increased fire power and mobility would mean very little in future operations without more effective command control.

To gain and maintain such control, a more rapid, accurate, secure and reliable means was needed—a system that would sustain single breakdowns and still provide rapid communications to all

215

units, even though they would be much more widely dispersed. This system must also be capable of summoning replacements, ammo, and rations in a hurry while the moving and shooting is going on. In short, a new system, with a new look, was mandatory. It was not long in coming.

By the mid-1950's, the Chief Signal Officer was well aware of the Korean experiences, and the weaknesses in the capabilities of the single axis system. He knew that, as a minimum, the communications system required to support our modern field army in this new era of warfare would have to: (1) be 100 per cent self-contained and mobile for quick reaction; (2) be operable and dependable even if one or more major communication centers are completely wiped out; (3) provide sufficient channels to satisfy user requirements, and furnish alternate routings as necessary; (4) provide coverage of the complete area of responsibility, including services to widely dispersed units. To meet these requirements, the Army Area Communications System was developed by the Signal Corps.

Today such a system for a field army is composed of an area communications system for each division, a system for each subordinate corps, an army area communications system, and facilities for other assigned or attached units. Throughout the overall system, radio-relay and multichannel cable-communications support is considered the workhorse of a field army. In addition, messenger, wire, and numerous low-, medium-, and high-power voice and radioteletype radio links are provided for special purpose communications, contact during fluid situations, and to backup the radio relay/cable networks.

Alternate routes are available from division to corps and to army, and vice versa. Each signal center is capable of providing communications channels to all units situated in the vicinity. As a result, no unit is ever far from access to the overall area system. When time permits, the radio relay circuits are replaced by cable to conserve radio frequencies.

So, what is so different? For one thing, we now have a reliable multiaxis, multichannel network with adequate routing facilities for effective command control while our forces are moving and shooting, and to get the replacements, ammo, rations, and other supplies up front at the same time. If the bombs fall, the word can still get through.

And what about cost? You guessed it—requirements for mobile multiaxis communications support has resulted in increased costs of several million dollars for equipment and personnel. But for reasons previously discussed, the importance of this support is of such a magnitude that the costs must, of necessity, be borne. Similarly, we must pay the increased costs for other military equipment in order to obtain the greater mobility and increased firepower required.

Already approximately twelve hundred of twenty-two different types of mobile self-contained electronic communications equipment configurations have been introduced in the Field Army Area Communications System. Several hundred more will soon be introduced to complete the system's requirements. These assemblages contain numerous functional combinations of the best radio, switchboard, teletype, telephone, multichannel telephone/teletype carrier, and security equipments available.

Approximately five thousand more highly trained Signal specialists are required to install, operate, and maintain the new equipment than were required within the Field Army for support of the old single axis system. Service school training programs must be constantly revised to provide the necessary skills required by responsible Signal units. Even then, in some instances, the nature of the assemblages requires additional special training by units in the field.

What are these "responsible Signal units," and what are their capabilities for supporting the Army Area Communications System? The answer depends upon the requirements of each component system. In place of the Division Signal Company previously provided to support the division single axis system, the Infantry Division now has an organic Signal Battalion capable of installing, operating, maintaining, and controlling the new division area communications system.

The Infantry Division Signal Officer (DSO), assisted by his staff, plans and directs installation and operation of the component system. The battalion S3, under the direction of the DSO, establishes and operates a division systems control and Signal information center which supervises circuit routing, circuit assignment, emergency rerouting, and designation of control terminals for the system. Similar support is provided the Armored and Airborne Division.

A Corps Signal Battalion, consisting of a headquarters and headquarters company, a command operations company, and a field operations company, is provided to install, operate and maintain the Corps communications system. Under direction of the Corps Signal Officer, it provides internal communications for all echelons of the Corps headquarters, trunk circuits from Corps headquarters to major subordinate units, and Corps messenger service.

The Field Army Area Communications System, under direction of the Army Signal Officer, is installed, operated and maintained by the Combat Area Signal Group (with its Combat Area Signal Battalions and a Signal Cable Construction Battalion), an Army Signal Battalion, a Signal Communications Center Operations Company, and such other units as required.

Combat Area Signal Battalions install, operate, and maintain the Army Area Signal Centers and the interconnecting trunk circuits all the way down to division level. The Signal Cable Construction Battalion installs field cable trunk circuits and field cable extensions as required.

The Army Signal Battalion provides the command Signal centers which serve the Field Army headquarters. It also provides personnel and equipment to install and maintain Field Army Operations Centers. The Signal Communications Centers Operations Company is equipped to provide internal communications for operational headquarters within the Field Army, as required.

In this manner, the Signal Corps has developed, fabricated, and implemented the new Field Army Area Communications System. But there is no intention of resting on laurels. Studies and development activities go on constantly to improve today's methods and techniques for providing Signal support to the Field Army.

No communications system is perfect; it is realized that messages can never be delivered rapidly enough, accurately enough, or with complete security. But accomplishment of the soldier's combat mission demands the very best communications possible. The Signal Corps is determined that you will have nothing short of the best in "Getting the Message Through."

A specialized form of tactical communications—the type which is required in such guerrilla fighting as is waged in Vietnam currently—is briefly described in this short but interesting narrative.

Signal Support of "Special" Warfare

✠ COL. HARVEY J. PENCE

Two American soldiers, in the vanguard of a South Vietnamese patrol, walk carefully down a narrow path toward a rectangular cluster of native huts. It is hot and sticky, and the jungle casts a gray-green pall over the trail. Their fatigues are sweat-soaked and the ground is slick with a thin film of mud.

The men comprise a two-man Signal team accompanying a South Vietnamese patrol. Their mission—to install a radio station to be used to link the village to the South Vietnam defense network. Without a radio link to the defense forces the village is, in effect, a sitting duck—without support or the ability to call for help against the elusive Vietcong.

Arriving at the village, the patrol advances past the defense moat, a deep ditch, half-full of water, with long sharpened wooden sticks pointing up and out. They are greeted effusively with wide grins by the village chief. He knows their mission and has been anxiously awaiting their arrival.

Moving swiftly, Private Smith and Specialist 4 Jones unpack their equipment. In short order, an antenna is erected and guyed, a radio transceiver placed inside the chief's hut with the battery nearby. A windmill-operated battery charger is erected and the chief and his assistants are briefed on operation of the set. In addition, they are given a check list of instructions—charge the battery, oil the windmill fan, dry off the surfaces and connections daily, and "yell for help" if it stops working.

A test is conducted to link up with the provincial governor's station and the nearest South Vietnamese battalion command post. The chief is now "in communication"—a phrase known to combat commanders since the beginning of time.

This episode is not solely an Army Signal Corps achievement, nor can any one element of the U.S. government claim credit. The State

219

Department's Agency for International Development (AID), formerly known as the United States Overseas Mission (USOM), bought the radio sets from an electronics firm in the Midwest, based on technical advice of an overseas representative of the Department of Defense Advanced Research Projects Agency. Some of the sets were flown to Vietnam by the Air Force, some were brought by the Navy, and the overall effort was supervised by Gen. Paul D. Harkins, Commander, U.S. Military Assistance Command, Vietnam.

It is a typically American unified effort, exemplifying the intent of President Kennedy's message to Congress in 1961 which stated, in part, "We need a greater ability to deal with guerrilla forces, insurrection, and subversion. We must be ready now to deal with any size of force, including small externally supported bands of men; and we must help train local forces to be equally effective."

The Army's response to Communist-inspired subversion, insurgency, guerrilla and psychological warfare has taken many forms. It includes phased organization and training of area-oriented, flexible Special Warfare task forces; provision of advisory and materiel support to indigenous forces; increased language training for personnel going to critical areas; improved service school instruction and unit training in counterinsurgency; expanded research and development in the field of Special Warfare; and greater emphasis on Army civic action programs.

Special Warfare operations pose unique communications-electronics problems not normally encountered in general or limited warfare. From the very beginning of an operation, the Special Forces commander is immediately challenged with difficult problems of command and control of his assigned forces.

His first concern is to establish communications from the friendly seat of government to the various areas of the country of operational interest to him. For this purpose, large, complex, permanent equipment employing the latest ionospheric and tropospheric scatter technique can be employed.

Adverse terrain and weather seriously complicate his ability to communicate with subordinate elements, higher echelons and friendly military forces. Yet without this capability, overall control and command is lost, so that "all the commander really commands is his desk."

From a communications point of view, the tough Special Forces soldier operates in the worst possible electromagnetic environments —in hundred-foot-high rain forests, jungle, arctic, or desert regions. Further complicating the overall communications-electronics problems, he arrives in the area of conflict by parachute or helicopter;

he operates in widely dispersed detachments and patrols; and he must be resupplied through devious and uncertain routes.

His concept of communications is based on security, accuracy and dependability as he goes about setting up an efficient, foolproof, indigenous, intelligence-gathering network. His communications equipment must be reliable, highly flexible, and responsive to the constantly changing tactical situation. Dense foliage and rapid moves call for devices that are small, reliable and compact enough to be carried in the pocket. The Special Forces soldier should only have to turn an "on-off" switch to be in instant, reliable, and secure contact with members of his immediate patrol or higher headquarters. Accelerated research and development effort is now under way to develop such a transceiver and radio.

Psychological operations units, by contrast, require specialized, high-power radio broadcast stations, recording-reproducing equipment, and special audio-visual equipment. In this area, the Army is developing an air-transportable radio broadcast station designated the AN/TRQ-20. The complete station will include essential studio and control facilities, three fifty-thousand-watt transmitters (one short-wave and two standard broadcast) all mounted in standard Army type shelters capable of being emplaced by helicopters.

Communication-electronics in support of the local civilian population poses still different requirements. To meet the need for a simple-to-operate radio set for use in an alert-warning and intelligence communications net, the Army now is working with the Department of Defense, the State Department, Navy, and Air Force on installation and maintenance of the village and hamlet radio sets in South Vietnam.

Maximum effort is currently being made to satisfy, in the shortest possible time, the unique Special Warfare requirements for communication-electronics equipments that are lightweight, readily portable and simple to operate. To satisfy a few high priority requirements, some "off-the-shelf" commercial items are being utilized as an interim expedient.

The Army has always possessed an inherent Special Warfare capability. However, the frequency and tempo of worldwide remote area conflicts within the past few years have caused the Army to reevaluate its normal programs in the light of these crises. Top priority attention is directed toward improving the Army's overall communication-electronics posture in support of Special Warfare operations, for it is in this area that the Army can most effectively support the foreign policy of the United States as enunciated by the President.

Ever since the late nineteenth century, when Gen. Adolphus Greely made photography a part of the Signal Corps' mission, pictorial support for the Army has become an increasingly important function. Here is a general description of what is being accomplished today in that field.

Pictorial Support for the Army

✠ COL. ARTHUR A. McCRARY

Pictorial support for the Army—an important Signal Corps responsibility—includes photography, television, and other audio-visual systems and techniques for command and control, carried out by Audio-Visual Communications Directorate, Office of the Chief of Communications-Electronics.

The photographic mission encompasses motion-picture and still photography for training, information, and historical record, production and distribution of motion pictures, film strips, transparencies, and other photographic audio-visual aids, as well as library and depository activities.

Television responsibilities include strategic, tactical and training applications of television and other electronic audio-visual systems, and the conduct of studies to determine feasible uses of this medium.

Motion pictures, a vital means of improving military training and increasing motivation of fighting men, are made at the Army Pictorial Center in Long Island City, New York. The Center produces "The Big Picture" television series, which helps tell the Army story to the troops and the American people. This facility carries out projects for Army research and development, information and education, and for other Department of Defense agencies.

Besides its production activities, the unit ships film material and equipment used in training and informing troops at Army installations all over the world. Films, film strips, transparencies, language tapes, and audio-visual equipment are loaned by film and equipment exchanges to Army units. Preview facilities, projectionist training, and audio-visual advice to training personnel also are provided. Each of the 258 exchanges in the Army system is thus a focal point from which instructors can obtain many forms of audio-visual support.

222

Still photography is the pictorial medium most extensively employed in the field. Relatively simple, rapid, and readily available, it has advantages over motion picture photography and television for field use.

Besides its value as a source of information, historical record, and identification, still photography supports the special needs of intelligence, operations, and logistics officers. Long-range cameras and infrared film have broadened the scope of intelligence photography and have augmented coverage from Army aircraft. The medium is also useful in military police investigations, and in research and development and test and evaluation.

The U.S. Army Photographic Agency in the Pentagon provides permanent storage and accessibility for over half a million Army still photographs—color and black and white—selected as record material from negatives sent from the field. It also operates a pictorial facility for the Departments of the Army and Defense. It is the only Army agency authorized to sell still pictures.

The struggle against Communism is requiring increased pictorial coverage on a global basis. To assist in this mission, the Department of the Army Special Photographic Office controls still and motion-picture teams in the Pacific, Caribbean, and the Middle East. It also maintains standby teams to rush to new trouble spots.

Photographic records by these teams augment the efforts of photographic units regularly assigned to overseas commands. This combined pictorial coverage is steadily building the photographic documentation of Army operations, with emphasis on world trouble spots. Such coverage supports studies of special problems, helping to blueprint the strategy and tactics for future military success.

Television, which entered the Army's pictorial capabilities a little more than a decade ago, is now utilized in varied ways. Closed-circuit television for classroom teaching is operative at nine Army installations; four more are expected to be in use by 1965. Special studies exploring its effectiveness in instruction were made at Fort Dix in 1962. Results indicate that savings in instructor manpower and preparation time will be possible both in current training and in case of mobilization.

Television as a military operational communications medium has long been hindered by problems in transmission bandwidth and security. Recent technical advances bring closer the day when television will be practical as an audio-visual means of communication for military operations.

Important strides have recently been made, and even greater advances are anticipated with the rapid expansion of electromechanical and electronic information display systems. The Signal Corps is studying strategic and tactical implications of these systems, to insure that the Army obtains maximum advantage from them.

In addition, still other important challenges face us. Among them —how to increase the versatility and responsiveness of pictorial systems and organizations to meet the operational needs of commanders at all levels; also, how best to use the pictorial equipment and processes that technology makes available to us.

A breadth of imagination and practical wisdom is constantly being brought to bear to find ever better ways to accomplish the vital pictorial communications mission.

224

Training films proved to be invaluable during World War II in helping train the millions of men summoned to military service within a short space of time. Because they can serve so many people at once, because they can explain certain military subjects better than any other means, and because they are relatively inexpensive per "man-showing," they have become firmly established as a primary training adjunct. Still, improvements can be made. Here are some ideas on the subject.

Training the Modern Soldier

✠ LT. COL. MAX L. MARSHALL, USA (Ret.)

Never before in history have military forces, relentlessly spurred by a galloping technology, been required to undergo such rapid and drastic evolution in tactics, weapons, materiel, and organization for combat. In a race against the time-clock of pressing necessity, a revolution in military doctrine and techniques rumbles on, as "advanced" or "unconventional" weapons and materiel—and above all, *ideas*—first become "operational" and relatively soon thereafter, become generally accepted as "conventional."

All the while, the new weapons systems must continuously be integrated into the Army's new organizations, optimum employment patterns must be worked out, and the troops instructed in their use. Considering this along with the requirement to fill the enormous soldier-skill reservoir needed to support today's military technology, the whole clearly comprises a training problem of staggering proportions.

Equally important, if not so apparent a training requirement, is the necessity of leading the *thinking* of officers and men alike *away* from the old, familiar and previously successful methods used during World War II and the Korean Conflict, *toward* the not yet fully developed modern tactics that the future will demand. France, during the peace interval between the two World Wars, wasted precious training time perfecting the tactics of World War I. The thinking of her officers and men was geared to the past. This resulted in her swift defeat early in World War II by an enemy who had improved the infant weapons of World War I—armor and air power—and formulated new and dynamic tactics for their employment—the *blitzkrieg*.

225

The modern United States Army and the tactics being designed to support it definitely are oriented toward the future. But the ultimate responsibility for the success of the enormous retraining program involved must rest directly on the shoulders of the commander and his staff, at all echelons.

The training methods available for use in this far-reaching effort necessitating the imparting and exchange of so much new, strange, complicated and detailed information are fairly well defined. These range from classroom presentations, through practical work in the field, to field maneuvers; from formal high level staff conferences to spontaneous informal discussions. Highly specialized presentations will be made to small groups of key planners, and large demonstrations will be held before masses of soldiers.

Training aids—mock-ups, transparencies, models, charts, and others—will be produced in quantity to support the various instructional means. Many of these the commander himself will have constructed; for some he will turn to his next higher headquarters. Others, reflecting the complexity of modern warfare, will be beyond the capability of even major units in the field to produce, and must be provided by staff echelons as high as Department of the Army.

Chief among these is the Army training film.

Training films are ideally suited to effectively, uniformly, and quickly instruct large numbers of officers and men concerning the operation and maintenance of the new weapons and equipment continuously being made available through the research and development program. Also, they are excellent for teaching officers and men the constantly evolving tactical doctrine on the integrated employment of the combined arms.

In the how-to-operate-and-maintain category, excellent film production work is being accomplished in connection with a vigorous overall program to insure that the troops who will use the new weapons and materiel are thoroughly trained, and simultaneously, to see to it that the technicians charged with their upkeep are well qualified.

A case in point is the success being attained in the Nike training film program, designed to make available to the field training films concerning new items of equipment which go into both the Ajax and Hercules antiaircraft defense systems *as the equipment is delivered to the troops*. This training supplement tends to reduce inches from the thick and unwieldly technical and training texts which otherwise would have to be prepared and distributed, speeds up the training, and improves its quality.

Throughout, the technical services actively exploit the advantages of the training film in order to provide mass technical instruction to large numbers of soldiers. The success of such programs is attested by the relatively favorable training status of Army technicians considering the large turnover due to losses to industry and the perpetual re-training effort this necessitates.

Research and development is another vital area in which Army pictorial support is making extremely worthwhile contributions. Though much of what is currently being done is classified, these efforts contribute substantially to the constant study and improvement of materiel now on hand, and to the introduction of new and completely different items.

Ultimately however, the efforts of those involved in the Research and Development Program and of the members of the technical services are aimed at supplying the field commander with the best possible weapons systems and supporting materiel, and providing him with trained men who can operate them. The integrated use of trained men, weapons, systems, and materiel involves the formulation of optimum combat organizations and fighting techniques—a key area where training films can make further substantial contributions.

Films can clearly show masses of troops how our powerful Army is organized for combat and the various ways it can be fought. Superior to any other means short of the real thing, the training film can impart the psychological "feel" of the new and strange battlefield over which our soldiers may some day be called upon to fight, thus reducing any fear of the unknown and imparting confidence which comes of knowledge and familiarity.

No phase of advanced tactics is too difficult to depict clearly, forcefully, and, with respect to the training time involved, economically. Nor is any portion of the training problem too complicated to illustrate.

If the action takes place in different geographical areas over different periods of time—a tactical exercise on the attack, for example —the whole can be meaningfully presented in a film of less than an hour's duration by means of the physical movement of only a handful of cameramen and technicians, rather than the laborious and inefficient hurry-up-and-wait process of having groups of observers go from one vantage point to another to see, piecemeal, seemingly unrelated facets of the maneuver.

If the instruction is being conducted by orientation teams touring various headquarters throughout the country and carrying with them highly-specialized training aids to orient commanders and their staffs concerning specific vital subjects, how much more efficient, faster and cheaper to film just one such presentation, then immediately release it to the field? All the designated headquarters simultaneously would receive information while it was still up-to-the-minute—as opposed to the possibility that a year might otherwise elapse between the first and the last presentations.

Because time is such a precious commodity to the military, it is indicated that a stepped-up program should be pushed immediately. It must be recognized that training film production, like many other aspects of modern war preparation, must be accomplished in peacetime—that what is left to be done later, may very well never be done. A prohibitive amount of time is required to produce a large number and variety of films even under the pressure of wartime emergency, and there is the possibility of early bomb damage to production facilities. *Now* is the time to begin pressing a comprehensive training film program designed to completely replace that which is outmoded in the existing training film inventory.

One concept of the attack of tomorrow envisions the initial dispersal of highly mobile fighting units capable of quickly falling upon and defeating an enemy force in conjunction with the exploitation of an atomic shot. Another considers the use of helicopter-borne troops in the vertical envelopment with or without atomic support.

Entirely new techniques will be demanded of the various branches which support the infantry, armor and artillery in future combat operations. Signal communications, for example, must change in kind and expand in degree and flexibility to enable the commander to retain control of his units. Again, films depicting in broad, general terms new techniques being evolved by the Signal Corps to support modern tactics—such as electronic warfare, area communications, combat surveillance—are being prepared. Films designed to train specific signal units in the details of tactical employment might well be speeded along.

Whether or not atomic bombs are used in any future conflict, there is an absolute requirement that a number of officers be highly proficient in planning and executing an atomic shot, and that the rest of the officer corps be sufficiently familiar with the weapon to favor its maximum exploitation. Here again, appropriate training films could hasten and improve current instruction conducted in these areas and ease the work load on the commander, the Service School and the student.

Represented above are but a few of the tactical subjects which should be in the hands of the troops before long. There are others, perhaps in an even higher priority category, which should be done first. The important thing is that full advantage be taken of the Army's most precious peacetime possession—*time*—and that necessary programs be pressed forward as rapidly as possible.

To accomplish this, certain difficulties must be dealt with.

Among these is the fact that evolving tactics by their very nature are fluid, subject to constant change and improvement, and as such, are a perishable product; training films which depict them will have to be brought up to date more frequently than previously.

A related obstacle, also caused by the evolutionary characteristic of modern tactics, is the cautious attitude sometimes taken to hold back on expensive motion picture production until doctrine becomes "firm." But, if one side of the coin of folly is the ill-considered and wasteful production of pictures which too soon will become obsolete, then the other side of the coin is an overly cautious approach which prevents the distribution to the field of sorely needed training films to meet legitimate training requirements.

Procedures involved in initiating, coordinating and clearing such films will have to be streamlined so that the elapsed time before a given film is distributed to the troops is held down as closely as possible to the six months required for actual production.

Another problem is to educate commanders and their staffs at every echelon and in every branch concerning the influence they can and should—indeed *must*—exert with regard to obtaining the kind of training films they need at a rate compatible with their increased training obligations.

In the final analysis, the sole reason for producing training films is to assist *the commander* in his mission of training his command, for which he alone is responsible.

The staffs of the respective top level agencies concerned with training-film production are largely composed of officers who themselves have had experience in troop command and staff positions. They understand the overall training problem and attempt to provide the best film program possible. But it is the commander *in the field today* who best understands the training problems he is faced with *now*, and it is necessary that he actively participate in procuring the kind of films and the number of films he needs to discharge his training responsibilities. When confronted with a situation in which a training requirement can best be met by means of a training film, a letter to the appropriate branch Service School, or to CONARC, is clearly indicated. By so doing, the commander

229

will not only contribute to having films produced that best fit his requirements, but will also promote a program which will improve the active Army's overall training capability and combat-readiness status.

The Reserve components of the Army, likewise, will benefit from the fruits of a vigorous training-film program. The Reserve Unit Commander, often faced with inadequate training facilities, always limited with respect to training time available, in many instances must depend heavily upon the film as the best—sometimes only— means of getting across his instruction effectively. Since support of the Reserve program becomes increasingly important as the Active Army becomes smaller, everything possible must be done to assist these units to achieve an acceptable level of combat readiness; this in itself provides heavy justification for producing up-to-date training films on a large variety of subjects.

A side benefit provided by the existence of an adequate inventory of training films has to do with the Allies who will fight with the United States in the event of future aggression. The term "foreign adaptation" is applied to a process wherein Army training films are renarrated into the language of friendly nations. Because many of these countries will be using U.S. weapons, and in varying degrees, adopting U.S. tactics in any future conflict, foreign adaptations— which completely surmount language barriers—will, as in the Korean Conflict, prove to be invaluable.

But however important such side benefits may be, the immediate requirement to step up the overall film production program is based on the following "Big-Picture" realities:

To prevent war, the United States must have an atomic and guided missile capability sufficient to counter and offset the large troop masses our potential enemies can muster. The Army is committed to a readiness posture which calls for it to be able to fight in a "brushfire" conflict, an atomic war, or any kind of action in between.

The degree of success obtained toward meeting this objective will depend upon the effectiveness of the Army's training program; this in turn is related to a number of factors—among them the effectiveness of the training aids made available to the commander to help him perform his training mission.

Training films are ideally suited to teaching large numbers of officers and men tomorrow's tactics today, generating discussion and thought which will lead to improvements in new doctrine, and to defining the new directions toward which future warfare is moving.

230

The Signal Corps accomplished much of the early pioneering in the use of television as a teaching medium. Its successes in this area have paid big dividends—not only to the Army, but to industry and education as well.

Teaching Through TV

✠ DR. JOSEPH H. KANNER

From all over the nation they came, some two hundred representatives of civilian institutions as well as all the military services, to attend the first Armed Forces Educational Television Conference in Washington, D.C., sponsored by the Office of the Chief Signal Officer.

They witnessed the opening of the Pentagon's first video tape facility, and the first extensive use of video tape for a military briefing. They heard what is being done in the military services, in civilian educational institutions, and by television networks, in the field of television education. They saw exhibits of equipment that has been developed for such endeavor.

Ten years ago such a conference would not have been possible because there weren't that many specialists—either civilian or military—with sufficient interest or experience to have made such a gathering possible. But today television is becoming increasingly important as an educational adjunct, and promises to become even more so as further experience is gained.

Introduction of the video tapes filmed at military installations throughout the country and projected by the Pentagon's new tape facility is one new advance in the field. Use of video tape is planned to speed communications between outposts of the armed forces and the Pentagon, since the tape can be shown immediately after it is taken. It was particularly fitting for the first demonstration to be carried out under auspices of the Army's Chief Signal Officer since the Army pioneered in the use of television in teaching.

Just ten years ago the first U.S. Army mobile television unit was delivered to Fort Monmouth, New Jersey, in one of the first attempts of the U.S. Army Signal Corps to carry out its newly assigned mission of developing television for military training and information uses. Today the Army is the leading user of television for training.

The unit's design and purchase reflected the faith of many key

231

personnel in the potential value of television for the Army. That optimism was reflected by the Army Pictorial Center personnel who were to operate it—but it was not matched by any data pertaining to the effects of television upon learning nor by development of effective production techniques. These had to be planned, tested, measured.

For the first year the mobile unit felt its way, visiting Army training installations, demonstrating the equipment, televising training presentations, learning how to apply television to many different teaching situations. Opinions and reactions of instructor personnel were sought. From all this, it was realized that much more had to be learned.

For two years, experimental facilities were operated at Fort Monmouth and at Fort Gordon to develop use of television for school training. A study was conducted by the Human Resources Research Office, George Washington University, under sponsorship of the Chief of Army Field Forces and the Office of the Chief Signal Officer. Major objective was to compare teaching effectiveness of conventional and television instruction.

The study was conducted at Fort Gordon, Georgia, since a basic training program was already being conducted there, and a closed-circuit television facility was available. Mobile television units from the Army Pictorial Center also participated.

Fourteen representative hours of basic training were selected. Groups of basic trainees were divided—one taking instruction by television, the other by conventional methods. They were then given written or performance tests to determine what they had learned. A month later, some groups were given a review using television recordings of original instruction to determine its effects upon retention.

Overall the study indicated that television instruction was never inferior to the conventional method and was actually superior for some types of learning such as recognition training, comprehending relations among parts, manipulation of equipment, and rote learning. There was evidence that lower-aptitude groups learned better from television than from conventional methods. At the same time, the television operatives were learning and developing many production techniques for effective presentation.

Since this first study was completed in 1953, the Signal Corps has continued with similar work at the Signal Schools, Fort Gordon and Fort Monmouth and other installations, making contributions of significance to military television and civilian educational programs.

232

Some original contributions made by the Signal Corps to the entire educational field include: (1) demonstration of the feasibility of training entirely by television for periods as long as a week; (2) demonstration of the feasibility of rapidly training effective television instructors; and (3) comparative study of the effectiveness of color as compared to black and white television.

As a result of these pioneer studies, the Army by 1956 was able to propound television doctrine through publication of AR 108-40, *Television*. In 1959 the first military television technical manual, TM 11-491, *Training by Television,* was published, describing the techniques of applying television to military training.

During this same period Army installations were receiving assistance from the Signal Corps in acquiring and installing equipment, obtaining personnel, and arriving at an effective television utilization program.

Today, thousands of students Army-wide are receiving instruction by television. Facilities at Fort Gordon and Fort Monmouth have tripled in size and scope since 1952. Several other major installations use television to varying degrees. These include Walter Reed Army Medical Center, the Transportation School, Air Defense School, Ordnance Guided Missile School, Quartermaster School, Army Information School, and the Army Language School. Additionally, several installations are currently studying their requirements or procuring equipment to further TV training.

In addition to live television instruction, the Signal Schools at Fort Monmouth and Fort Gordon transmit films, kinescopes, video and tape recordings. Use of video tape recorders greatly expands the usefulness and flexibility of television as a training medium.

At both schools, television is utilized in one or more of the following ways—in mass training, adjunct training, film transmission, television recordings, and mobile field use.

Mass training. By this method, an outstanding instructor may simultaneously teach a number of classes or large groups. Advent of video tape has eliminated the requirement for simultaneous instruction. In either case, economies are effected in instructor and training aid requirements.

Adjunct training brings into the regular classroom materials which would ordinarily be unavailable. Thus a new piece of equipment may be televised to groups in the classroom.

Film transmission makes available training films, television recordings or kinescopes and video tape recordings. Hundreds of hours of such material are presented over the television system weekly.

233

The instructor simply notifies the television studio of the film subject and the time he desires it to be presented.

Television recordings are used to teach repetitive materials; they are also useful for review purposes.

Mobile television units have been developed to travel into the field to televise direct, or to record for later use, field exercises for transmission to classroom or auditorium. Such coverage eliminates or reduces the need for transporting spectators to an exercise; it insures that the viewing audiences see the most important aspects of the demonstration.

At Walter Reed Army Medical Center, a compatible color television system has been used since 1956 in surgery and other procedures where the closeup advantages of television permit many viewers to see as well as though they were directly at the surgical table.

Panel discussions among medical and research personnel also are televised. Exchanges of information or transmissions of medical and scientific programs frequently take place between Walter Reed and other nearby medical installations. Special transmissions over closed circuit systems are used at medical and dental conventions.

A unique utilization of the facilities at Walter Reed occurred last November when The Adjutant General transmitted a course in effective writing over closed circuit television to military and civilian personnel at Fort Meade, Fort Belvoir, Fort Detrick, the National Naval Medical Center, and Andrews Air Force Base. Primary purpose of the eight hour course was to teach some five hundred government employees who write letters and staff studies to make their writing more effective through brevity, simplicity, strength and sincerity.

The Ordnance Guided Missile School (OGMS), Huntsville, Alabama, has made important contributions to use of television for Army training since acquiring its extensive facility in 1958. At OGMS, both fixed and mobile facilities permit transmission from missile field activities back to the classroom. Six video tape recorders permit recording of valuable information for later use. These can be edited to bring changes in techniques and materials up to date quickly and cheaply.

The school transmits by closed circuit television to the Armor School at Fort Knox, Kentucky, two hundred and fifty miles north. This method enables the Fort Knox students, many of them high ranking officers, to obtain information on missile maintenance without traveling to Redstone Arsenal. It also avoids duplication of costly equipment at the two schools.

234

Radio frequencies are nebulous things. We can't feel them, we can't see them, and we can't operate electronic devices without them. The frequency spectrum is only so big and cannot be stretched; in any given time frame, technological advance can exploit it only to a finite degree. Frequency management is the art of squeezing every last channel out of the crowded airwaves.

Frequency Management

✠ COL. W. M. VAN HARLINGEN

Within the Chief of Communications-Electronics sphere of responsibility, the management of the radio frequency spectrum for the Department of the Army has become one of the most critical areas. Like its sister services, the Army has become a titan in the use of radio frequencies beside which the communication-electronic operations of World War II and Korea seem incredibly simple.

The Director for Frequency Management exercises the Chief's responsibility in radio-frequency management, extending from the birth of new equipment concepts and their development, to production and operational employment of new equipments and systems.

Although no longer having responsibility for research and development, he must closely monitor R&D programs to provide timely guidance on radio-frequency matters having an impact on those programs. The objective is to provide frequency allocations that are technically satisfactory and capable of supporting our operational requirements in both peace and war. These frequency allocations— *i.e.,* authority to proceed with experimental, developmental, and production efforts in specific radio-frequency bands—are issued by the Chief of C-E.

Since the radio-frequency spectrum is a national resource of all nations, political and economic factors influence the degree of availability of frequencies. Of major concern is the availability (or limited availability) of frequencies to support the Army's worldwide tactical and training requirements in peacetime. Many equipments and systems—air defense, for example—must be immediately responsive in a peacetime environment. In such cases, there is no clear distinction between "peacetime" and "wartime" frequencies; in effect, they are synonymous.

The Seventh U.S. Army in Europe presents a prime example of the problems besetting peacetime frequency management. The Seventh Army lives, maneuvers, and stands alert in the arena of cold war. Its communications-electronics are extensive; and operational readiness is a peak requirement. Nevertheless, it must operate in what is essentially a civilian radio-frequency spectrum.

The Chief of C-E has significant support responsibility for the Seventh Army and all other tactical forces. He appraises the total situation affecting the frequency spectrum, and provides guidance to Department of the Army agencies on means of satisfying operational requirements in the field. He seeks to answer such questions as—Where can the existing and programmed equipment inventory best be utilized? What frequency bands must be considered for the development of new equipment? What interim equipment measures can be taken to ease immediate operational problems?

In order to improve responsiveness to frequency-management requirements, the Frequency-Management Directorate is developing a computer-oriented automatic data-processing system that will eventually be utilized at field army level.

The U.S. Army Signal Radio Propagation Agency (USASRPA) provides the Army with scientific data which permits the most efficient use of high frequencies for both strategic and tactical purposes. Short courses are conducted in propagation and frequency-selection techniques applicable in the field at tactical levels. Considerable emphasis is given to support for Special Forces activities. USASRPA also provides propagation prediction support as required by the Navy, Air Force, and various government agencies.

Our armed forces requirement for more and better communications-electronics equipment has loaded the frequency spectrum to the point of overflowing. To handle the problems stemming from this myriad of equipments, the Department of Defense has established the Electromagnetic Compatibility Program (ECP) concerned with predicting and resolving frequency problems in joint operations. Heart of this activity is the Joint Electromagnetic Compatibility Analysis Center (ECAC) at Annapolis, Maryland. The Chief of C-E is the Department of the Army member of the Military Communications Electronics Board which coordinates ECAC joint operating procedures and reviews the ECAC recommendations on problems referred to it.

While the Defense program is intended to centralize control of the combined compatibility effort, each service has the responsibility to do its utmost to assure intra-service compatibility of

236

equipments and systems. Within the Army, extensive efforts are underway. The program is concerned with predicting interference and establishing compatibility on an intra-Army basis. Thus both the Army and Department of Defense programs are geared to provide invaluable data in developing frequency allocations for tomorrow's new equipments.

237

Before any new electronics equipment can be mass produced and issued to the troops, it must undergo a rigorous testing process. Here is the story of how and where this is done.

Quiet Please! Electronics Being Tested

✠ JOHN B. SPORE

The trouble with people is that they tend to mass together in urban areas and then insist on flooding the air with static-producing devices like radio broadcasting stations and receivers, electric toothbrushes, and power generators. These necessities and pleasures of civilized existence are the cause of so much electronic distemper that communications engineers charged with the task of testing electronic equipment become Thoreaus in their desire for solitude. The Walden Pond that the Signal Corps found when it looked around in 1954 for an isolated spot to establish an electronic proving ground was this eighty-year-old Indian-wars post hidden away in the Huachuca Mountains of southern Arizona.

Both people and electromagnetic devices were scarce at Fort Huachuca and environs in 1954. It is mountainous, desert country, lying some fifteen miles north of the Mexican border and seventy miles south of Tucson. But now, ten years later, one wonders.

Arizona is bursting out all over with people, and the U.S. Army Electronics Proving Ground (USAEPG) has worked against itself by bringing more people and their dependence upon electronic gadgets into the area. Not many years ago the old soldier-hamlet of Fry, just outside the gate, was in a state of somnolence. Today the thriving new little city of Sierra Vista has swallowed Fry and boasts a population of 6,000. A smaller community with the ambitious name of Huachuca City has sprouted outside of another gate of the Fort. The combined military-civilian work force at Fort Huachuca numbers about 8,000, and is increasing.

But Arizona is big, with clear, spacious skies from rim to rim. There's still lots of open desert and the Electronics Proving Ground uses big hunks of it. The post itself covers some 73,740 acres; outlying test areas bring the total to some 113,000 acres. But that's only part. Stretching westward across the state from Huachuca to Yuma,

238

there's an instrumented flight corridor approximately two hundred and eighty miles long by forty miles wide. One test facility, about which we'll have more to say later, seems to cover most of the southern third of the state.

What goes on here? What does the Electronic Proving Ground do? Maj. H. H. Todd, the present orientation officer, says its purpose is "to bridge the gap between the scientist in his laboratory and the soldier on the battlefield who must rely on the scientist's product." This is a revealing statement, somewhat simplified, perhaps. I found a fuller one in some of the material given me to read. It said: "The U.S. Army Electronics Proving Ground has as its major responsibility the engineering and service tests of communications-electronics systems and individual items of equipment."

"These tests," the statement continued, "include susceptibility of radio interference at varying power and ranges; the feasibility of a potential enemy to employ electronic countermeasures against the device; and the effect of friendly electronic equipment in a realistic tactical field environment."

The electronic stuff USAEPG tests may be off-the-shelf items that seem to have a military application or equipment built to government specifications by defense industry. USAEPG thinks of itself as the representative of the ultimate user. It doesn't tell the maker what to make or how to make it. In the jargon of economics it is consumer oriented.

We will look at some typical tests later on. But a quick, but not dirty, example of USAEPG's work are the tests it gave the new AN/VRC-12 radio—the one that will eventually replace the AN/GRC-3 through -8 series. It put this radio through all kinds of tests over all types of terrain and varying climatic conditions during a considerable period of time.

"We rattled, shook and abused it. We tried to make it fail," Major Todd said. "But it stood up through all our tests of ruggedness, reliability and performance. We now know that it will do what it was designed to do. As a result the battlefield commander will have a reliable radio with 920 channels and with double the range of the old GRC-3. He will be able to communicate with artillery, infantry, and armor units with one radio instead of three."

The work of USAEPG goes beyond the testing of combat radios. Major Todd mentioned six of what he called "commodity areas" of interest to USAEPG: communications, combat surveillance, meteorology, automatic data processing, avionics, and electronic warfare.

The present commander of USAEPG is Maj. Gen. Benjamin H.

239

Pochyla, a tall, well-set-up, soldierly, articulate Texan. A graduate of Texas A&M, he was first commissioned in the cavalry reserve but transferred to the Signal Corps after going on active duty in 1941. Since becoming a general officer in 1960, he has been the Commanding General of the Army's Signal Training Center at Fort Gordon, Georgia, and served a hitch as Deputy Director, J-6, Communications-Electronics Directorate of the Joint Chiefs of Staff. He arrived at USAEPG in 1963 and after a few months as Deputy Commanding General took over the command.

The nerve center of USAEPG is the Electronics Test Agency, bossed by General Pochyla's deputy commander, Col. Geoffrey D. Ellerson, an artillery type. For scientific advice he and General Pochyla have the services of a chief scientist. The incumbent, Mr. John H. Troll, is a newcomer to USAEPG. There is a healthy sprinkling of other civilian scientists in all departments of USAEPG, and a number of the officers assigned to the command have advanced degrees. Also the Army's program for identifying educated young draftees brings in fresh talent.

Colonel Ellerson's Electronics Test Agency is engaged in some ninety-eight tasks on which either test planning, evaluation of tests, or reporting on tests is required. To perform these tasks the Agency is divided into these three departments:

(1) The Test Programs and Evaluation Department. The people in this department have to ask the right questions. If the test plans they prepare are searching and relevant, the answers obtained during the engineering and service tests will provide usable knowledge. The department monitors and coordinates each test and sees to it that the data used in each evaluation report are scientifically valid. It is on the basis of these reports that recommendations are finally made.

(2) The Test Operations Department performs the tests following the plans made by the Test Program and Evaluation Department. Its job is to produce data, both in the field and laboratory. These go to the evaluators.

(3) The Field Test Facilities Department operates and maintains all range and supporting instrumentation necessary for test operations. Its principal facilities fall into three parts: (a) the surveillance system test facility (this includes a western terminal at Yuma which largely concentrates on the testing of avionics and surveillance drones); (b) the electromagnetic environmental test facility; (c) all common test facilities at Fort Huachuca.

Headquarters of all of this activity is the modern, three-story, all-concrete, and completely air-conditioned and temperature-controlled Greely Hall which contains 407,000 square feet of floor space. Completed in 1959 (a new wing is presently being added), Greely Hall houses technical test facilities and the administrative offices of the command. Local wags, who have worn themselves out pacing its lengthy corridors, call it Arizona's Little Pentagon.

Among the technical test facilities in Greely Hall are the Data Reduction Center and Automatic Data-Processing Center. The technical nature of the testing and the immense amount of data required and obtained can only be assimilated by reducing it to digital form for the IBM 7090 and 1401 computers of the Automatic Data-Processing Center. The test plans of the Test Programs and Evaluation Department and the data produced by the Test Operations Department are all reduced to digital form. The 7090 computer is a recent addition, replacing a smaller model 709.

Going back to the all-important work of the Test Programs and Evaluation Department, it is instructive to consider its general philosophy. A member of the department has put it this way: "Somebody expected the equipment we test to perform a function, solve a problem, or do a task better. Consequently our tests must be designed to tell us if these objectives have been achieved."

But the department attempts to find out more than if the item will meet some minimum materiel requirement. It tests actual performance, looks for changes that may improve the item, and finally makes an evaluation of how the item may best be employed and supported.

One of the members of the department observed that evaluation must include both engineering and operational factors. "We have a number of simple basic questions that we seek answers to," he said. "These are: Is it better? Does it perform? What are its weaknesses?"

This involves what is called operational-validation testing and, as I understand it, some people question whether a proving ground should go beyond purely engineering tests and begin to ask such questions as how much better is this product than the one it will replace, and what are the shortcomings of this product and what can be done to overcome them.

Those who believe a proving ground should go into these questions say that evaluation is a part of the development process and produces valuable data that can be cranked into the cycle. Even when operational tests are negative, the validation tests should continue just for this reason, they will tell you.

Whatever the scope of the testing may be, the tricky part, as one member of the Test Programs Department said, "is to produce a thorough evaluation without overtesting."

241

General Pochyla added a significant thought to the discussion:

The stuff we test is usually costly and almost always the product of some advanced technology. In many instances it is equipment that has never before been tested and until we get it no one has really given much thought to how to test it. Many times the product is so new that there is simply no test equipment as far advanced. So we have to produce it.

This requires a lot of thought and ingenuity by some of the fine brains we have here. It can also be costly in time and money. We are constantly urged to hold down our costs by reducing the test and evaluation phase of the R&D cycle to a minimum. This we make every effort to do, but at the same time we want to keep USAEPG the finest electronic proving ground in the world. The job of being on top of our work without being lavish or wasteful is a constant challenge to our management and to our engineers and scientific personnel.

A good starting point for a look at some of USAEPG's projects is the testing of absolute altimeters—an endeavor that was not costly, but did require considerable ingenuity in devising test equipment. Barometric altimeters have, of course, been used for many years by aircraft navigators and pilots. While these are admirable for their purpose, they do not operate within close tolerances and are unsatisfactory for the Army aviator who must fly close to the ground and wants a device that will tell him within inches of how close he is to mother earth.

A new technique for measuring the distance from aircraft to ground involves a radar sensor and read-out device. Called an absolute altimeter, it has a theoretical accuracy of plus twelve inches at low altitudes. It does this by sending radar signals to the ground which are reflected back to the aircraft where computations are performed to determine the distance these signals have travelled. This information, displayed on an instrument panel in the cockpit, provides the pilot with continuous information.

Five newly developed commercial models of absolute altimeters were delivered to USAEPG for testing and the project was turned over to a young second lieutenant by the name of Clifford R. Holland, a graduate mechanical engineer. One of his tasks was to find out just how accurate these altimeters were at altitudes varying from two to fifty feet. His solution was remarkably prosaic and involved techniques that were known to George Washington. He had a simple platform built on which to mount the altimeters.

This he suspended from a catenary by a cable and pulley system which can fix the platform at selected heights. A surveyor's transit was used to measure the height of the platform and the read-outs on the altimeters were checked against this known height. The devices are also being tested in aircraft flying over different kinds of terrain and over the ocean from a naval base in Southern California. If out of this testing a reliable absolute altimeter can be procured, Army aviators will owe a small debt to young Lieutenant Holland and his associates.

At last count there were some eighty thousand electromagnetic radiating devices in the field army. All are presumably essential items but all are also quite capable of creating radio-frequency interference problems. An intimation of the growing magnitude of the problem can be seen in the fact that at the end of World War II a field army had less than a third as many, some twenty-five thousand. Beyond the fact that electromagnetic interference can play hob with vital communications and essential control of the battle, there is the added complexity of having to know whether the interference is enemy-induced—an interesting form of electronic warfare—or self-induced. Until you know what or who is hurting you, you can't do much to ease the pain.

To study electromagnetic problems the USAEPG has established an Electromagnetic Environmental Test Facility covering some twenty-four hundred square miles of southern Arizona. The area approximates that of an army corps, which has about 15,000 electronic emitters. Since it was economically and physically impracticable to place 15,000 communications emitters in the area, USAEPG put in 412 emitters employed in bands with each band representing tactical unit deployments from platoon to division. These emitters are grouped around what are called environment generator vans and buildings. Twenty-six of these have been established and more than 4,000 miles of wire and power cables connect them. To test a given piece of equipment these emitters are turned on in such a way as to create a desired environment.

Results of the tests do much more than determine incompatibilities in existing equipment and systems, important as this is. They suggest possible modifications that will reduce interference, or provide a basis for the establishment of realistic standards for new equipment. The tests provide valuable data on frequency assignment methods of the Army. Finally the system is used to test new equipment.

In addition to this test facility, USAEPG is preparing a computer

243

mechanized interference prediction model that when validated by field data, can be used to depict with a high degree of accuracy the interference that will be experienced by communications-electronics equipment in any tactical unit deployed on any terrain or in any climate.

In its testing USAEPG takes into consideration the effect of the operator on the machine and the effect of the machine on the operator. This is recognizably the application of "human engineering," and while the connotation of the words is disagreeable, the importance of what they mean cannot be discounted. A single example of human engineering at USAEPG was in the testing of a manpack radio. This radio had a rigid telescopic antenna that failed to bend when the soldier carrying it had to crawl under brush or through a fence. This, some old-timers recalled, was exactly the problem encountered with a manpack radio produced some twenty years ago. Sometimes our advancing technology gets so balled up in its belief that it reverses direction and travels back towards horse cavalry and wigwagging semaphores without knowing it.

The same manpack radio offered another, more subtle, exercise in human engineering. It was discovered during tests that some of the controls were so close together that the operation of one of them caused the operator inadvertently and invariably to nudge another control knob out of tune. There simply wasn't room for his fingers. Finger-shrinking may become mandatory if miniaturization continues unabated.

The soldier or platoon or division that is lost and can't relate the ground it's on to the maps it has is in a predicament potentially as disastrous as that of the commander plunging into an ambush because he didn't know the whereabouts of the enemy. In fluid warfare of fast moving, dispersed battalions and companies, dependent upon air vehicles for logistics, fire support, and intelligence, the need to know accurately where you are is essential. The intricacies of command and control under modern conditions are difficult enough without the added worry of misplaced forces.

What the soldier on the ground and the flyer in the air needs is a system that will tell him instantaneously and accurately where he is. This the Army is attempting to provide through an electromagnetic grid which will cover the field army area. Called a Battlefield Position Fixing and Navigational System, such a grid is being tested by USAEPG. It is designed to be used by an individual soldier with his helmet radio, by a tank or jeep, or by aircraft flying above the battlefield.

244

In its testing of the system, which is as much unlike the English Decca Navigation System as it is like it, a number of imperfections have shown up. USAEPG found a number of technical problems that had to be solved before the system could be fully tested and evaluated. It is working on these with the contractor and developer, and with various service test boards. It hopes that the isolation and correction of the recognizable deficiencies will result in a second generation navigation system that will provide the necessary performance and reliability.

The science and art of interpreting aerial photographs of enemy-held territory grew into an important element of the target selection activities of Anglo-American forces during World War II. This was especially true of the bombing effort against Germany, and the greatest achievement of the photo interpreters of that era has gone down in the books as the detection by a woman officer of one of the British military services of the German V bomb sites.

Today image interpretation is much more advanced, depending more on scientific analysis and less on art and intuition, although the curious mind is still a very necessary ingredient.

At Fort Huachuca, an image-interpretation facility is engaged in interpreting data produced by a variety of airborne sensors. These include not only the familiar black-and-white photographs of airborne cameras, but also images produced by infrared sensors and side-looking airborne radar. The work of this branch of the Surveillance Division of Test Plans and Evaluation Department is directed by Mr. Henry F. Hauser, a former Army officer. Mr. Hauser's group provides technical assistance to project officers testing airborne sensors. Their work is central to the eventual evaluation of the ability of the sensors to satisfy specifications. One of the important elements is the reduction in the time it takes to transmit the images captured by airborne sensors to the laboratory for evaluation and the conveying of the information to the forces that can make prompt use of it. The goal, according to Mr. Hauser, is "near real time," which I interpret to mean the practically instantaneous transmission of an image from an airborne drone to the photo interpreters.

Mr. Hauser's group also provides technical assistance to the Combat Development Command's Communications-Electronics Agency, which is tenanted on Fort Huachuca. New techniques it develops in the course of its work are forwarded to the Intelligence School at Fort Holabird to be developed into doctrine. It also sends selected samples of its work to Holabird for use in the instruction of photo interpretation specialists. The group is also constantly called on to provide photo interpreters and technical assistance to commanders of large maneuvers.

An example of electronic warfare instruments tested by USAEPG is a VT-fuze jammer recently put through a test to see if it would predetonate fuzes at tactical ranges. This jammer, carried in a three-quarter-ton truck, had also to be compatible with the field army's other communications-electronics equipment. USAEPG okayed the fuze jammer, provided certain modifications were made.

Space unfortunately prohibits a discussion of other interesting and important test projects in meteorology, avionics, combat surveillance, automatic data processing and communications. Nor is it possible to describe the activities of "tenanted" activities on the post. These include the Army's Combat Surveillance School; the Fifty-second Army Security Agency Special Operations Command; The Electronics Research and Development Activity, Arizona; and The Combat Developments Command Communications-Electronics Agency.

As it looks to the future, USAEPG sees two parallel developments that will vitally affect the Army's future capabilities. The development of military devices using laser beams may, USAEPG believes, revolutionize present communications-electronics equipment. It is studying the possibilities and adding to its store of knowledge and facilities in order to be ready to test laser devices as they come along. Already it has tested two range-finder lasers. Both are lightweight, optical target-ranging devices.

The second important trend in the Army that USAEPG believes may have a vital effect on communications-electronics is the emphasis on mobility with, as it has said, "all its implications on more versatile and higher performance aircraft." That quotation comes from a special report prepared by the Proving Ground. And the report goes on to say:

> *In the electromagnetic environment area, there will be a considerably higher density of emitters and receivers both at ground level and at levels up to roughly five thousand feet. The ability to evaluate mutual interferences of this high-density, more mobile complement of communication and navigation devices becomes increasingly necessary.*
>
> *The effects of nuclear radiation and the electromagnetic pulse on electronic equipment must be given increasing consideration.*

Another evaluation consideration suggested by the mobile nuclear army is the susceptibility of our own weapons systems to detection, and the ability of our surveillance devices to detect enemy weapons systems. Targetry may increasingly include low-level airborne forces, and either rapidly dispersing or underground tactical targets—which requires evaluation of optical, infrared and radar devices in these additional dimensions.

Everyone at Fort Huachuca has a strong feeling of pride in the Electronic Proving Ground and its accomplishments. They are quite aware, as General Pochyla had said, that it is the finest test agency of its kind in the free world and quite probably in all of the world. It is quite unlikely that the Russians have anything like it. He is quite conscious of the importance of USAEPG as an agency that contributes to providing the best communications and electronics to the Army's combat forces. "We keep the combat soldier constantly in mind," he says. "In our work we remember that our task is to come up with the equipment that will fit the man and not the other way around. Compatible equipment for the soldier and effective communications-electronics systems for his commanders must be our contributions to victory on the battlefield."

In the final analysis, it is men—trained men—who make the difference between victory or defeat on the battlefield. To ensure that all signalmen, officers and enlisted men alike, obtain the best possible training, the U.S. Army has established a thorough schooling system—a system which does not look back over its shoulder toward the past, but instead keeps its eyes fixed toward the new horizons of future communications-electronics techniques.

A Step Ahead of the Future

✠ BRIG. GEN. JOHN C. MONAHAN

The philosophy of training Signal communication specialists is based on the inexorable military logic that command implies control, which implies communications, which implies equipment and people trained to plan, install, operate and repair it.

That's where Signal schools come into the picture—at the end of the line, but a line that starts right at the top, for communications people have to be masters of the systems that make the will of the commander known. It is this mastery that we train for, in many varied fields of communication, at Fort Gordon, Georgia, and Fort Monmouth, New Jersey. Here budding signalmen are schooled in seventy-one courses, ranging from pole-line construction to newborn ones like troposcatter.

The difference between the old and the new brings home just how far we have come in a short time. A generation ago, it was perfectly possible for every Signal officer to know intimately all the Signal equipments used by the Army. Now no one can know them all thoroughly. Indeed, the training tasks that at one time constituted our mission are only introductory to the tasks we face today, yet we often have less time to devote to them. In World War II for example, our field radio course ran thirty-two weeks. Now it is only twenty-three, although equipment is far more complex.

Today at Forts Monmouth and Gordon we train about 32,000 officers and enlisted men a year in fifty-one enlisted MOS courses and twenty officer courses. Civilians and allied military personnel are included. This represents about 25 per cent of all resident students in Army schools. At any one time there are likely to be almost 10,000 students at both locations. We also have 16,637 others enrolled by our Department of Nonresident Instruction.

248

A glance at the types of enlisted specialists indicates the scope and complexity of the training task. The more familiar include pole-line construction, communications center operator, teletype-writer repair, dial central office maintenance, carrier and repeater repair, radio, microwave, and television equipment repair, and radar repair. But there are others—meteorology and meteorological equipment repair, automatic data-processing programming and equipment repair, electronic warfare equipment repair, crypto-graphic equipment repair, surveillance photography, and aviation electronic equipment repair.

This impressive array of skills is vitally important in accomplish-ing the communications mission; for the equipment we train on, when properly organized into systems, provides the crucial element of command control. Within the theater of operations, integrated radio and wire equipment form an area communications system. Radio, microwave, carrier, and cryptographic equipment make it work. Planning and management of this system are the skills we teach Signal Corps and other officers. Installation, operation, and maintenance skills are taught to enlisted specialists.

The worldwide Strategic Army Communication Network (STAR-COM) includes equipment of startling complexity, demanding highly skilled managers and maintainers, which we have been pro-viding for years. It operates terminals and relays at such widely separated points as Orleans, Asmara, Hawaii, and Ankara.

Even the briefest consideration of these two areas of operation impresses one with the magnitude of the training task. Further, there are still other related areas in which variety and complexity become even more evident. A small sampling of these may be of interest.

Troposcatter. Equipment for multiple voice and teletypewriter channels that will span one hundred miles of terrain with a reliabil-ity of up to 99 per cent, easily transported and quickly installed, already is in use with the Pershing missile system. This versatile equipment—a communicator's dream—quadruples the range of conventional microwave equipment, drastically reduces need for relay points, minimizes effects of unfavorable terrain, and reduces vulnerability to guerrilla action. Troposcatter systems are not beamed directly at each other, but at the skies near the horizon, to benefit from ability of atmospheric layers to reflect radio waves back to earth. The equipment is extremely sensitive, and requires spe-cially trained maintenance personnel.

Combat surveillance has had its impact on Signal training. For example, we teach the installation, operation and maintenance of the KS-61 photographic system used in the Mohawk aircraft. This electronically controlled system automatically computes camera angles and settings, and controls the movement of film to compensate instantly for speed, altitude and camera angle, to produce aerial photographs over a wide range of altitudes, speeds and light conditions. But to use it properly, we need trained people. Training them is our job.

Portable radar. AN/PPS-4A resembles a small searchlight on a tripod. It detects personnel and vehicular movement in frontline areas, giving a direct-range reading in meters. A far cry from the heavier radars weighing tons, this small, compact but still complex equipment requires thorough and practical instruction.

Surveillance aircraft. Training in this area concentrates on equipments designed for the tracking, plotting and control of both manned and drone surveillance aircraft.

ADPS. For some years we have been training in the field of Automatic Data Processing Systems—a field where not only equipment had to be taught, but techniques, procedures and teaching methods had to be evolved. The Officers' Department at Fort Monmouth offers a three-and-a-half-week course in ADPS for staff officers and key civilians of all the services. Thus far almost eighteen hundred have attended. Special courses train officers to manage field army level systems like MOBIDIC (mobile digital computer) and smaller ones like BASIPAC, a tactical general-purpose digital computer. Enlisted specialists are being taught to operate and maintain ADPS equipment, and to program computers.

Satellite communications. If surveillance and ADPS are new, this field is even newer. Our concern is not so much with satellites as spacecraft, but as links in a communications system. We are now seeing the first stirrings in research and development in this area, and already are sending selected staff and faculty members for special training.

Radar. New equipment keeps us occupied constantly in planning new courses of instruction. The AN/GPS-5, a radar chronograph developed for artillery use, is an example. It is essentially an electronic device which measures precisely and rapidly the muzzle velocity of a projectile so that artillery fire can be pinpointed with far greater accuracy. Like all other new items, this set is being analyzed with a view to developing an effective training course.

Because developments like those cited are new, they attract great attention. But other less exotic training tasks are nonetheless criti-

250

cal. We still have the task of training on the more usual communications equipment and systems—the wire and radio systems that carry the big traffic load as the backbone of our tactical and strategic communications system. Our Officers' Department courses must produce highly trained career officers as well as specialists in fields like electronic warfare, countermeasures, microwave, telephone and teletypewriter and communications center operations. Our twenty officer courses, from the eight-week basic officers orientation course at Fort Gordon to the twenty-seven-week Signal officers career course at Fort Monmouth, are producing the communications staff officers of the space age. They learn not only communications, but the tactical and strategic settings within which a communications system operates.

Consequently, the officers' orientation course at Fort Gordon incorporates extensive field training, especially in the defense of communications installations, tactical movements, and individual weapons. The officer career course at Fort Monmouth has recently been revised to increase instruction in counterinsurgency from fifteen hours to seventy-eight. Stress is placed on special communications for counterinsurgency operations including, where appropriate, the counterinsurgency aspect of normal communications operations.

To accomplish these many training functions, we take advantage of the latest techniques of modern scientific teaching methods. In 1951 the school at Fort Monmouth pioneered in educational TV for military instruction. It now has two studios, video tape and kinescope recording facilities, and fifteen miles of coaxial cable making up a seven-channel system which serves 485 receivers. A similar setup at Fort Gordon provides nine channels. Together, both schools transmit an average of 412 hours of televised instruction each week. Substantial savings in student and instructor time and effort are realized by bringing into the classroom instruction that would normally require moving a class outdoors. Close-ups of equipment add to teaching effectiveness.

At both schools we have also moved into the field of programmed instruction, sometimes referred to as "teaching machine" instruction. Programs have been devised in electronic fundamentals, message center procedures, and basic mathematics. This approach is being carefully evaluated.

All our attention to communication equipment, procedures, and techniques, all our striving for excellence as instructors, do not blind us to the part we play in the total picture—training men to establish and keep open the channels of information essential to success in war. Military operations are controlled by orders which have to be transmitted, and orders are based on plans, which in turn rest on information. In the modern Army, not only is information transmitted by Signal equipment, but very often the equipment itself gathers the information which gives rise to the plans and orders.

Everything we do in communications training finds its justification in the support we give the commander. Our mission is combat support—making command control not only possible, but timely, reliable, and secure. In this role more than intricate machinery and engineering ingenuity is needed—alert and capable communications are essential. The only way we in the schools can continue to provide such men is to keep not merely abreast of the present—but one step ahead of the future.

Radio amateurs—more often called hams—have been a prime source of support for the Signal Corps in past years. In recognition of the importance of the amateur radio community, the military services have organized the MARS program, which is described in this selection.

MARS – Military Affiliate Radio System

✠ MAJ. H. C. BECKER, JR.

A soldier in Korea gets a message from a relative in Kansas. A helicopter operator at the South Pole sends a message to South Bend. From all parts of the globe to all parts of the United States such messages and replies are the training media for a unique network—the Military Affiliate Radio System.

Known as MARS, and operating under jurisdiction of the Chief of Communications-Electronics, the system has enrolled some six thousand amateur radio operators, most of them in the fifty states of the Union. They are organized into local, district, state and Army area-wide radio-net facilities, with the Army area or command headquarters MARS radio stations as the top echelon net control station.

While these net facilities provide an emergency communications potential for military use, the full potential of the amateur radio operators has not yet been realized. There are more than 225,000 licensed amateur radio operators in the United States alone. In every city, village, metropolitan area, on remote farms and atop distant mountains, they man their personally owned, self-sufficient radio stations, capable of communicating over wide areas on a number of frequencies. They use continuous wave-telegraphy, amplitude modulation, single sideband voice operation and, often, radioteletype. Some also have mobile equipment in cars or trucks.

All of this capability is available to the military with no cost or requirements for support—other than use of military frequencies and necessary training publications.

MARS can serve a military commander's requirements in many ways. Where Army communications facilities are nonexistent, MARS stations can provide radio links to the Army Headquarters Station or to the nearest Army radio facility. Other local military, government and civil personnel can use local MARS member stations for emergency link-up with Army Headquarters.

The average MARS member is public spirited, dedicated, and versatile. He is eager to prove that he can perform worthwhile communications services. Since MARS networks were first organized in 1948, the many public service deeds by its members have won for the Military Affiliate Radio System an honored place in communications annals.

A recent Chief Signal Officer looks at future requirements in Army field communications.

U.S. Army Objectives in Field Communications

✠ MAJ. GEN. EARLE F. COOK, *USA (Ret.)*

I would like to re-examine the evolving nature of communications-electronics requirements in the combat zone, and to outline what the Army has already done about them and also what still needs to be done, or improved upon. Most of all, I want to point out some of the areas in which industry can help.

We are all aware that tremendous advancements in firepower and mobility have served to steadily increase the size of the combat area. During World War II the area required for one hundred thousand fighting men to maneuver in had increased by about four-fold over that required in World War I. In any future war, the size of the battle area will be substantially more than double that which was required in World War II.

This is largely due to the nuclear weapon and the availability of supersonic aircraft, missiles, and other means to deliver it. Against nuclear weapons, dispersion is an effective and necessary defense. But it is the *offense* that wins the battles, and to take the offensive a high degree of concentration of forces is required. This concentration must be effected quickly, the thrust swiftly made, and dispersion effected immediately afterwards, to preserve our units from a devastating counter-blow by enemy nuclear attack. It is because of this that our forces must be highly mobile. The ability to move will be tantamount to life or death on such a battlefield.

There are other considerations which must enter into our planning. The degree of violence any specific conflict may encompass, and the extent if any that nuclear weapons may be used are among the foremost. We must be ready for all contingencies. We must be prepared to fight any type of warfare across a broad spectrum. We must recognize that even if conflict should initially involve conventional weapons only, nuclear weapons *could* enter the picture at any moment.

What do these factors do to our communications requirements? First, the demand for communications equipment increases. We must have better radio communications at both higher and lower echelons to retain necessary command control. Every unit must have a means of quick communication extending over a suitably broad area.

Second, there will be an increase in traffic beyond that experienced in past warfare. This greater volume demands greater capacity, and at the same time complicates the problem of security. Increased traffic in an expanded combat area invites more possibilities for compromise of security, interception of messages and sabotage.

Third, mobility, flexibility, maintainability, and survivability become the watchwords for all electronics gear.

These factors are accompanied by a greatly compressed time factor. The tactical environment of modern warfare dictates the need for an all-weather round-the-clock mobile capability under any and all conditions. Whereas, in times past, a fast-moving force might have been described as "here today—gone tomorrow." By modern standards, a fast-moving force is better described as "here they come—they they were." Darkness and inclement weather no longer provide the protection they once did, and vital situation changes no longer will await the dawn. Taken together these factors will drastically reduce the time margin for decision-making.

Now, what have we already done, what are we now doing, and what do we want to do in the future about this evolving tactical environment confronting us?

First of all, we have set about establishing an improved communications complex throughout the geographical area of the Field Army, with a substantial increase in the equipment authorized. This is illustrated at the division level by the fact that a current Infantry Division, for example, is authorized 25 per cent more radios of all types than the Infantry Division of 1950.

We have developed this complex in accordance with what is known as an "area" concept—a new communications system which is composed of multiple signal centers which are interconnected, primarily by multichannel radio.

With this area communications system, considerable freedom of movement is allowed our troop units without the necessity for major changes in the trunking system, as access to any one of the Signal centers provides access to the entire network. This system overcomes the disadvantages encountered in the old single-access system which was short on flexibility and mobility, and was vulnerable at any link in the chain of command.

In addition to revamping the old communications system which no longer meets our needs, we have attempted to achieve a greater measure of flexibility by means of better equipment performance. An entire new family of compatible FM voice inter-operable radio sets has been developed. These are lighter in weight and provide more channels and range than the multiplicity of sets they replace.

Our new transistorized manpack set, the PRC-25, is designed for use by all arms and services in the forward area. Its principal advantages are its greater range, reduced weight, modular construction, greater frequency coverage, and a 50 per cent reduction in bandwidth per channel. This individual equipment will net with the new vehicular sets which have been developed and will be issued to the troops in the near future. In turn, a new vehicular series of voice radio sets for use by battalion and higher headquarters, has been designed for utilization by all arms and services and is much lighter than any of the sets it replaces; it has 920 available channels.

Existing mobile radio relay sets provide twelve voice channels between brigade and division headquarters. At the same time this equipment also provides twelve voice channels for communicating with adjacent brigades, as two twelve-channel radio relay systems are installed in a single shelter. Also at the division level, we have a mobile telephone central used for switching from trunk circuits provided by the radio-relay system to local telephones.

Although the various items of equipment I have described can provide a considerable communications capability, this must be surpassed in order to meet future operational requirements, principally from the standpoint of flexibility, mobility, reliability, and maintainability.

Despite the substantial progress already made, more needs to be done, and here industry's assistance will be of great value in supplementing our own efforts.

In this connection, we have under development new equipments which will provide for reduced weight and cube factors, and higher reliability. Substantial reductions in size and weight will be achieved through the use of modular construction techniques and transistorization. For example, the transistorized manpack set which I described earlier is to be further reduced in size by micromodularization, and maintenance will be simplified by this same construction feature, as well as by means of throw-away components.

An effort to further meet the challenge of increased reliance on radio communications during maneuver, has led to the development of a Radio Telephone Central Station for interconnecting the division echelons with its brigades and support command. Present limited production models have a capability of providing for as many as forty-eight subscriber stations. Each subscriber will be able to communicate with any other subscriber through this base central, in a manner similar to that utilized in the tactical telephone system, except that radio is used instead of wire.

Another problem area of great concern to us is frequency engineering. While our radio needs increase, the useable frequency spectrum does not, and the problem of operating more and more radios in noninterfering nets becomes increasingly difficult. Although we are pursuing a number of spectrum saving techniques to alleviate this frequency congestion, much more needs to be done. New single sideband radios and mobile radio centrals using either single sideband or random time-division pulse modulation techniques are among those that offer much promise.

Small tactical tropospheric scatter systems, mobile and rugged enough for use in forward combat areas are needed to provide improved reliability and substantially more range than is currently available in existing very high frequency radio relay equipment. These new scatter techniques must increase existing ranges by a factor of three or four times in order to eliminate the need for relays when line-of-sight is not available.

Improvements are also needed to alleviate the increased security problem which accompanies increased traffic. Unacceptable time delays would be imposed in the future, if we attempt to secure all anticipated traffic prior to transmission by means of present known methods. A quick method of providing voice security within the standard three-kilocycle bandwidth, simple enough for use by forward combat elements, could greatly increase our battlefield security.

The fields of combat surveillance and target location offer many additional challenges. Weapons of longer range and greater firepower demand surveillance systems capable of locating appropriate enemy targets over a much greater area than before. We are presently developing aerial sensor platforms, both manned and unmanned, for use at Army, Corps, and Division level. These platforms require improved versions of the radar, infrared, and photographic sensors. Ground surveillance devices, on the other hand, will be required at the lower tactical echelons, to provide company-size units with the ability to maintain a twenty-four hour systematic all-weather watch over its area of responsibility.

But the entire surveillance field is still a relatively new one and the ultimate in contributions that surveillance systems can potentially offer are not yet in sight. For example, though radar is a good surveillance sensor, the doppler types detect movement only. Their effectiveness tends to be reduced by severe weather conditions, and penetration of heavy foliage is a problem. Good mapping radars, with enough resolution to replace aerial photographs and detect stationary targets do not adapt easily to drones and aircraft which must fly at high speeds on evasive courses, to protect them from enemy air defenses.

Along with the need for such a radar, or substitute day-night camera, there is the parallel requirement for a data link that can transmit high definition radar or camera photography in real-time back to the ground station. Otherwise the information acquired will be brought back too late to be of use; this is particularly true in a nuclear environment. Combat surveillance and target location then, is truly a field where exploration by the electronics industry will assist us in attaining technological breakthroughs and in providing material contributions of the greatest significance.

The concept of command and control encompasses all of those activities which assist the commander in making and executing tactical decisions. Before discussing this problem of command and control any further, let us first attempt to visualize a possible future battlefield:

Some missiles stand ready to fire on targets being searched out by drones and other surveillance devices; other missiles are in the process of intercepting enemy aircraft; our own Army aircraft and helicopters are conducting their assigned missions; the tactical aircraft of our Air Force is contesting the air space with the enemy's forces; conventional artillery and antitank missiles are engaging targets suited to their close support fires; fighting men are maneuvering in a life or death struggle.

Now, from all these simultaneous movements, the commander must evaluate that information which is pertinent, swiftly make his decisions and communicate them in time for effective execution. Electronics alone can provide the means, timewise, by which he can do his job.

To assist him, the commander must have integrated electronic air defense systems to aid in protecting his forces. He needs mobile tactical operations centers to provide him with real-time automatic display of all data pertinent to the tactical situation. Mobile automatic data-processing equipment must be available to increase the accuracy and effectiveness of his surface-to-surface missile attacks, his employment of artillery and to speed his intelligence collection and production processes.

259

He must have a highly efficient system for battle identification—a means whereby he can discriminate between friend and foe, both on the ground and in the air. He must also have an almost instantaneous warning net which will permit him to give warning to his own combat elements when they must take cover against a nuclear burst, his own or one from the enemy.

It is our job—both military and industry—to see that he gets the things he needs. To a large extent, our national survival depends on it.

The present Chief of Communications-Electronics sees in the electronic computer important battlefield application in the years that lie ahead.

Computers Aid Command and Control

✠ MAJ. GEN. DAVID PARKER GIBBS

Command and control—always essential to military success —today has become increasingly critical. The reasons—the potential of the nuclear battlefield and the increasing stress on greater mobility, dispersion, and employment of highly complex weapons systems.

The commander on the battlefield of tomorrow will be forced to make vital decisions—decisions which may well affect the fate and future of nations—with speed matching the missiles and rockets he and the enemy will have available.

To make these decisions, commanders must have timely and accurate information upon which to base them. Fortunately, the same technological advances that have caused some of these problems have produced the means to solve them. Communications-electronics, as an integral part of command and control systems, offer us a means of obtaining superiority over our enemy—a decisive factor on any battlefield.

In the logistics and administrative area, the needs of the commander are being met through communications and automatic data-processing systems (ADPS) that make possible significant advances in timely and accurate data handling.

Coupled with existing communications systems, the digital computer is being widely and effectively used in Army administration. This system has the potential of providing the commander with the means of handling the overwhelming flow of data furnished by the various devices used for sensing and identifying enemy action.

When adapted to the tactical field, ADP would permit the staff to present the commander in very short time a graphic display of a digest of a vast mass of information. Such an automated command and control system would allow the commander and his staff to assimilate and better understand the information from the balance of the system.

261

The commander thus will have presented to him the significant relationships, conflicts, correlations and extrapolations which can be quickly, clearly and correctly comprehended. Displays will allow important information and intelligence to be understood in context with the whole situation and, conversely, allow the whole situation to be examined in detail.

Improvement in quality, clarity and length of briefings through use of improved information handling is also possible. The electronic information system will assist in reducing briefing preparation time below that currently required by manual methods of preparing and posting displays of the type used in appraising key personnel of status, problems, and plans.

The full potential of ADP systems has not yet been realized, obviously. In the next few years the impact of the computer in areas of strategy and tactics will increase as new computers and techniques are introduced and as commanders understand their use more fully. One particular area of promise is the possibility that tactical computers and communications may make it possible to establish austere headquarters and alternates.

At present, several problems exist in the realm of automatic data processing systems. Some are created by the variety of machines in use, others in the field of operating personnel.

Lack of compatibility in existing systems is a serious problem—programs for one computer or system will not work with those of another manufacturer; output data from one system cannot be used with another; parts are not interchangeable; personnel trained in one system need retraining for another.

One approach to meeting this problem is use of one of the standard compiler languages such as COBOL, ALGOL, and FORTRAM. Use of more and more Automatic Digital Network (AUTODIN) switches and terminals also will aid in this area.

Another problem stems from the fact that automated information gathering, correlation, and display systems go to the very heart of the commander's decision-making process and exercise of command and control. Thus development and programming primarily must be under the control of Army personnel who are responsible for doctrine as well as the ADP system.

This is a grave and serious matter which must be continually affirmed by the Army, or we will find ourselves in danger of turning over a major element of our decision-making process to computer programmers, engineers and systems designers. Indeed, it is far better, safer and easier to teach a professional soldier ADP than to

262

teach computer specialists the military profession. As a step toward solution of this problem, the developer and user are co-located wherever possible—an arrangement which enables Army doctrine personnel to work directly with the developer.

In short, the commander cannot turn over his decision making to a machine, no matter how efficient that instrument may be. The commander must use the machine as a tool—a remarkably efficient, swift, and accurate tool which can supply him with data very much faster than existing methods; a tool that can provide the information with which to react against the increasingly swift tempo of modern warfare—but still a tool.

The Army must possess the capacity to provide supply and maintenance support for computers and ADP devices in our oversea commands as well as the capacity to develop, install, and operate them. The most important problem facing the Army today in ADP, therefore, is the attainment of logistical and personnel self-sufficiency. We must be able to plan, operate, maintain, and supply ADP systems by means of Army personnel. The Army school and training systems should be geared to meet the challenge and supply the needed analysts and technicians and, most of all, informed user personnel.

We are making some advances in attaining this posture of self-sufficiency. The Army program known as CCIS-70 (Command and Control Information Systems of the 1970 era) is designed to put an integrated communications and data-processing system into the field army. It will put mobile, rugged, militarized computers down to division level, to serve as information-processing systems for logistics, personnel, fire control, intelligence, and tactical operations centers.

In addition, ADP courses, both orientation and specialist, have been established in several Army schools—Signal, Adjutant General, Army Management Engineering Training Agency (AMETA), and others.

The Army now is indoctrinating its senior officers in ADP techniques and applications. Young officers are being sent to civilian institutes and universities for graduate training in the ADP-related fields of business administration, electrical and industrial engineering, mathematics, and operations research.

Use of computers in the Army has increased rapidly since they first came into prominence in the 1950's. In fact, the Army was largely instrumental in original development of these instruments.

Today we have left the first generation of computers characterized by milisecond (thousandths of a second) operations and are well into a second generation characterized by microsecond operation (millionth of a second). Development of transistorized elements has permitted this increase in capability. Not long ahead for purposes of Army utilization lies the third generation, operating in nanoseconds (billionths of a second) utilizing new techniques in integrated circuits, thin film memories, tunnel diode devices.

There now are more than two hundred general-purpose digital computers in use in the Army. ADP systems used in the administrative—or business-type—areas are generally devoted to the processing of data used in logistic and personnel management, finance and accounting, general record maintenance, and the like.

One example of ADP administrative application is the system currently being installed under staff supervision of The Adjutant General at the six Continental U.S. Army headquarters, and at headquarters U.S. Army Europe. Similar computers will later be installed at major headquarters in the Pacific area.

The system is now being used primarily for personnel management on a limited scope. It will be expanded to encompass the entire field of personnel accounting. Thus, through the use of long-haul strategic communications, it will provide the Chief of Staff with more complete control over all personnel on an Army-wide basis. It also will help insure a more flexible personnel system to provide the swift reaction time necessary in today's Army.

Other examples are those in use at the Finance Center and by The Surgeon General.

Without these machines, it would be virtually impossible to cope with the work of processing actions at the Finance Center. The Chief of Finance also will pioneer for the Army the use of optical character readers which can discriminate among many fonts of type. These are designed to read automatically certain classes of documents and convert the data to computer-recognizable language.

The Surgeon General now is planning installation of computers in Class II hospitals to maintain supply records, provide management data on assigned personnel and patients, and process finance and accounting records. They also will be used in correlation of patient diagnostic data.

In still another area of application, computers are used in the academic field—at the Signal School and the Military Academy, for example. Still other areas concern scientific and engineering applications which necessarily use many mathematical computations, equations, and techniques.

War gaming and systems simulation are now being carried on with the aid of digital computers. At present, extensive efforts are under way to automate the information handling techniques in the Army War Room. Here the Department of the Army is undertaking to develop a communications and control system, including data transmission and display techniques combined with automation processes. By incorporating a digital computer as the data processor, and an assemblage of display devices, incoming data will be quickly presented in usable form.

One of the newest and most challenging areas in the entire field is the concept of using digital computers for processing of information received on a real-time communications basis—that is, they will not operate in the standard batch-card processing manner, but will receive information electrically direct from the communications system. They will then operate upon the information immediately and deliver the data to the appropriate output device.

These techniques will be employed with the store-and-forward type message switching computer which will be used in AUTODIN for teletype and data service.

Programming a real-time system offers many difficulties not normally encountered. More sophisticated methods of control will be required. In this area particularly, the importance of a close working relation between computer and communications engineers cannot be overemphasized.

From closer contact with CCIS-70, commanders will be able to gain more experience in utilizing computers in command and control. The first of these computers is operational in Europe, where the MOBIDIC computer is in use in the Seventh Army Stock Control Center. A second MOBIDIC computer is being checked out at the Ordnance Stock Control Center at Maison Forte, France. Others—MOBIDIC, BASICPAC (medium scale computers)—now are undergoing tests at Fort Huachuca, Arizona.

From these intensive trials in the field will come the computer that will enter the Army in quantity. Whatever or whichever it may be, it will be compatible with the FIELDATA specifications designed to make the CCIS-70 system an integrated, compatible data processing system.

Within CCIS-70 the most dynamic subsystem is ARTOC (Army Tactical Operations Center). This is an experimental computer, communications, and display information handling system designed for the field army. Its data processing device consists of a special MOBIDIC version with associated random access disc files.

265

New modern input devices known as TACDEN and GRAPHDEN are available with ARTOC. TACDEN permits entry of preformated alphanumeric data from a remote location. GRAPHDEN permits linear or point information, such as a front line trace, to be entered directly into the computer. Individual displays and group displays are both available. Chart-form information and overlay information are available from programs written for the ARTOC system, which now is under final acceptance tests.

Thus, in a variety of applications, automatic data processing systems are moving into ever more challenging areas. Commanders will find them ever increasingly useful as tools to aid in assembling and displaying a mass of incoming information, thus enabling them to react more swiftly to the demands of the nuclear battlefield of the future.

GLOSSARY OF TERMS

ALGOL	Algebraic Oriented Language
AUTODIN	Automatic Digital Network
AUTOVON	Automatic Voice Network
BASICPAC	Basic processor and computer of medium capacity, mounted in 2½-ton truck shelter.
COBOL	Common Business Oriented Language
FORTRAN	Formulae Translator
GRAPHDEN	Graphic Data Entry
MOBIDIC	Mobile Digital Computer, large scale, mounted in standard Army van.
FIELDATA	Family of Army militarized mobile processors, data communications, and peripheral devices.
REAL–TIME SYSTEM	A system by which data describing an event is processed in a sufficiently rapid manner so that the information produced is available in time to influence the course of the event.
BATCH–CARD PROCESSING	A technique by which items of data to be produced are coded and collected into groups prior to processing.
THIN FILM MEMORIES	A special plate on which minute particles of magnetic material are thinly deposited so as to provide a compact and reliable internal computer storage unit which has a faster access time than the conventional internal storage units.

The U.S. Army Signal Corps can be credited with much of the early work done in the field of communications satellites. At present, communications via satellite is the joint responsibility of many government and civil agencies.

Signals in Space

✠ MAJ. GEN. R. T. NELSON, *USA (Ret.)*

With the dawn of the Space Age, a tremendous new dimension has been added to man's earthly existence.

Arrival of the Space Age can be said to date from man's first contact with the moon, which was achieved by Army Signal Corps engineers at Belmar, New Jersey, in the Evans Area of sprawling Fort Monmouth on January 10, 1946. Known as Project Diana, this achievement represented a real scientific breakthrough and gave strong impetus to further electronics research activities in space.

Since then, despite the high costs and the superhuman effort required, the national space effort has proceeded on a broad scale for reasons variously ascribed to man's consummate thirst for greater knowledge, to a desire for scientific advancement, and to the requirements of national defense and even national survival.

Whatever the motives, United States progress in the mastery of space has been substantial and of far-reaching significance—of much greater significance than is generally realized. The U.S. Army Signal Corps is proud to have had an essential part in it.

Why is the Army Signal Corps interested in space?

For some quite practical reasons, this interest is intimately related to the Signal Corps' mission and the role of the Army in national defense. The Signal Corps is the Army's combat arm of command control. Also a technical service, it has the mission of providing the means of command control. This means communications, the transmission of intelligence of all kinds, and the acquisition of intelligence through combat surveillance and target identification.

In effect, the Signal Corps comprises the nervous system of the Army. The provision of various means of communication, combat surveillance, and target acquisition is inseparable from research in many scientific areas. Consequently, the Corps has had to delve deeply into studies of physics, materials, power sources, meteor-

267

ology, electromagnetic wave propagation and other aspects of the world of science.

In seeking to provide communications support to Army units and elements deployed throughout the world—in seventy different countries—there is an implacable need for global communications facilities of ever greater capacity, reliability, and speed.

By far the most promising solution to the Army's growing communications problem lies in the tremendous possibilities offered by satellites for the relay of encoded audio and even video communications. While they will probably never replace all of the various existing systems, ultimately they will provide a reliable and efficient means of spanning the oceans and polar regions where today many reliability problems exist. They give promise of greatly increased traffic capacity which would relieve the congestion on existing facilities.

Along with other new developments, satellites also give promise of greater speed in communications service—speed closely approaching the real-time, user-to-user transmission which would be particularly advantageous. Undoubtedly, satellites will ultimately provide truly global communications for both military and commercial purposes.

Step by step, the necessary technology for exploring the possibilities of and exploiting the opportunities for space communications has been developed by the Army Signal Corps or by private enterprise laboratories. Many of the really significant technological advancements—in the development of new materials, new techniques of miniaturization and microminiaturization, new power sources; and in the exploratory research of such areas as solid-state sciences, nuclear physics, plasma physics, mathematics—cannot compete with the "big bang" or the "flaming launch" when it comes to newspaper headlines. This, however, in no way detracts from their significance or essentiality.

Miniaturization techniques developed by the Signal Corps have contributed immeasurably to reduction in necessary missile-vehicle sizes or conversely to increase in the capabilities of the pay load that can be carried by a vehicle of a given size. Printed circuit techniques developed in 1949 and combined with the transistor and other miniaturized components permitted the initial development of systems having a parts density of the order of 50,000 per cubic foot and point to further potentials of 250,000 parts per cubic foot or more. Today, with solid state circuitry techniques, our researchers are thinking in terms of density possibilities of more than a million parts per cubic foot.

New special and heat-resisting materials developed by the Signal Corps have likewise contributed to the effective design and operation of the vehicles themselves and of the satellites in their space environment.

While Signal Corps research and development has contributed much to the development of the missile-vehicles by which satellites are launched, its areas of greatest achievement lie in the sophisticated utilization and the developed capability of the satellite in orbit. This is all the more significant since a mere piece of hardware, orbiting in space without some intelligent application, is of little profit except for the boost in morale of the launching personnel.

The Signal Corps, in a sense, is a "hitchhiker" on missile-vehicles provided by others, but it has earned the ride because of its contributions to development of the vehicles themselves and because of its capability for intelligent employment of the satellite in its orbit-destination.

In the dramatic Diana project of January 10, 1946, Signal Corps engineers, using a modified SCR-271 long-range radar, succeeded in bouncing its radar signals off the moon and receiving them on earth seconds later. The equipment used for the moon contact was an adaptation of an older radar set designed for early warning of enemy air attack. The contact demonstrated that very high frequency radio waves can penetrate the electrically charged ionosphere around the earth and proved the feasibility of space communications.

Following the success of the Diana moon-bounce, Signal Corps activities relating to space began to broaden considerably. Renewed emphasis was placed on meteorology. In 1948, new radar equipment at Fort Monmouth observed a rain storm at a distance of one hundred and eighty-five miles and then tracked the disturbance to zero range, giving accurate precipitation forecasts for various areas down to the minute. This equipment, or some modification of it, is now in wide use in the military services and the Weather Bureau.

During this time also, Signal Corps weather experts started looking higher, using V-2 rockets at first, and later cheaper carriers for probing temperatures, wind direction, and velocity up to 250,000 feet.

Techniques were further developed and extended during the 1957–58 International Geophysical Year (IGY) to widely separated spotchecks of the high altitude mass currents which spawn our weather. Using specially equipped Aerobee rockets, air currents were thoroughly explored at altitudes up to eighty miles.

On another front, shortly after the Diana moon-bounce, Signal Corps scientists and engineers began participating in postwar atomic bomb tests. These experiments resulted in major contributions to long-range detection of high-energy explosions, new dosimeters, tracking of radioactive clouds, and determination of vulnerability of electronic equipment in highly radioactive environments.

Electronic support for guided missiles began in 1949 at the Army's White Sands Missile Range, New Mexico, and soon grew into the large U.S. Army Signal Missile Support Agency. Experience and early participation in this phase of communications-electronics enabled the Army Signal Corps to provide major science and electronics support to subsequent missile and space programs.

The advent and rapid development of Army missiles also brought forth a relatively new and expanding electronics mission area for the Signal Corps—that of combat surveillance and target acquisition. Essentially this involves gathering information day and night, in all weather, about the enemy, for employment of weapons systems against him. In support of this mission, research and development effort was intensified and expanded to include, among other things, a variety of such sensors as radar, photographic, TV, infrared, seismic, and acoustic devices.

Permeating all such research is the ever-nagging requirement for certain scarce strategic materials. Significant Signal Corps solutions to some of these problems included learning how to grow synthetic mica in 1946, large quartz crystals in 1950–51, and how to synthesize diamonds in 1959.

A rare material, gallium phosphide, grown in Signal laboratories, has been used to build an electronic diode which has withstood temperatures seven times higher than materials previously used. Still under evaluation and study, gallium phosphide holds promise of helping to solve heat-barrier problems encountered by electronic parts in missile nose cones.

Use of a synthetic ruby in the development of a new "electronic ear" has given the Corps one of the most sensitive listening devices invented to date—one that can detect "beeps" from space vehicles millions of miles away and pick up signals from distant stars.

Signal Corps patience and perseverance in these many areas related to space research have paid off handsomely, and have steadily advanced the national space effort to dramatic levels of sophisticated scientific achievement.

The Vanguard I satellite, launched on March 17, 1958 under Navy direction, is still sending signals from outer space, courtesy of Signal Corps-developed solar converters for powering its radio transmitter. With little perceptible loss of power, these radio signals have continued to come in as regularly as clockwork and almost as strong as when first launched. On its third anniversary this year, Vanguard I had completed approximately 11,750 orbits, and traveled 408,004,164 miles through space. It is now expected that its solar cells will permit continuous and effective radio signals to earth for several lifetimes.

Vanguard I marked the first use of solar cell power in a satellite by anyone, anywhere. Because of continued success in this first application by the Army, solar cells have been employed in numerous succeeding satellites. As of January 1, 1961, the seven satellites that were still orbiting and transmitting were all of American manufacture. The continuous supply of significant data provided by the tiny Vanguard I, initially referred to with some derision as the "grapefruit" satellite, has caused many knowledgeable scientists to pause in respect.

The development of solar cells for converting sunlight into electrical power is but one area in which the Army has pioneered in the search for dependable power sources, but it is one of far-reaching implications—for both ground and space operations. Other developments particularly applicable to missiles and satellites include special chemical batteries of various types.

Early attempts to transmit radio messages by "lunar reflection"—after the Army's first contact with the moon—always came back scrambled. However, techniques for transmission of intelligible messages were eventually perfected by the Navy.

These were followed by the successful Army Signal Corps development of the communications "package" for the Project Score satellite. Launched into orbit on December 18, 1958, the Score satellite made possible relay of the first message from outer space—a Christmas message to the world from President Eisenhower.

The communications "package" of Project Score—meaning Signal Communications by Orbiting Relay Equipment—was developed by the Army Signal Corps Research and Development Laboratory in cooperation with industry and under jurisdiction of the Advanced Research Projects Agency of the Department of Defense.

Project Score demonstrated for the first time that voice, teletypewriter, and even multiple teletypewriter signals could be received, stored, and then retransmitted by a satellite orbiting in space. This satellite was used successfully as both a delayed repeater and as a real-time relay station. To obtain stored messages from the communications relay, a ground station triggered the relay transmitter by electronic command. As long as the satellite was in range, the ground station could also transmit its own message by relay directly to another station. Messages could be relayed from one station to another without storage.

Installed inside the Atlas, using the missile itself as the carrier, the relay consisted primarily of two transmitters, two receivers, and two recorders using erasable loops of magnetic tape. The total pay load, including antennas, was about one hundred and fifty pounds. The transmitter produced eight watts of power and used zinc-silver oxide batteries with an estimated life of four to six weeks. Solar cells were not used, as in Vanguard I, because of the expected short life of the huge Atlas satellite in orbit.

Global meteorological research took a giant step forward, and upward, with the launching of the Vanguard II, or United States Cloud Cover Satellite, on February 17, 1959. Equipped with a revolutionary type of meteorological observation and reporting system, the electronic instruments arranged inside the satellite shell were designed and built by Army scientists and engineers at the U.S. Army Signal Research and Development Laboratory, Fort Monmouth, New Jersey.

The satellite's "eyes" were two photocells placed on opposite sides of the sphere to scan the earth's surface and cloud systems from vantage points as far out as two thousand miles in space. These were so mounted behind circular gridded windows that direct sunlight would not reach them and so that one optic would always sweep the earth.

As the satellite orbited, the photocells scanned the light and dark areas—*i.e.*, clouds and ground—converting the changes in light intensity into electric signals. These signals were recorded on erasable magnetic tape and transmitted to ground stations upon demand, thus re-creating a pattern of light corresponding to the top surface of the cloud areas over which the satellite passed.

Because of its orbit, about 25 per cent of the earth's surface could be observed. Prior to this time regular observations had been made of only five to ten per cent of the surface.

A series of photographs of areas three hundred miles square presented data that made possible a graphic representation of the clouds and weather over a given area of operation. The purpose of this experiment was to give Signal Corps physicists an opportunity to study dynamic cloud systems and to detect and track the early development of cyclonic systems, including hurricanes and typhoons.

The tape recorder stored about fifty minutes of data and then transmitted it on command in one sixty-second burst. Powered with mercury cells with a life expectancy of only two weeks, the "package" included a solar cell-operated switch which halted the tape when the satellite was in the earth's shadow, thus saving battery power.

When transmission stopped on March 7, after approximately eighteen days, the satellite had been successfully interrogated 152 times on 211 trips around the earth. The tape recorder and solar switch worked perfectly. Temperature of the satellite was within *one degree* of its thermal design value.

As a first and limited effort to explore the use of satellites for meteorological studies, Vanguard II—a project of the National Aeronautics and Space Administration—performed a very useful purpose. A wealth of intelligence was provided by an electronic package weighing twelve pounds, eight pounds of which were batteries. Total weight of the twenty-inch diameter satellite was twenty-one and a half pounds.

A later satellite of this type, known as Tiros I (Television Infrared Observation Satellite) was launched on April 1, 1960, also under sponsorship of NASA. In its nearly three months in orbit, it took approximately 23,000 useful photographs of the earth and its cloud cover from vantage points ranging from 430 to 467 miles in space and relayed them back to earth. The instrumentation which made this feat possible was developed under technical direction of the U.S. Army Signal Corps by the Radio Corporation of America.

Tiros I, weighing 270 pounds, was equipped with two television cameras to photograph the earth's changing cloud patterns—one for large area photographs giving an 850-mile square view and another for pinpointing smaller sections about 80 miles on each side. Both provided meteorologists with detailed pictures of hurricanes and cyclonic patterns, with resolution roughly comparable to commercial television.

Information gathered by the two TV cameras was stored on magnetic tape in the satellite and then fed, on radio command, to ground stations. These stations could order photographs three orbits in advance, when the satellite's position and the sun combined for the best picture possibilities. When the satellite was in range, it could be commanded by ground stations to transmit the TV picture of the moment directly to earth, without being taped.

Shaped like a round pillbox, Tiros I was forty-two inches in diameter and nineteen inches high. Electrical power was provided by banks of ninety-two hundred solar cells, which operated directly when the vehicle was in the sun and also charged lightweight storage batteries to provide power when it was in the earth's shadow.

An entirely new design of spin control, similar to a gyroscope,

273

was installed to prevent any wobbling such as experienced in Vanguard II. However, in its later stages, management of the attitude of Tiros I caused difficulties because of a gradual attitude shift traceable to influence of the earth's magnetic field.

Techniques for counteracting this earth magnetic influence were developed by RCA engineers for Tiros II, launched November 23, 1960. Tiros II also incorporated infrared sensors, omitted from Tiros I, for mapping relative temperatures of the earth's surface.

Malfunctioning of the wide-angle TV camera in Tiros II caused disappointments from a reliability standpoint—particularly since this equipment had worked well in Tiros I. Overall, however, the innovations in weather satellite techniques proved in Tiros II represented an important advance in general technological capability over Tiros I.

In the meantime, communications satellite projects known as Courier and Advent were set in motion, with management responsibility for both eventually assigned to the Army.

The first into orbit was Courier 1B, launched by an Air Force Thor-Able Star missile from Cape Kennedy on October 4, 1960. The Army Signal Corps had responsibility for technical direction of the satellite system development and operation of the two ground stations.

Courier was an experimental research and development vehicle designed to explore the feasibility of providing a delayed repeater satellite at a 640-mile altitude. As a delayed repeater, it stored information until commanded to transmit rather than relaying it directly.

Satellites of this type can be envisioned as a messenger system providing a trunking capability for storing and forwarding messages in an eventual worldwide network of orbiting satellites. Like the Score equipment, it could also relay directly between ground stations when both were in range of the satellite.

The remarkable ability of Courier to send approximately 68,000 words a minute, and to receive and store the same amount simultaneously, has been amply demonstrated. Staying within operable range of a ground station for a five-minute period, it was capable of transmitting approximately 340,000 words each way on a single pass—while moving through space at 24,000 feet per second. This wordage is equivalent to approximately three novels.

Circling the globe nearly fourteen times a day, it exchanged an average total of some 6,000,000 words a day with its two ground stations at Fort Monmouth, New Jersey, and Salinas, Puerto Rico. Both stations also sent and received sixty facsimile photographs.

The significance of these performance figures to an Army requirement for greater capacity in global communications is evident.

As an experimental research and development vehicle, Courier used frequencies in the ultra-high range, never before used in a satellite for communications. The use of this band has several advantages. It is a relatively unused part of the radio spectrum and is generally free from interference by other man-made signals. It also is not disturbed by natural causes such as magnetic storms which can blanket the lower frequencies.

The fifty-one-inch, five-hundred-pound Courier included a pay load of 300 pounds of electronic equipment. Design of the entire system was a cooperative effort of the military and of industry, representing teamwork at its best.

Despite its comparatively great weight, Courier was a triumph of miniaturization, using printed circuits, tiny modules and transistors. It contained only four conventional vacuum tubes—for the microwave circuits—and 1,300 transistors. Power was derived from a "skin" of 19,200 solar cells for charging miniature nickel cadmium batteries.

While these end products of our research may seem fantastic and sometimes visionary, they are the result of a carefully planned, painstaking, step-by-step process, wherein each new venture is evaluated on the basis of its practicality and its usefulness. Such is the stuff of which real scientific progress is made.

We of the Army Signal Corps have made a beginning in this new dimension, as we did in electrical communications a century ago and in meteorology some ninety years ago. But it is only a beginning!

APPENDIX A

Chief Signal Officers, U.S. Army

Brig. Gen. Albert J. Myer	1860–1863; 1866–1880
Col. Benjamin Franklin Fisher	1864–1866
Brig. Gen. William B. Hazen	1880–1887
Brig. Gen. Adolphus W. Greely	1887–1906
Brig. Gen. James Allen	1906–1913
Brig. Gen. George P. Scriven	1913–1917
Maj. Gen. George O. Squier	1917–1923
Maj. Gen. Charles M. Saltzman	1924–1928
Maj. Gen. George S. Gibbs	1928–1931
Maj. Gen. Irving J. Carr	1931–1934
Maj. Gen. James B. Allison	1935–1937
Maj. Gen. Joseph O. Mauborgne	1937–1941
Maj. Gen. Dawson Olmsted	1941–1943
Maj. Gen Harry C. Ingles	1943–1947
Maj. Gen. Spencer B. Akin	1947–1951
Maj. Gen. George I. Back	1951–1955
Lt. Gen. James D. O'Connell	1955–1959
Maj. Gen. Ralph T. Nelson	1959–1962
Maj. Gen Earle F. Cook	1962–1963
Maj. Gen. David P. Gibbs	1963–1964

APPENDIX B

Congressional Medal of Honor Winners, Signal Corps

BARNES, WILLIAM C. *Rank and Organization:* Private First Class, Signal Corps, United States Army. *Place and Date:* At Fort Apache, Arizona, September 11, 1881. *Entered Service at:* Washington, D.C. *Birthplace:* San Francisco, California. *Date of Issue:* November 8, 1882. *Citation:* Bravery in action.

GREELY, ADOLPHUS W. *Rank and Organization:* Major General, United States Army, retired. *Entered Service at:* Louisiana. *Birthplace:* Newburyport, Massachusetts. *G. O. No.:* 3,W.D., 1935. Act of Congress, March 21, 1935. *Citation:* For his life of splendid public service, begun on March 27, 1844, having enlisted as a private in the United States Army on July 26, 1861, and by successive promotions was commissioned as major general February 10, 1906, and retired by operation of law on his sixty-fourth birthday.

JOHNSTON, GORDON. *Rank and Organization:* First Lieutenant, United States Signal Corps. *Place and Date:* At Mount Bud-Dajo, Jolo, Philippine Islands, March 7, 1906. *Entered Service at:* Birmingham, Alabama. *Birthplace:* Charlotte, North Carolina. *Date of Issue:* Unknown. *Citation:* Voluntarily took part in, and was dangerously wounded during, an assault on the enemy's works.

KILBOURNE, CHARLES E. *Rank and Organization:* First Lieutenant, United States Volunteer Signal Corps. *Place and Date:* At Paco Bridge, Philippine Islands, February 5, 1899. *Entered Service at:* Portland, Oregon. *Birthplace:* Fort Myer, Virginia. *Date of Issue:* May 6, 1905. *Citation:* Within a range of two hundred and fifty yards of the enemy and in the face of a rapid fire climbed a telegraph pole at the east end of the bridge and in full view of the enemy coolly and carefully repaired a broken telegraph wire, thereby reestablishing telegraphic communication to the front.

LANE, MORGAN D. *Rank and Organization:* Private, Signal Corps, United States Army. *Place and Date:* Near Jetersville, Virginia, April 6, 1865. *Birthplace:* Monroe, New York. *Date of Issue:* March 16, 1866. *Citation:* Capture of flag of gunboat *Nansemond*.

277

APPENDIX C

"AN" Nomenclature System

MIL-STD-196, "Joint Electronics-Type Designation System."

EQUIPMENT INDICATOR LETTERS

1st Letter (Installation)	2d Letter (Installation)	3d Letter (Purpose)
A Airborne	A Invisible light, heat radiation	A Auxiliary assemblies
B Underwater		
C Air transportable	B Pigeon	B Bombing
D Pilotless carrier	C Carrier (wire)	C Communication
F Fixed	D Radiac	D Direction finding
G Ground, general	F Photographic	G Gun or searchlight directing
K Amphibious	G Telegraph or teletype (wire)	
M Ground mobile		H Recording
P Pack or portable	I Interphone and public address	L Searchlight control
S Water surface craft		M Maintenance and test assemblies
T Ground, transportable	K Telemetering	
U General utility	L Countermeasures	N Navigational aids
V Ground, vehicular	M Meteorological	P Reproducing
	N Sound in air	Q Special or combination of types
	P Radar	
	Q Sonar	R Receiving
	R Radio	S Detecting and/or range bearing
	S Special types	
	T Telephone (wire)	T Transmitting
	V Visual	W Remote control
	X Facsimile or television	X Identification and recognition

Example: AN/VRC = 12 is a vehicular radio used for communications.

Significant Dates in the History of the U.S. Army Signal Corps

1860, June 21. *Birth date of the Army Signal Corps.* The appointment of a signal officer for the Army was authorized by Congress.

1860, July 2. *First Signal Officer: Albert J. Myer.* Assistant Surgeon Albert J. Myer, who had patented a system of wigwag signaling in 1856, was appointed the first Army Signal Officer.

1861, March–April. *First Signal units.* In the spring of 1861, Major Myer began training a nucleus of Signal personnel adept at flag and torch signaling, using the Myer system. This training was performed at Fort Monroe, Virginia.

At about the same time, Alexander—a lieutenant in the Confederate army, and a student of Myer prior to the war—organized a handful of soldiers as a provisional Signal Corps. This unit—using Myer's original system of signaling saw effective service with the Confederate army at the battle of Manassas-Bull Run in July of 1861.

1861, June 12. *First combat Signal units.* For service with the Union army, the first Signal parties were detailed at Fort Monroe, Virginia.

1861, June 15. *First use of signals to direct gunfire.* By means of signal flags, fire of the battery at Fort Wool in Hampton Roads, Virginia, was directed on the Confederate works at Sewell's Point. One Signal detail of four men, including Major Myer, observed the effect of the firing from a tugboat and reported their observations by signal flag to the shore battery.

1861, June 26. *First permanent communication line in war.* Using flags and torches, the first permanent line of communication was established between Fort Monroe and Newport News, Virginia.

1861, July 10. *First Signal school.* The first Signal school was established at Fort Monroe, Virginia, by Maj. Albert J. Myer.

1861, July 21. *First use of balloon for military purposes.* The first balloon built in the United States for military use was inflated in Washington, and an attempt was made to transport it to the headquarters of McDowell's Union forces in Virginia. The balloon and its handlers were under the command of Maj. Albert J. Myer, the Army Signal officer. Along the line of march, however, the balloon was damaged and never reached the field of battle. Myer proceeded without it, reported to McDowell's headquarters, and served with distinction as a mounted messenger—the only Signal officer of the Union forces during the Battle of Manassas-Bull Run. Subsequently, balloons were used occasionally by both sides during the war, but were provided and operated by civilians under temporary contracts.

1861, July 21. *First Confederate use of signals.* Using flags, a Confederate signal party of four men maintained communications between a forward observation post and the main Confederate forces at the Battle of Manassas-Bull Run—a major contribution to victory by the Confederacy in that engagement.

1861, August. *First military telegraph train.* The War Department procured the first telegraph train for military use. Known as a "Flying Telegraph Train," it consisted of horse-drawn wagons equipped with Beardslee magnetoelectric telegraph sets, field wire, flags, rockets, and other equipment—much of it obtained from commercial telegraph companies. Army telegraph trains, using the Beardslee magnetoelectric set especially procured by the Signal Corps, were first employed in the Peninsular Campaign in the spring of 1862.

1862, January 1. *First Union use of Myer flag code in war.* Using flags, the Union army and navy first employed Myer's code of signals during the combined land and sea attack on Port Royal Ferry, where Federal troops first touched the mainland of South Carolina. Signal flags were used both to direct fire from Union gunboats and to maintain communication between Union vessels and army-navy shore parties. As a result of its success, Myer's code of signals was adopted for instruction purposes by the Union Naval Academy at Newport, Rhode Island.

1862, March-July. *First Army signaling for Marines.* During the long Union campaign to capture and control the Mississippi River from New Orleans to Vicksburg, a Federal army signal party served actively with the Marine Brigade and with elements of the Federal navy. After the fall of New Orleans in April of 1862, the signal party continued such effective action that it was cited for service under fire during the attack and fall of Memphis in June of 1862 and the attack and fall of Vicksburg in July of 1863.

1862, March 9. *First Army signaling for Navy.* During the naval battle between the *Monitor* and the *Merrimac* at Hampton Roads, a Confederate army signalman aboard the *Merrimac*—correctly known as the *Virginia*—relayed messages by flag and torch to a shore-based signal party. This was the first use of an Army signalman on board a naval warship. Subsequently signal officers were used on almost all blockade-runners of the Confederacy throughout the war. They were also used aboard Union warships during several expeditions and in blockading Southern ports during the war.

1862, June 1. *First air-to-ground communications.* Using a telegraph instrument aboard a captive balloon during the Battle of Fair Oaks, a Union observer reported his aerial observations via a connecting line to his headquarters on the ground. This was the first use of telegraphy from a balloon, and the first air-to-ground communication during the war.

1863, July 3. *Signaling at the Battle of Gettysburg.* During the Battle of Gettysburg, Union signal stations strategically located on the mountain peaks, Big Round Top and Little Round Top, played crucial roles in observing Confederate forces and communicating this information to Federal troops. Although there were other factors which led to the defeat of Confederate forces during this major battle of the Civil War, the occupancy by signal troops of the stations on Big Round Top and Little Round Top was of singular and historic importance, and established beyond doubt the significance of signal communications toward victory in warfare.

1863, August. *First use of signal cipher equipment.* During the fall of 1863, after continued interception of Federal messages by Confederate signalmen, a cipher disc invented by Myer was utilized for all Union messages. The code was subsequently broken through the efforts of Bryan, a Confederate secret service operator. This, in turn, led to the continued development of other cipher devices by both Union and Confederate forces.

1867, October. *Signal Corps a supply agency.* Functioning as a supply agency, the Signal Corps furnished two full sets of signaling equipment and two copies of the *Manual of Signals* to every company and post of the Army. Telescopes and binoculars were also furnished on requisition. All signal equipment was accounted for by the Chief Signal Officer.

1870, February 9. *Signal Corps Weather Bureau.* Congress assigned responsibility for forecasting storms on lakes and seacoasts to the War Department, which charged the Army Signal Corps with these new duties. Weather stations were erected throughout the nation, connected by telegraph lines, to provide meteorological data. This work continued until 1891, when all non-military meteorology was transferred to the Department of Agriculture; in 1940 it was transferred to the Department of Commerce. Thus, the original organization and operations of the Signal Corps led ultimately to our present-day Weather Bureau.

1877, August. *First American heliograph.* After experimentation during the summer of 1877, the first military heliograph was developed at Fort Whipple, Virginia (later designated Fort Myer), by the Army Signal Corps. Although it had an effective range in clear weather of about thirty miles, it was not used extensively for nearly ten years, when it began to be employed during campaigns in the Southwest to link isolated forts and outposts. One of these, Fort Huachuca, where the U.S. Army Electronic Proving Ground is now located, was connected into an elaborate network of heliograph communication stations.

1877, October. *First use of military telephone by Signal Corps.* Less than two years after Bell's invention of the telephone, the Army Signal Corps experimented with it successfully over an existing ten-mile field telegraph line at Fort Whipple, Virginia. In the spring of 1878, a forty-mile telephone line was constructed of two iron wires.

1878, July. *First American military use of pigeons.* Homing pigeons, obtained and trained by the Army Signal Corps, were first used experimentally in the Dakota Territory with limited success. Flights were later attempted between Cuba and Florida during 1888.

1880, August 24. *Death of Albert J. Myer.* Brig Gen. Albert J. Myer died at the age of fifty-two. In the following year Fort Whipple, Virginia, was renamed Fort Myer in his honor.

1881 to 1884. *First Army Arctic Exploration.* Participating in a joint international effort to obtain meteorological data in Arctic areas, the Army Signal Corps dispatched one expedition to Point Barrow under command of Lt. Phillip H. Ray and another to Grinnell Sound under command of Lt. Adolphus W. Greely. This was the first official peacetime enterprise in which the United States participated internationally. Collecting meteorological, magnetic, tidal, and natural history data, Greely's expedition penetrated the farthest north of any at that time.

1889, June. *First military field telephone kit.* A combination of the Bell telephone and a telegraph instrument, the first military field telephone kit, was developed by the Army Signal Corps.

1891, July 1. *Transfer of meteorology to the Weather Bureau.* Nonmilitary meteorology was transferred by Congress to the Weather Bureau which had been established in the Department of Agriculture in October, 1890.

1897, July. *First electrical fire control.* After considerable experimentation, the Army Signal Corps developed the first electrical fire control systems for the Coast Artillery.

1898, July 27. *Genesis of the First Signal Company.* Among the new Signal Corps organizations were Companies A and D. After action in Puerto Rico during the Spanish-American War, these two groups were reorganized as the Second Field Battalion, which subsequently served with the First Division during World War I. At Fort Dix in February, 1921, it was renamed the First Signal Company.

1899, April. *First radio operations of Army Signal Corps.* Radiotelegraph communication was established between Fire Island and the Fire Island Lightship, a distance of twelve miles. A year later radio-telegraph stations for controlling traffic were installed adjacent to New York Harbor and San Francisco Harbor.

1900, May 26. *First Alaskan Communications System.* To provide an extensive system of military telegraph lines and undersea cable for Alaska, the Army Signal Corps organized the Washington-Alaska Military Cable and Telegraph System. After several years of construction, most of the principal towns of Alaska were linked with the United States and Canada by undersea cable and overland wire. Beginning in 1903, radio communication supplemented the wire and cable system. In 1936 the system was renamed the Alaska Communications System.

1903. *First long-distance military radio circuit.* The Army Signal Corps installed a radio circuit spanning one hundred and ten miles between Nome and St. Michael, Alaska, to handle both military and commercial traffic.

283

1907, August 1. *First Army avaiation division.* The Aeronautical Division of the Office of the Chief Signal Officer was established and charged with "all matters pertaining to military ballooning, air machines, and kindred subjects." Congress designated this the Aviation Section of the Signal Corps in July, 1914.

1907, December 23. *First military airplane.* The Army Signal Corps issued the first specification and advertisement for a military flying machine. It stated that the machine had to carry a pilot, a passenger, and enough fuel for one hundred and twenty-five miles; fly forty miles per hour, make a sustained flight of one hour, maneuver in any direction, and alight without damage; and be capable of being dismounted and loaded into Army wagons. A contract was signed with Orville Wright on February 10, 1908 to build such a machine. The plane was delivered for testing at Fort Myer, Virginia, on August 20, 1908.

1908, May. *First ground-air radio communication.* By means of an antenna suspended below the basket of an Army Signal Corps free balloon over Washington, radio signals were received aloft from the Navy Yard at Washington and from Annapolis. This was the first known military use of radio for ground-air communication.

1908, August 4. *First military dirigible.* A powered gas-filled dirigible was first tested by the Army Signal Corps at Fort Myer, Virginia, piloted by the builders, Glenn Curtiss and Thomas Baldwin. It was accepted by the Aeronautical Board of the Signal Corps, and designated *Dirigible No. 1.* Subsequently, more than a dozen airships of this type were procured by the Signal Corps for training purposes.

1908, September 3. *First flight of first military airplane.* The first test flight of the Wright airplane was made by the Army Signal Corps at Fort Myer, Virginia. Tests continued until September 17, when the plane crashed, killing the pilot, Lt. Thomas E. Selfridge. He was the first person ever killed in a crash of a heavier-than-air engine-driven craft. With similar planes, tests were continued by the Signal Corps during July 27–30, 1909. The official board of the Signal Corps approved purchase of the Wright machine for military purposes on August 2, 1909. This was the beginning of the era of powered flight for military purposes.

1909, August. *First training of Army pilots.* The first formal training of two Army pilots was conducted by the Signal Corps at College

Park, Maryland. After three weeks, both students made solo flights. The airfield was closed when one of the two planes crashed, and the other was transferred to Fort Sam Houston, Texas. At this time the entire air force of the Army consisted of a single aircraft.

1910, September 18. *First wire-wireless communication.* Over a single twisted-pair wire telephone circuit between the Signal Corps laboratory at the National Bureau of Standards and a small laboratory on Pennsylvania Avenue in Washington, two separate telephone conversations were carried simultaneously.

1917–1919. *First Signal Corps participation in a major war.* Although the Army Signal Corps troops comprised only about four per cent of the total troop strength, they provided communications far more extensive, reliable, and efficient than those known by any previous Army. While doing so, the Signal Corps sustained battle casualties second only to those of the Infantry by percentage: 301 killed and 1,721 wounded.

1917, May 16. *Signal Corps training camps.* The establishment of signal training camps was authorized by Congress. The first and principal installation was located near Red Bank, New Jersey. Officially opened on June 17, 1917, it was named the Signal Corps Camp, Little Silver, New Jersey. On September 15, 1917, it was renamed Camp Alfred Vail. In 1925 it was established as a permanent Army post and was redesignated Fort Monmouth, New Jersey.

Other signal training camps were established during 1917 at Camp Samuel F. B. Morse in Texas, at Fort Leavenworth in Kansas, and at Monterey in California. The Signal Corps Radio School was activated at College Park, Maryland, during this period in 1917.

1918, April. *Establishment of radio laboratory.* To conduct research and development of new communications equipment for the Signal Corps, the Radio Laboratory was established at Camp Alfred Vail, New Jersey.

1918, May. *Separation of the Air Service from the Signal Corps.* The activities of the Air Service were separated from the Signal Corps. Subsequently this service became a separate corps of the Army and ultimately, the United States Air Force.

1919, August 24. *First public radio broadcast.* The first Signal Corps radio broadcast for the general public was a service from Trinity Church in Washington.

1921, March 12. *First War Department Radio Net.* The War Department Radio Net was established as a responsibility of the Army Signal Corps. A control station in Washington was designated WVA; it was operated by the Seventeenth Service Company, later named the Seventeenth Signal Service Company of the Signal Corps.

1937, May 18. *First American radar.* An experimental model of the first Army radar set, designed and developed by the Signal Corps, was successfully demonstrated at Fort Monmouth. Known as the SCR-268, it was used to detect and locate aircraft and to direct searchlight beams for antiaircraft batteries. It was the progenitor of many Army radar sets developed by the Army Signal Corps. Chief among these were the SCR-270 and SCR-271 long-range aircraft detection radar sets.

The first overseas installation of radar sets—SCR-270 and SCR-271—was at Fort Sherman in the Canal Zone, early in 1940.

The first SCR-268 radar set was installed in Iceland during September of 1941. Seven of these sets were installed in gun-battery positions in Panama by October of 1941.

1941, December 7. *Attack on Pearl Harbor.* Personnel operating an Army Signal Corps radar set at Opana, Hawaii, reported a large flight of unidentified aircraft aproaching the island. Their warning was ignored, and almost an hour later the surprise attack by Japanese aircraft was successful.

1942, March 30. *Signal Corps Photographic Center.* To produce the vast amount of training films and other motion pictures required for the expanding Army, the Signal Corps Photographic Center was activated in Long Island City, New York.

1942, April. *First use of Army airborne radar.* The SCR-517 radar set was first put to use in aircraft to search the Atlantic sea lanes for vessels. This was the first microwave radar set developed by the Army Signal Corps for use in aircraft.

1942, May 30. *Lexington Signal Depot.* To provide needed additional signal supply and storage facilities, the Lexington Signal Depot was dedicated at Lexington, Kentucky.

1943, January. *Military radio-relay system.* Engineers of the Army Signal Corps arrived in Algiers with mobile FM radio equipment and built the first radio-relay system used in combat.

1943, June 1. *Sacramento Signal Depot.* The Sacramento Signal Depot was established in California.

1943, June 30. *La Plata Receiving Station.* The receiving station of the Army Command and Administrative Network was established by the Signal Corps at La Plata, Maryland, with probably the greatest concentration of radio antennas ever assembled to receive signals simultaneously from any part of the world.

1944, February 24. *First combat use of SCR-584 radar.* The newly developed microwave gun-laying SCR-584 radar set was rushed into position near Anzio, Italy, and broke a sustained German air attack. In its first use, five of the twelve German Junkers were dropped with the first radar-directed salvo. From this time, enemy high-level night bombing attacks diminished sharply.

1944, June 6. *Signal Corps landings in France.* The first U.S. Army Signal Corps troops to land in the great D-Day invasion of Normandy were twenty-eight men of the 101st Airborne Signal Company. They parachuted with the division headquarters group and landed near Hiesville.

First Signal Corps troops to come ashore afoot in France were personnel of the 294th Joint Assault Signal Company at Omaha Beach. Within a few minutes personnel of the 286th Joint Assault Signal Company landed at Utah Beach.

The 165th Signal Photographic Company landed with the first infantry elements at Omaha Beach. The commanding officer, Capt. Herman Wall, was the first Army Signal Corps casualty of the Normandy invasion on June 6, 1944. His pictures were the first photographs of the invasion to reach England and be reproduced.

1944, December 16–24. *Operations during Battle of the Bulge.* During the Battle of the Bulge, Army Signal Corps troops rerouted and installed more than two thousand miles of new communication circuits in only seven days.

1945, April 28. *Fastest message around the world.* Through facilities of the Army Signal Corps, a nine-word radioteletype message was transmitted around the world in 9.5 seconds to set a new record for speed. This broke a previous record of 3.5 minutes set in May, 1944.

1946, January 10. *First radar contact with the moon.* Using a modified SCR-271 long-range radar set, engineers of the Army Signal

Corps at Belmar, New Jersey, succeeded in making radio contact with the moon. This was known as Project Diana.

1946, June 1. *Decatur Signal Depot.* The Decatur Signal Depot was established in Decatur, Illinois.

1948, August. *Electronic Countermeasures Program.* The Army Signal Corps was assigned responsibility for the entire Army Electronic Countermeasures Program.

1948, October 1. *Training Center at Camp Gordon.* The Signal Corps Training Center was established at Camp Gordon, Georgia. It was redesignated the U.S. Army Signal Training Center on January 31, 1957.

The Signal Corps Replacement Training Center was established at Camp Gordon in September, 1950, and discontinued in November, 1954.

Camp Gordon was redesignated Fort Gordon on March 21, 1956.

1949, September 26. *First Army electronic automation technique—"AUTO–SEMBLY."* The "Auto-Sembly" system of automation, promising high-speed manufacture of subassemblies, was announced by the Signal Corps Engineering Laboratories. The new process combined the best features of printed circuitry and conventional component usage.

1952, January 1. *Signal Corps Supply Agency.* The Signal Corps Supply Agency was established in Philadelphia by merging two formerly separate activities, The Procurement Agency and the Stock Control Agency. On March 1, 1956 it was redesignated the Army Signal Supply Agency. On January 31, 1957 it was redesignated again, this time called the U.S. Army Signal Supply Agency.

1952, May 19. *Woodbridge Transmitting Station.* A radio transmitting station at Woodbridge, Virginia, was activated by the Army Signal Corps as an integral part of the global Army Command and Administrative Network. This station replaced the old Fort Myer and Battery Cove transmitting stations.

1952, December 17. *First military automatic teletypewriter system.* At Fifth Army Headquarters in Chicago, the first automatic teletypewriter relay system was established by the Army Signal Corps.

1953, February 1. *Tobyhanna Signal Depot.* The Tobyhanna Signal Depot was established in Tobyhanna, Pennsylvania.

1954, February 1. *Army Electronic Proving Ground.* The Army Electronic Proving Ground was established as a Signal Corps activity at Fort Huachuca, Arizona. Fort Huachuca was designated a permanent Army post in August, 1954.

1957, January 15. *Army Combat Surveillance Agency.* The U.S. Army Combat Surveillance Agency was established in Washington, D.C.

1957, December 5. *First operational electronic system for coordinating and controlling antiaircraft missile batteries.* The first operational electronic system—the Missile Master—for controlling and coordinating the use of Nike and Hawk missile batteries was placed in action defending the Washington-Baltimore area. Developed for the Army by the Martin Company working with the Army Signal Corps, the system was received by a group of Department of the Army representatives headed by the Secretary of the Army and turned over to the U.S. Army Air Defense Command at its installation at Fort George G. Meade, Maryland. The system collects information on the location of aircraft and their identity, presents this information on electronic displays, and distributes this data to the missile firing batteries.

1958, January. *First calibration of satellite tracking station by bouncing signals from moon.* On January 14, 1958, the Space Sentry, a giant radio transmitter of the U.S. Army Signal Corps, bounced signals from the moon to insure close tracking of the U.S. satellites. The calibration tests assured that the Minitrack listening posts throughout the Western Hemisphere and on the West Coast of Africa would be precisely tuned to the same frequency—in effect "their watches would be synchronized." The signals were transmitted from Fort Monmouth, New Jersey, on each test date for five hours between January 14–28. The Space Sentry was erected by the U.S. Army Signal Research and Development Laboratories at Fort Monmouth in conjunction with the Naval Research Laboratory, Washington, D.C.

1958, March. *First use of rockets and metallic confetti to plot winds of the upper atmosphere at more than fifty miles altitude.* Army scientists conducted tests, using rockets which release metallic confetti more than fifty miles above the earth, to plot winds in the upper atmosphere. The new method was devised by scientists at the U.S. Army Signal Research and Development laboratories, Fort Monmouth, and employs small Loki II rockets carrying packets of confettilike aluminum chaff. At a certain altitude, a cloud of chaff is released and tracked by radar to produce a fast and accurate wind profile. The purpose of the tests, in which the Loki rockets reached an altitude of fifty-four miles, is to provide accurate information on wind behavior at high altitudes, which is necessary for delivery of an intercontinental missile on target.

1958, March 17. *First conversion of solar cells to use sun power for electrical energy in satellites.* Vanguard I was launched and placed in orbit using Army-developed solar converters to provide power for one of its two radio transmitters. Engineers of the U.S. Army Signal Research and Development Laboratories, Fort Monmouth, developed a solar converter which used commercially available solar cells to provide electrical power for the satellite's radio. The Vanguard I radio powered by these Army-developed solar converters is still functioning after more than two years in orbit. The solar cells were invented by Bell Telephone Company and produced by Hoffman Electronics Corporation.

1958, December 18. *First satellite communications relay to actively relay voice and teleteypwriter signals through space.* The Atlas was successfully launched and placed in orbit by the Air Force carrying an Army communications package that became the first radio communications relay in outer space. Under the direction of the Advanced Research Projects Agency, the U.S. Army Signal Research and Development Laboratories developed with industry the space communications relay and the associated ground stations. The achievement—called Project Score—marked the first time that human intelligence was actively relayed through voice and teletypewriter signals by communication equipment in outer space. A goodwill message by President Eisenhower stressing America's wish for "peace on earth" was the first voice to be transmitted in space. Contributing firms who worked with Army scientists were Radio Corporation of America, Eagle-Pitcher Lead Company, Porter Bromfield, Convair-Astronautics Division of General Dynamics, Radiation, Inc., and R. F. Laboratories.

1959, February 17. *First cloud-cover instrumentation in a United States satellite.* NASA's Vanguard II was launched and placed in orbit carrying an Army-developed cloud-cover instrumentation package. The cloud-cover satellite instrumentation was developed by the U.S. Army Signal Research and Development Laboratories and was housed in a satellite shell prepared by NASA's Vanguard

Division. The twenty-one-and-a-half-pound sphere contained two photocells mounted behind circular, gridded windows and was the first effort to measure from outer space the distribution of cloud cover over the earth and relate it to the overall meteorology of the earth. A quarter of a million feet of taped signals were obtained by Army scientists at Fort Monmouth, New Jersey, from the cloud-cover satellite signals before the expected termination of the satellite batteries.

1959, February. *First successful firings of a meteorological rocket that can be launched by a two-man crew.* Successful test firings of a new low cost meteorological rocket that can be fired by a two-man crew were made by the U.S. Army Signal Missile Support Agency at the White Sands Missile Range, New Mexico. Named ARCAS (All-Purpose Rocket for Collecting Atmospheric Soundings), the rocket was made for the Office of Naval Research by the Atlantic Research Corporation. The Navy requested the U.S. Army agency to test fire the ARCAS at the White Sands Missile Range because of the Army's previous successful experience in shooting such atmospheric measuring vehicles as the Loki, Nike, Cajun, and Aerobee Hawk. One of the four ARCAS missiles fired reached a height of 174,000 feet with its instrumented pay load, which averaged thirteen pounds.

1962. *Major reorganization in Signal Corps.* The Chief Signal Officer relinquishes many of his command functions, and becomes primarily a Department of the Army Staff Officer.

1964, March 1. The Chief Signal Officer's staff functions are broadened. He is redesignated the Chief of Communications-Electronics.

Index

294

295

296

flagmen, 8, 18, 81, 85
  in Civil War, 21–62
  in Confederate Army, 63–75
flags, 8, 9, 11–13, 18, 20, 24, 26, 28,
    34, 35, 42, 43, 47, 48, 62, 67, 70,
    71, 84, 142, 146, 149
Florida, 26, 138
Floyd, John B., 14
Foch, Marshal, 152
Force Development, Ass't Chief of
    Staff for, 204
Fort Belvoir, 234
Fort Bennett, 90
Fort Bliss, 90
Fort Bragg, 210, 214
Fort Buford, 93
Fort Concho, 91
Fort Conger, 95–98, 105
Fort Davis, 85, 90, 113, 114
Fort Detrick, 212, 234
Fort Dix, 223
Fort Egbert, 113–119
Fort Ellis, 85, 92
Fort Gaines, 61
Fort Gibbon, 113, 116, 118–120
Fort Gordon, 232, 233, 240, 248, 251
Fort Greble, 81, 82
Fort Hamilton, 13, 121
Fort Holabird, 245
Fort Huachuca, 238, 240, 245, 247,
    265
Fort Keogh, 93
Fort Knox, 234
Fort Leavenworth, 110, 212
Fort Lewis, 214
Fort Liscum, 113–115, 117, 119, 126
Fort Macon, 28
Fort Malate, 140
Fort Mason, 122
Fort Meade, 234
Fort Monmouth, 140, 158, 174, 179,
    193, 195, 196, 198, 231–233,
    248, 250, 251, 267, 269, 272, 274
Fort Monroe, 21, 22, 24, 26, 27, 29,
    34, 38, 40, 81
Fort Myer, 89, 129, 132
Fort Omaha, 129, 143
Fort Pulaski, 27
Fort Riley, 107, 108, 134
Fort St. Michael, 112, 114, 116, 118–
    122
Fort Sam Houston, 133, 134
Fort San Antonio, 140
Fort Seward, 113, 117, 119
Fort Shafter, 169, 173
Fort Sill, 85, 90, 129

Fort Sumter, 19, 22
Fort Wadsworth, 13
Fort Washington, 37
Fort Whipple, 82, 88, 89, 91
Fort Wool, 22
FORTRAM, 262, 266
Foulois, Lt. Benjamin D., 131, 133,
    134
411th Telegraph Battalion, 151
Fourth Signal Battalion, 188–191
France, 10, 142–157, 159–161, 165,
    166, 171, 184, 225, 265
Franklin, Sir John, 94, 98
Frayser, Richard E., 65, 66
Frederick, Md., 44
Frederick Sound, 125
Fredericksburg, battle of, 48–50, 68
French, Lt. Col. Edward F., 172
French Revolution, 11
Frequency Management, 203, 235–
    237

Gaines' Mill, battle of, 73
gallium phosphide, 270
Garfield, James A., 97
Garfield Mtns., 97
general communications, 41
General Electric, 158
General Myer, 127
Geneva College (*see* Hobart)
Georgetown Aqueduct Bridge, 23
Germany, 10, 142–156, 245
Gettysburg, battle of, 52, 53, 68, 74
Gibbs, Lt. George S., 118–120, 140
Glassford, Lt. William A., 127
global communications (*see* STRAT-
    COM)
gold rush, 112
Government Printing Office, 108
Governors Island, 121
Grant, Gen., 44, 68, 77–79
Grant Land, 97
GRAPHDEN, 266
Great Plains, 5
Great Seneca River, 37
Greely, Adolphus Washington, 84,
    90–111, 113–117, 120–122, 124,
    127–129, 136, 141
Greely Hall, 241
Greene, Col. Frank, 138
Greenland, 93, 96
grids, 244
Grinnell Land, 93, 97
Groveton Heights, 65
Guantanamo Bay, 138
Guenes, 4

297

298

303